Price $5.75

TACO ENGINEERING DEPT.

WAVE PROPAGATION
AND ANTENNAS

by

GEORGE B. WELCH

Professor of Physics
Northeastern University

D. VAN NOSTRAND COMPANY, INC.
PRINCETON, NEW JERSEY

TORONTO   LONDON
NEW YORK

D. VAN NOSTRAND COMPANY, INC.
120 Alexander St., Princeton, New Jersey (*Principal office*)
257 Fourth Avenue, New York 10, New York

D. VAN NOSTRAND COMPANY, LTD.
358, Kensington High Street, London, W.14, England

D. VAN NOSTRAND COMPANY (Canada), LTD.
25 Hollinger Road, Toronto 16, Canada

Published simultaneously in Canada by
D. VAN NOSTRAND COMPANY (Canada), LTD.

Library of Congress Catalogue Card No. 58-9431

PRINTED IN THE UNITED STATES OF AMERICA
BY LANCASTER PRESS, INC., LANCASTER, PA.

PREFACE

This book is the outgrowth of a series of lectures first given to sophomores at the Lincoln Institute of Northeastern University in the fall of 1949, and is the successor to a mimeographed edition prepared to meet the needs of rapidly increasing classes of students. Written primarily for readers who are presumed to be familiar with general physics, trigonometry, and a little analytic geometry, the text is designed to provide in general a background knowledge of electromagnetic wave propagation and in particular an understanding of the fundamental principles of antennas.

Throughout the text basic principles upon which the student may build and ultimately extend his knowledge are emphasized. An understanding of these principles is developed through physical reasoning, aided by elementary mathematics and graphical methods. Every effort has been made to integrate carefully the entire subject matter. The propagation of electromagnetic waves along wires, in waveguides, and through space is shown to be basically the same. Similarities between optical and radio waves are constantly stressed. The subject of antennas is not confined to designated chapters; it is a central theme which runs throughout the book. Graphical methods for obtaining radiation patterns are based on the single principle of interference. Mathematical rigor, which is necessary in advanced theory, plays a secondary role. By confining the scope of certain phenomena to specific cases, and by indicating clearly the limitations, the material has been presented in such a manner that the reader should have nothing to unlearn.

Basic unification of the subject matter has made it possible to include the fundamental principles of topics not heretofore treated at this level. Recent developments, such as radar, forward scatter, and radio astronomy, fall naturally into the plan of the book.

As a consequence of a steadily growing interest in the subject matter of the text, the preprint edition has been adequately tested in the classroom by various instructors. The individual teacher, of course, will include details and supplementary material derived from his personal background. Experimental demonstrations and the showing of some of the excellent films now available should be considered a necessary part of the course. The problems appended to each chapter are an integral part of the text. The references for additional reading are briefly reviewed for the guidance of the student.

To the physicists who, as colleagues and teachers, have all unknowingly contributed to the writing of this book, the author gratefully acknowledges his debt. In particular, extended thanks are due to Professor Hollis S. Baird, who has also taught the course, for many helpful discussions, and to the author's wife, Edna F. Welch, for valuable advice throughout the preparation of the book.

GEORGE B. WELCH

Boston, Massachusetts
March 1, 1958

CONTENTS

Chapter 1

SIMPLE HARMONIC MOTION

1.1. Diverse Viewpoints in Physics. Physical phenomena may often be recognized and described in several ways. No question should arise as to which is the *proper* or *best* way. The choice is one of convenience. Certain problems may be solved easily when attacked from one point of view; from another, they may be all but impossibly complicated. Either, however, is correct in principle.

As an illustration consider a closed "black" box, with two small holes in the bottom, from which the strings A and B are hanging. When A is moved down 2 ft, B moves upward 1 ft. In general, the motion of A over a predetermined distance in a given direction produces a motion of B over half this distance in the opposite direction. The reader can easily propose a number of mechanisms by means of which the motion may be correctly described and future results predicted. The final choice will be a conveniently simple device whose mode of operation may appropriately be called the *theory* of the enclosure. But if there is no way of opening the box, the "true" mechanism must forever remain unknown.

In considering the flow of electrical energy, particularly by direct current or low frequency alternating current, we assume that the motion of electrons is restricted to wires or conductors of relatively small cross section. The product of voltage and current gives the rate at which energy is transported. This is a *convenient* method because instruments called voltmeters and ammeters are easily constructed and read. In many cases the description and analysis of the behavior of charged particles constitute the conventional method of thinking about electrical phenomena. In electron tubes, for example, charges are represented as moving from cathode to plate (electron flow) or in the opposite direction (conventional current).

But there is another way of viewing these phenomena. In the neighborhood of every electric charge there is an electric field. That is, the space surrounding the charge is modified so that another charge, when placed in the field, will experience a force. By convention, the direction of the field

1

is that in which a *positive* charge will tend to move. For a static *point* charge the lines picturing the field are the radii of a sphere of which the charge is the center. If the charges are located on two parallel plates, set rather closely together, as in a capacitor, the lines are between the plates and perpendicular to them. In the vicinity of the grid in a triode the field lines take on more diversified shapes, which depend on the spacing of the wires and the applied voltages. In free space at distances far enough from a straight antenna for the waves to be considered plane, the direction of the electric field is parallel to the antenna wire. In any case the electric field exists whether the charge is in motion or at rest.

For charges in motion, however, there is in addition a magnetic field, the direction of which may be determined by the familiar right-hand rule if conventional current is assumed. For example, the magnetic field about a wire may be represented by concentric circles in planes perpendicular to the axis of the wire. In problems dealing with antennas, transmission lines, and waveguides it may be assumed that the electric and magnetic fields are always at right angles in space. The combined electric and magnetic fields form the electromagnetic field.

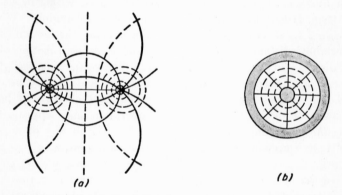

(a)   (b)

FIG. 1.1. Electric and magnetic fields of (*a*) an open-wire transmission line and (*b*) a coaxial cable.

——————— Electric field   — — — — Magnetic field

In Fig. 1.1 are shown the electric and magnetic fields for two types of radio-frequency transmission lines, (a) the open-wire line and (b) the coaxial cable. The currents in the conductors give rise to a magnetic field and the potential difference between them sets up an electric field. The diagrams are drawn on the assumption that the conductors are materials of low resistivity.

Although it is usually more convenient to analyze conventional electrical circuits in terms of the flow of charge within wires, it must be remembered that it is done solely from the standpoint of convenience. We may alternatively view the transmission of electrical energy through the agency of the electromagnetic field, the wire serving as a *guide*. Wired radio was introduced before World War I. Today coaxial cables and waveguides are well known devices for conveying electrical energy in communications circuits.

In radio, using the term in its general sense, the method of energy transfer is truly "wireless." No material medium is required; no wire acts as guide. Clearly it will be convenient to analyze the phenomena in terms of the electromagnetic field. To this type of analysis we shall give considerable attention. We shall not, however, hesitate to shift our point of view when it is convenient for our purpose. In the meantime, certain fundamental groundwork must be laid.

1.2. The Vibrating Spring. From the beginning there must be a clear understanding of simple harmonic motion. In mechanics we conveniently define this type of motion as that in which the force is proportional to the displacement and oppositely directed. Now we must be able to put our definition into mathematical language; for mathematics is a language—just as English and Russian are languages—and a truly universal one. Good translation requires an adequate working knowledge of the languages involved. Translating from English to mathematics, we write

$$F = -ky \tag{1.1}$$

where F is the unbalanced force (recall Newton's second law of motion) and y is the displacement from the equilibrium position, say in a vertical direction. The minus sign indicates that the displacement and the force are oppositely directed. The symbol k is a constant, the value of which depends on the system in motion.

A physical picture of simple harmonic motion may be obtained by supposing we have a mass m attached to a spring hanging vertically. This spring must be of a special type, one that follows Hooke's law. That is, the displacement of the spring must always be proportional to the force applied. If 1 pound will stretch it 2 in., 2 pounds will extend it 4 in., etc.

If the system is displaced downward and released, the elastic force of the spring which is always proportional to its displacement, measured from the equilibrium position, will act upward. Note that force and displacement are always oppositely directed. As the system approaches its equilibrium position the force diminishes, and at that point it becomes zero.

The system, because of its inertia (recall Newton's first law of motion), does not come to rest at its equilibrium position, but continues to move upward. The spring is now compressed and is thus enabled to exert a force, again proportional to its displacement and oppositely directed, which brings the system to rest. Then the compressional force of the spring pushes the system downward. It should be reasonably clear that, in the absence of friction, the motion will repeat itself indefinitely.

For convenience we have neglected gravitational forces. As an alternative we may allow the system to move in a horizontal plane on a *smooth*, i.e., frictionless surface.

It should be noticed that the system, in order that it may execute simple harmonic motion, must have the fundamental properties of *inertia* and *elasticity*, or must possess *mass* and *stiffness*.

1.3. Technical Terms in Simple Harmonic Motion. By employing a familiar method of analysis a physical meaning for the constant k in Eq. (1.1) may be found. Solve for k neglecting the minus sign and including the units.

$$k = F \text{ (measured in newtons)}/y \text{ (measured in meters)}$$

Thus k is numerically equal to the force which will stretch the spring unit distance. It may, of course, be expressed in newtons per meter, pounds per foot, or any other convenient set of units. It is called the *force constant* or the *stiffness constant* of the spring. For a stiff spring the value of k will be relatively large.

We now need to make certain that some of the technical terms associated with simple harmonic motion are well understood. The *displacement y*, as already mentioned, is the distance of the "particle" from its equilibrium position. The conventions of mathematics are followed in assigning positive and negative values to the displacement.

The maximum displacement is called the *amplitude A*.

The time for a complete to-and-fro motion is called the *period T*. The number of vibrations per unit time (usually, per second) is called the *frequency f*. Since either of these quantities is the reciprocal of the other, they are related by the equation, $f = 1/T$.

It should be clear that if the phenomenon of simple harmonic motion were confined to the oscillations of a spring, it would not warrant our attention here. An understanding is important because the variations in a-c voltages and a-c currents, as well as fluctuations in electric and magnetic fields, may be analyzed by methods which are identical with those for a vibrating spring. The inductance of a circuit element is analogous to the inertia factor and the reciprocal of the capacitance to the elastic or stiffness factor.

1.4. Sinusoidal Representation of Simple Harmonic Motion. From what has been said at the beginning, it may be suspected that Eq. (1.1) does not always provide us with the most convenient description of simple harmonic motion. A different, albeit equivalent viewpoint will prove to be of use.

Consider a line of length A with its origin at O and its termination at P_0 (Fig. 1.2). Let this vector (more accurately called a *phasor*) rotate with constant angular speed, the period being T. P_0 may be projected upon a vertical diameter of the circle at P. Let us begin to count time—the mathematical parlance is, $t = 0$—when A is horizontal and directed to the right. P will first be found at the center of the circle. P will then move

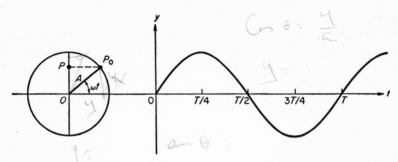

FIG. 1.2. Displacement in simple harmonic motion represented by a sine curve.

upward a distance A, stop, move downward until its displacement is $- A$, and finally move upward to the center of the circle, in the time T. The motion of the point P is evidently similar to the motion of the mass attached to the spring.

If we plot the displacement y of P as a function of the time t we have the curve shown in Figure 1.2. Since we have some familiarity with mathematics, we strongly suspect that this is a sine curve. We know that the sine is zero at $0°$, increases to a maximum, returns to zero, etc. This idea is confirmed when we notice that in the right triangle POP_0 the displacement OP is proportional to the sine of the angle ωt.

A sine is a mathematical function which repeats itself after an elapsed period. We classify it as a *periodic function*. Might we not have suspected that the periodic vibration of a spring must have its mathematical counterpart in a function which changes periodically? We proceed to write an equation which will describe the curve and consequently the motion.

$$y = A \sin \omega t \qquad (1.2)$$

The sine varies between $+ 1$ and $- 1$. Hence y will vary between $+ A$ and $- A$. Therefore y is considered to be the displacement and A is the amplitude.

What is the meaning of ω? The so-called argument of a trigonometric function (in this case, ωt) must be a pure numeric, i.e., without units, such as feet or pounds. Since t is usually measured in seconds, ω may be expressed in reciprocal seconds. Actually it is represented by radians per second but, as we have learned, a radian is also a pure numeric, as its definition shows it to be the ratio of two lengths. Thus ω is the angular speed of P_0. It may, however, be more convenient to express ω differently. In one revolution P_0 describes an angle of 2π radians in the time T. Since the speed is constant, $\omega = 2\pi/T$, and we may write

$$y = A \sin 2\pi t/T \tag{1.3}$$

When the observations are begun, $t = 0$ and $y = 0$. By substitution in Eq. (1.3) we may find the values of y for values of t corresponding to $T/4$, $T/2$, $3T/4$, etc. These values check with the curve which repeats itself after $t = T$. Evidently the displacement in simple harmonic motion may be expressed as a sine function. As we shall see, this is of the greatest importance in the discussion of many electrical problems.

From elementary physics we recall that in simple harmonic motion the velocity is zero when the displacement is a maximum. This is easily seen by noting that the particle must stop at the ends of the path in order to reverse its direction of motion. At the center of the path the velocity is the greatest. Furthermore, since the acceleration is proportional to the displacement, the former will be a maximum at the ends of the path and zero at the center. A little analysis will show that both velocity and acceleration may be expressed as periodic functions of the time.

The speed of P_0 is constant and may therefore be written equal to $2\pi A/T$, which is equivalent to the speed of P at the center of its path. That is, the velocity of P is a maximum when $t = 0$. Clearly, if we should write for the velocity, $v = 2\pi A/T \cdot \sin \omega t$, and substitute the value, $t = 0$, the result would not be in accordance with observation. But if we notice that, after all, the cosine curve is identical with the sine curve, except for a shift of $90°$, a way out of the difficulty presents itself.

If we try the equation

$$v = 2\pi A/T \cdot \cos 2\pi t/T \tag{1.4}$$

we find that the results are satisfactory. When $t = 0$, the velocity is a maximum, $2\pi A/T$; when $t = T/4$, $v = 0$, etc.

In elementary physics it is shown that the acceleration of P_0, a particle moving with uniform speeed in a circle is v_0^2/A, where v_0 is the speed and A the radius of the circle. Since $v_0 = 2\pi A/T$, the acceleration of P_0, equivalent to the maximum acceleration of P, is $4\pi^2 A/T^2$. Since, by definition, the acceleration of P is proportional to its displacement, we should feel reasonably confident that we may return to the sine function and write

$$a = -4\pi^2 A/T^2 \cdot \sin 2\pi t/T \tag{1.5}$$

By trial we find that the results are wholly satisfactory. The acceleration is zero at the center of the path and a maximum at the extremities. Note that the minus sign is important. It indicates that the acceleration and the displacement are oppositely directed.

In electrical theory it is customary to speak of frequency rather than period. Since these two quantities are related reciprocally, we may write Eq. (1.3), (1.4), and (1.5) in the convenient form

$$y = A \cdot \sin 2\pi f t \tag{1.6}$$

$$v = 2\pi A f \cdot \cos 2\pi f t \tag{1.7}$$

$$a = -4\pi^2 A f^2 \cdot \sin 2\pi f t \tag{1.8}$$

If the value of y in Eq. (1.6) is substituted in Eq. (1.8) we have

$$a = -4\pi^2 f^2 y \tag{1.9}$$

Since $4\pi^2 f^2$ is a constant, the acceleration is shown to be proportional to the the displacement; the minus sign, of course, indicates that the two quantities are oppositely directed.

A presentation of the phase relations among displacement, velocity, and acceleration is given in Fig. 1.3. It should be carefully studied and its relation to the mathematical equations derived above thoroughly understood.

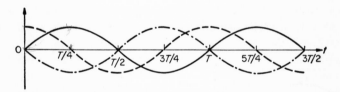

FIG. 1.3. Simple harmonic motion. The displacement, velocity, and acceleration are represented each as a function of the time. ———— Displacement —————— Velocity —·—· Acceleration

For a given mass and spring the period in simple harmonic motion is independent of the amplitude. Physically, changing the amplitude involves changing the maximum unbalanced force with its accompanying acceleration. The resultant velocities are such that they just compensate for increases and decreases in the path to keep the period unaltered. An expression showing that the period depends only on the attached mass and the stiffness of the spring may be obtained as follows.

From Eq. (1.1), $F = -ky$. From Newton's second law, $F = ma$. Writing Eq. (1.9) in terms of the period, instead of the frequency, $a =$

$- 4\pi^2 y/T^2$. If these three equations are combined so as to eliminate F, y, and a,

$$T = 2\pi \sqrt{\frac{m}{k}} \tag{1.10}$$

This result agrees qualitatively with the physical reasoning, that a smaller mass or a stiffer spring should decrease the time required for a complete oscillation.

Recalling from Sec. 1.3 that inductance is analogous to mass and capacitance to the reciprocal of stiffness, the frequency of an electrically oscillating circuit is found to be

$$f = 1/2\pi \sqrt{LC} \tag{1.11}$$

The equations for displacement, velocity, and acceleration which have been derived above are based on the assumption that observations are begun, $t = 0$, when the particle moving with simple harmonic motion is in its equilibrium position and is moving in a positive direction. If such is not the case, an adjustment equivalent to shifting the origin of the curve in Fig. 1.2 must be made.

For example, let $t = 0$, when $y = A/2$; that is, let the particle be first observed when it is halfway between its equilibrium position and maximum positive displacement. Furthermore, let it be moving upward. The time elapsed since the particle was at the origin is the value of t for which sin $2\pi t/T = \frac{1}{2}$. Sin^{-1} $\frac{1}{2} = 30°$. Considering $360° \equiv T$, a complete period, $30° \equiv T/12$ (Fig. 1.4). The origin may now be pushed back $T/12$ in time in

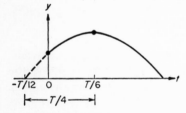

FIG. 1.4. Displacement of origin when the particle is not initially in its equilibrium position.

order to make the curve coincide with that in Fig. 1.2, whereby the displacements, velocities, and accelerations may be computed, using Eq. (1.3) to (1.8). To compensate for this shift, however, $T/12$ must be added to the value of t used in these equations. Suppose we wish to find the displacement of the particle at a time $T/6$ after the observations are begun. Since we have shifted the origin to the left by $T/12$ in order to use Eq. (1.3), we must set $t = T/12 + T/6 = T/4$. Hence, $y = A$ sin $2\pi T/4T = A$ sin $\pi/2 = A$. This is easily verified, for if the particle had been observed $T/12$

earlier it would have reached its maximum displacement in one-quarter period.

Other methods of analyzing the problems may suggest themselves to the reader. That which is most convenient and best understood should be used.

It should be clear from the nature of simple harmonic motion that the particle *does not move uniformly* in time along its path. Even a casual reflection will reveal that the object must necessarily slow down in order to come to rest at the extremities. In the example cited, the particle traveled a distance equal to half the amplitude from its equilibrium position in the time $T/12$; to travel the remaining half, twice this time was required.

1.5. Sinusoidal Voltages and Currents. In the study of alternating currents the relation between simple harmonic motion and a sine curve will prove exceedingly useful. If a coil of wire is rotated with constant

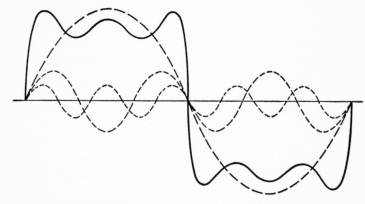

FIG. 1.5. The first three terms of the Fourier series and their resultant representing an approach to the ideal square waveform.

speed in a uniform magnetic field an alternating electromotive force (emf) will be developed. Since this emf is proportional to the *rate* at which the lines of flux are cut, it will be a maximum when the plane of the coil is parallel to the field and zero when it is perpendicular. The direction of the emf will change at each half-rotation. We may think of the magnitude of the emf varying as does the displacement of a particle moving with simple harmonic motion and treat these variations in accordance with the behavior of sine and cosine curves.

We speak of such an emf and the current associated with it as *sinusoidal*. Most a-c power generators develop emf's which, for practical purposes, may be considered sinusoidal. Many electronic oscillators too develop sinusoidal voltages, although frequently such is not the case. However, there is a mathematical method, known as Fourier's series, which enables us to treat these cases as if they were combinations of sine and/or cosine voltages. For example, a square waveform may be expressed by the series

$$y = \frac{A}{\pi} \left(\sin \omega t + \tfrac{1}{3} \sin 3\omega t + \tfrac{1}{5} \sin 5\omega t + \cdots \right)$$

This equation states that a square waveform may be represented by a series of sine waves with frequencies which are odd integral multiples of the fundamental or lowest frequency, and with appropriate amplitudes. Fig. 1.5 shows how closely the first three terms of the series approach the ideal waveform. A square waveform may be used to test the uniformity of frequency response in an amplifier by comparing the patterns before and after the signal passes through the apparatus.

Sinusoidal voltages are developed and sinusoidal currents flow in the antennas connected to the transmitters of radio and television broadcasting stations. The electromagnetic fields by means of which these antennas radiate energy into space are, in turn, also sinusoidal. When this energy is intercepted by a receiving antenna sinusoidal voltages and currents are again produced.

1.6. Simple Harmonic Motions at Right Angles. In the study of polarization of electromagnetic waves we shall have occasion to consider the effect when two simple harmonic motions of the same frequency, but not necessarily in phase, are impressed simultaneously on a particle. The combining of the motions may be accomplished in various ways. Analytically, two expressions, similar to Eq. (1.2), may be set up, e.g., $x = A_1 \sin \omega t$ and $y = A_2 \sin (\omega t + \Delta)$, where Δ is the phase angle. The time t is then eliminated and the equation of the curve determined. Here a graphical treatment, of which there are several, has been chosen to give a clearer idea of the physical principles involved.

Let it be assumed that the motions are identical except that the displacement in the y-direction leads the x-displacement by 30°. As in Fig. 1.6, lay off on each axis, in both positive and negative directions, distances proportional to the sines of say, 30°, 60°, and 90°. (To the reader who may wish to reproduce the diagram, it is suggested that these distances be made 2.5, 4.3, and 5.0 cm, respectively.) The starting point $(t = 0)$ for the horizontal motion is $x = 0$, i.e., the origin. For the vertical motion, which is leading by 30°, the starting point must be advanced a distance proportional to the sine of the phase angle, i.e., one-half the amplitude, or 2.5 cm. The starting point of the resultant motion is thus represented by the coordinates $(0, 2.5)$. The next point is located $(2.5, 4.3)$ by advancing 30° along each axis. By continuing the procedure for a complete cycle the resultant path of the particle is obtained. Notice that equality of angle change is equivalent to equal time intervals but not to equal distances traversed, a point which has already been strongly emphasized.

Of course the interval chosen need not be 30°, but conveniently 90° should be an integral multiple of the interval. Its value should be selected in accordance with the requirements of the problem.

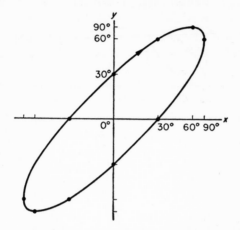

FIG. 1.6. Graphical composition of two simple harmonic motions at right angles. Equal frequencies and amplitudes. Phase angle, 30°.

If the pattern has already been obtained, the phase shift may be determined as follows. In Fig. 1.6 the displacements are $x = A \sin \omega t$ and $y = A \sin (\omega t + 30°)$. When $t = 0$, $x = 0$, but $y = A \sin 30°$. The y-intercept will be $A \sin 30° = A/2$. Since the vertical amplitude is A,

$$\sin \Delta = (A/2)/A = \tfrac{1}{2} \text{ and } \Delta = 30°$$

or, in general,

$$\sin \Delta = \text{vertical intercept/vertical amplitude}$$

The reader should be able to see from the figure that the above statement is equivalent to

$$\sin \Delta = \text{horizontal intercept/horizontal amplitude}$$

Moreover, these relations are not contingent upon the amplitudes being equal. True, an ambiguity may result. For example, a value of $\tfrac{1}{2}$ would also be obtained for $\sin \Delta$ if the phase angle were 150°, 210°, or 330°. The difficulty may be resolved by observing the orientation of the major axis of the ellipse and the direction of rotation of the particle.

The pattern shown in Fig. 1.6 is known as a *Lissajous* figure. If presented on the screen of a cathode-ray oscilloscope, to be described in the next section, Lissajous figures are invaluable in making frequency comparisons in electronic circuits. In Fig. 1.7 examples of Lissajous figures for equal frequencies and amplitudes, but with different phase angles, are shown. In verifying the statement that the path is always an ellipse when the frequencies are equal, the reader should recall that the circle and the straight line are limiting forms of this conic.

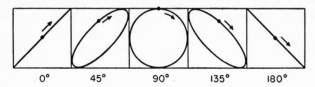

FIG. 1.7. Lissajous figures. Equal frequencies and amplitudes. Different phase angles.

1.7. The Cathode-Ray Oscilloscope. Voltage phenomena are now almost universally observed with the aid of a cathode-ray oscilloscope, the principal component of which is a deflection tube similar to the picture tube in a television receiver. The essentials are shown diagrammatically in Fig. 1.8, the entire assembly being enclosed in a highly evacuated container having a glass window.

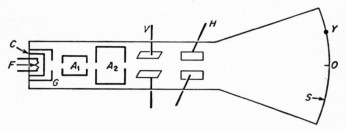

FIG. 1.8. Essentials of a cathode-ray tube with electrostatic focusing and deflection.

The heater F is a coil of wire through which an electric current passes in order to maintain the cathode C at a high temperature. The latter is a small cylinder coated on the end with an oxide which, when heated, emits electrons. The so-called grid G, which bears no resemblance to the grid of a triode, is a metal cylinder surrounding the cathode. By varying the negative potential on the grid a double purpose is accomplished: the emission from the cathode is controlled and the electrons are concentrated into a small beam after emerging from the hole at the right.

The divergence of the electron beam as it proceeds on its path requires additional focusing. It is accomplished by making use of the forces which the electric fields in the two cylindrical anodes A_1 and A_2 exert on the electrons. As they traverse an electric—or magnetic—field their paths are bent similar to the way in which light waves are refracted when they pass from one medium to another. The electric field between the anodes, the second of which is at a higher potential than the first, is equivalent to a converging lens. With proper adjustment of the grid and anode potentials, the electrons are brought to a sharply defined spot at the center O of the glass window. The inside of the latter is coated with a phosphor chemical which emits light when bombarded with electrons. The components which produce and focus the electron beam are known collectively as an electron gun.

In order that variations in voltage or current may be observed, an electron deflecting device, which may be electrostatic or magnetic, must be provided. Electrostatic deflection is proportional to the voltage; magnetic, to the current. The latter is preferred for picture tubes in television receivers. The former is usually employed in cathode-ray tubes of the instrument type and will therefore be described here.

Let a potential be applied to the pair of plates marked V, such that the upper plate is positive. Since the electrons carry a negative charge they will be attracted upward while passing between the plates and the direction of their path will be changed. After leaving this region the electrons will no longer be subject to a force and will travel in an upwardly directed straight line, producing a spot above O, say at Y. (A quantitative discussion is given in Sec. 7.9.) If the potential applied to the V plates is alternating, the spot will move up and down in a straight line, but persistence of vision and the afterglow of the phosphor will usually cause the spots to appear as a continuous line. If a potential is applied to the horizontally deflecting plates H, similar effects are obtained. When potentials are applied simultaneously to both pairs of plates, the pattern is the resultant of both deflections.

A device called a sweep circuit, which is contained within the instrument, may be used to apply to the H plates a voltage which increases linearly with the time for a period which may be adjusted to a given value. This produces a horizontal straight line on which equal spaces are swept out in equal times, thus providing a linear time scale. The intensity of this trace is the same over its entire length. When the sweep voltage reaches its maximum value the spot on the screen is farthest to the right. It then moves back to the original left position so rapidly that ordinarily the return trace is not seen on the screen.

If a sinusoidal voltage is applied to the V plates alone, the vertical motion of the electrons will be simple harmonic, the trace on the screen appearing as a vertical straight line. Unlike the trace of the sweep voltage this line will not appear uniformly bright. The speed with which the electrons are deflected vertically is slowest near the ends of the path, thus making the extremities of this trace somewhat brighter than the center.

If the linear horizontal voltage and the simple harmonic vertical voltage are of the same frequency and are applied simultaneously, the resultant path of the electron beam will be one cycle of a sine curve. The geometry of the trace is identical with that of Fig. 1.2. If the frequency of the sweep alone is halved, the period of the horizontal trace will be doubled and two cycles will appear on the screen.

The distances the electrons are deflected, horizontally or vertically, from the center of the fluorescent screen depend on the geometry of the tube, the speed of the electrons, and the potential difference between the plates. In a given tube the first two factors may be held constant. Thus an electrostatically controlled oscilloscope is essentially a voltage measuring instrument.

When conditions are such that one or more cycles of a sine curve appear on the fluorescent screen, a calibrated transparent scale placed in front of the screen will enable the observer to read the voltage between the upper and lower extremities of the curve. This value, as its name implies, is the *peak-to-peak* voltage, V_{p-p}.

It is not however the same value which would be read on an ordinary a-c voltmeter. Since the voltage is changing at every instant, the instrument must be designed to record some kind of "average" reading. Clearly this cannot be the arithmetic mean, for the sine curve has just as many positive as negative values and the resultant would always be zero. If, however, the instrument is designed so that its deflections are proportional to the *squares* of the voltage, the readings will always be positive.

If all the values of the sine squared are taken over a complete cycle, the arithmetic mean is found to be $\frac{1}{2}$. (The exact solution can be worked out only with the use of the integral calculus, but a satisfactory approximation may be obtained by the method of Problem 1.10.) Although the deflections of the needle are proportional to the average squares of the voltage, the scale of the instrument is calibrated to read the square roots of these values. Hence they indicate the roots of the mean or average squares and are called *root-mean-square* (*rms*) values. Since the root of $\frac{1}{2}$ is $1/\sqrt{2}$, the rms voltage V is related to the maximum voltage V_m by the expression, $V = V_m/\sqrt{2}$.

We are now in a position to convert the peak-to-peak readings of the oscilloscope to the rms values on the voltmeter. Since the peak-to-peak readings are twice the maximum voltages, $V = V_{p-p}/2\sqrt{2}$.

Since many of the voltage curves appearing in electronic circuits are not even approximately sinusoidal, it should be emphasized that the numerical conversion factors given above can be used only when the pattern is a sine or cosine curve. Otherwise the rms value must be worked out from first principles, as illustrated in the example below.

The cycle in Fig. 1.9 may be divided into five equal parts. For one part the voltage is 10; for the others, zero. The average or mean square is

$$\frac{(10)^2 + 4(0)^2}{5} = 20$$

The rms value is $\sqrt{20} = 4.46$ volts.

The Lissajous figures described in the preceding section may be readily presented on the screen of an oscilloscope. The two sinusoidal voltages, whose frequencies are to be compared, are connected separately to the

Fig. 1.9.   One cycle of a nonsinusoidal voltage.

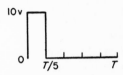

horizontal and vertical deflecting plates and the resultant pattern is observed on the screen. If the frequencies bear simple integral ratios, easily interpretable patterns may be obtained (Fig. 1.10). If the integers are greater than, say five, the pattern usually becomes too complex to be interpreted readily. In the case of the 1:1 ratio the phase angle stays constant, but when the frequencies are different it varies with the time. The statement under Fig. 1.10 that the phase angle is zero means that the two "particles" have zero displacement at the beginning of the motion and are moving in a positive direction.

2:1   3:1   3:2

Fig. 1.10.   Lissajous figures. Typical patterns obtained with simple frequency ratios. The phase angle is 0°.

In practice the voltage of known frequency is usually connected to the H plates and the unknown to the V plates. If the ratio of the latter to the former is 2:1, the diagram at the left in Fig. 1.10 will be obtained; if this ratio is 1:2, the pattern will be rotated through 90°.

The illustrations show that, in some cases, the 2:1 and 3:2 ratios, the figure is a closed curve; in others, the 3:1 ratio, the forward and return traces coincide. In any event, the form of the curve is determined by the frequency ratio and the initial phase angle. The correct frequency ratio may always be obtained by the following method. All Lissajous figures fit into a rectangular area. If the curve is closed, begin at a point where the figure is tangent to one side of the rectangle and trace the curve back to the starting point, counting the number of times each dimension of the rectangle is crossed. The ratio is given by

$$\frac{\text{Frequency on } V \text{ plates}}{\text{Frequency on } H \text{ plates}} = \frac{\text{number of vertical crossings}}{\text{number of horizontal crossings}}$$

For example, an examination of the 2:1 figure shows four vertical and two horizontal crossings. If the figure is not closed, the curve is traced from beginning to end and the ratio is obtained as before.

PROBLEMS

1.1. Radio station WJR has a frequency of 760 kc. In what time will an electron placed in its electric field make a complete oscillation? Give the answer in microseconds.

1.2. Assume that an electron is moving in a field where the frequency is 1 Mc and is first observed when in its equilibrium position and moving upward. If it attains a maximum displacement of 1 mm, what will be its displacement, velocity, and acceleration one-eighth of a period after the initial observation? Find these values first in metric units. Then find the velocity in miles/hour, and the number of times the acceleration exceeds that of gravity.

1.3. A weight hung from a spring of negligible mass stretches it 6 inches. A small displacement causes the system to oscillate with simple harmonic motion. What is its frequency?

1.4. Two coils, each with an inductance of 1 millihenry, connected in series, and two capacitors, each with a capacitance of 10 micro-microfarads, connected in parallel, form an oscillating circuit. Calculate the frequency in kilocycles per second.

1.5. A particle moving with simple harmonic motion has an amplitude of 10 cm. When first observed it has a displacement of − 7.07 cm and is moving towards its equilibrium position. Find the position of the particle 5/24 T later. Diagram.

1.6. A sinusoidal 60 cycles per sec voltage has a maximum value of 250 volts. At $t = 0$, $V = + 75$ volts and is increasing. What *minimum* time must elapse before $V = + 75$ volts again? Diagram.

1.7. For readers having a knowledge of the differential calculus: The velocity of a particle is the first time derivative of its displacement; the acceleration is the second time derivative. With this information, obtain Eq. (1.7) and (1.8) from Eq. (1.6).

1.8. Plot the Lissajous figures for two simple harmonic motions of equal amplitude and frequency with phase differences of (a) 150° and (b) 330°. Compare similarities and differences with respect to Fig. 1.6.

1.9. Show by eliminating t from the equations

$$x = A_1 \cdot \sin \omega t$$

$$y = A_2 \cdot \sin (\omega t + \Delta)$$

that the equation of the resultant path is

$$\sin^2 \Delta = \left(\frac{x}{A_1}\right)^2 - \frac{2xy}{A_1A_2}\cos\Delta + \left(\frac{y}{A_2}\right)^2$$

Show that the curve is a straight line when $\Delta = 0$, and a circle when $A_1 = A_2$ and $\Delta = \pi/2$.

1.10. Tabulate the values of $\sin \alpha$ and $\sin^2 \alpha$ by 10° steps from 0° to 90°, inclusive. Show that the average value of $\sin^2 \alpha$ is approximately 0.500, and hence the rms value is 0.707, i.e., $1/\sqrt{2}$. (Carry to three decimal places only.)

1.11. A cathode-ray oscilloscope is calibrated for 20 volts per in. and its sweep circuit set for 6 milliseconds. Three complete sine curves, with a distance of 2.25 in. between their upper and lower extremities, appear on the screen. Find the frequency and the rms voltage.

1.12. Two nearly equal frequencies are to be compared. The Lissajous figure is an ellipse which is not stationary but makes one complete rotation in 4 sec. If the known frequency is 50 cycles per sec, what is the frequency of the unknown?

1.13. A voltage waveform has a value of $+10$ volts from 0 to $T/4$, 0 volts from $T/4$ to $3T/4$, and -5 volts from $3T/4$ to T. Draw the waveform and find the rms value over the cycle.

1.14. Plot the Lissajous figure with a vertical to horizontal frequency ratio of $2:1$ for a phase angle of 90°. The phase angle is to be interpreted as follows: at the beginning of the motion the x-particle has zero displacement and is moving in a positive direction; the y-particle is at its maximum positive displacement.

Chapter 2

WAVE MOTION

2.1. Transfer of Energy and Momentum. In order to clear up any misunderstanding that may exist, let it be emphasized in the beginning that wave motion *is not* synonymous with simple harmonic motion.

Consider the transfer of energy and momentum from one particle to its neighbor. This may be shown in a general way by rolling an elastic sphere, say a billiard ball, so that it strikes a row of identical spheres placed in contact along a shallow groove. At the collision a force is applied which compresses slightly the first sphere in the row. There is an elastic reaction. According to Newton's third law of motion, action and reaction must be equal and opposite. Since the masses of the two objects are equal, the reaction force applied to the moving sphere during the time of contact is just sufficient to bring it to rest. The force in the forward direction is applied to the next ball and the process continues to the end of the line, the last sphere moving off because there is no other object to which it can transfer its impulse or momentum.

If the row were infinitely long energy and momentum would be transferred indefinitely. This transfer, however, cannot take place instantaneously, for the spheres have both inertia and elasticity. The speed with which the energy is transferred depends upon these two properties of the spheres. Note carefully that there is no displacement of spheres along the line. Energy and momentum, not matter, are transferred in wave motion.

2.2. Graphical Representation of Waves. Let us now assume that the spheres are separated from one another by spiral springs, that the row is infinitely long, and that the sphere at the left is given a motion which is simple harmonic in character. This motion will be conveyed successively by each sphere to its right-hand neighbor. Energy and momentum will be transferred along the line. But all of the spheres will not have, say, maximum forward displacement at the same time. With a fast camera we may take a snapshot of a section of the line at a given instant of time.

Suppose, after the motion has progressed a little, the first sphere is at its equilibrium position, moving to the left. The sphere immediately to the

18

right, having started its motion a little later, will also be moving backwards, approaching its equilibrium position from the right. If a curve is plotted, *displacement* against *position of the spheres*, the graph will have the appearance of the first curve in Fig. 2.1 for the time $t = 0$. A positive value of y for a given sphere indicates that its displacement is towards the right. The arrows attached to the dots representing the spheres, or particles, as they will hereafter be called, show conventionally the directions in which they are moving, i.e., an arrow pointing upward indicates motion to the right. The lengths of these arrows indicate the approximate magnitudes of the velocities.

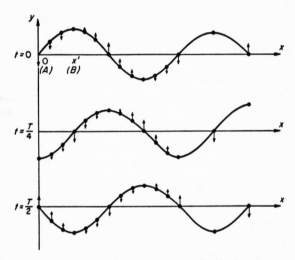

FIG. 2.1. Displacements and velocities of a longitudinal wave at three instants of time.

Note that the variables are the displacement y and the distance x; they are not the same as those in simple harmonic motion. The graph of the latter (Fig. 1.2) shows how the displacement varies with the time—for a single particle. That is, we select any particle and observe its displacement as time progresses. In Fig. 2.1 each curve represents a snapshot of the *particles within a given range* taken at a *given instant*.

Suppose, at the time $t = 0$, we place two observers, A at $x = 0$, and B at $x = x'$. Observer A will see the particle at zero displacement, moving to the left at its maximum speed; B will see the particle with maximum displacement to the right, momentarily at rest. At $t = T/4$ observations are again made, the positions and velocities of the particles being shown on the middle curve of Fig. 2.1. Notice that B's particle now has the same displacement and velocity which A's particle had a quarter-period earlier. B's particle is said to *lag in phase* with respect to A's, in this case, by 90°. The third part of Fig. 2.1 shows the situation at $t = T/2$. Notice that the maximum displacement has progressed *uniformly* down the line.

A study of the curves will show that the displacement and velocity of a particle depend on its position in the line and the time of observation. Translated into mathematics, y and v are functions of x and t, or $y = f(x,t)$ and $v = f(x,t)$.

2.3. Velocity, Frequency, and Wavelength. Notice that the individual particles move with simple harmonic motion which is essentially a *non-uniform* motion. The maximum displacement, which may be thought of as traveling from particle to particle, is essentially a *uniform* motion.

It is this maximum displacement—or its minimum, or zero—which, traveling along the x-axis, may be said, in a sense, to constitute a wave. Since its motion is uniform the equation for the velocity is simply

$$v = x/t \qquad (2.1)$$

This velocity is a function of the inertial and elastic properties of the medium in which the wave is traveling. The electrical analogs are the inductance and the reciprocal of the capacitance, respectively.

As in simple harmonic motion we need to define certain technical terms. Since the particle executes simple harmonic motion, it may be taken for granted that the definitions for displacement, amplitude, period, and frequency are identical with those given in Chapter 1. In Fig. 2.2, where the

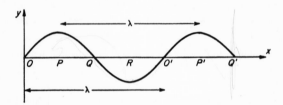

FIG. 2.2.   Diagram showing phase and wavelength relations.

displacement is plotted against the distance along which the wave is propagated, at a given time of observation, the displacement at O' is identical with that at O, both as to magnitude (zero) and phase (0° and 360°, or 0 and 2π radians). Although the displacement at Q is also zero, the velocity is opposite; the particle is therefore 180° out of phase with the particles at O and O'. The shortest distance between two successive particles in the same phase is called the *wavelength*. It is universally denoted by the symbol λ. The distance OO' is one wavelength; similarly, the distance PP'.

If we make our observations a quarter-period later, the crest at P has, we may say, reached Q, a quarter-wavelength farther along the x-axis.

Then, in successive quarter-periods, this crest will reach R, O', and P'. In other words, during the period T the wave travels one wavelength λ. Because the *rate is constant* the velocity with which the wave is propagated may be written

$$v = \lambda/T$$

Since $f = 1/T$, this relation may assume the more convenient form

$$v = f\lambda \qquad\qquad (2.2)$$

which is a fundamental equation of wave motion and is applicable to all waves.

TABLE 2.1.   TYPES OF WAVES

Examples	Velocity, meters/sec	Frequency	Wavelength, meters
Sound waves	344*	344 cycles/sec	1
Electromagnetic waves	3×10^8†	300 Mc/sec	1

* Depends upon, i.e., is a function of the temperature.   Medium: air.
† In free space; for many purposes the same value may be used for air.

2.4. Longitudinal and Transverse Waves.   The examples given in the table represent two different types of waves.   In the first the displacements of the particles are parallel to the direction of wave propagation, the situation being somewhat analogous to the row of spheres separated by springs. When sound energy is transmitted in air small "particles" of the gas are alternately compressed and expanded along the line of wave propagation. The particles move, say to right or left, always towards a pressure minimum. This motion results in a maximum being formed where a minimum previously existed.   Thus, a maximum, or a minimum, is propagated at a constant rate in a given direction.   Waves, in which the simple harmonic motion of the particles is parallel to the direction of propagation, are called *longitudinal* waves.   Sound or compressional waves may be generated in liquids and solids, as well as in gases.

Preliminary to a more detailed discussion of the second example, helpful information may be obtained by considering the vibrations of the particles in a rope.   The oscillations are simple harmonic, the particles moving in a plane perpendicular to the length of the rope along which the wave is propagated.   If the rope is stretched horizontally, the particles may vibrate up and down or in any other direction provided the line of motion lies in a plane perpendicular to the length of the rope.   The maximum displacement, for example, moves along the rope at a *uniform* speed, a procedure which constitutes a *traveling* wave. Since the displacements of the particles are in a plane which is perpendicular to the direction of wave propagation, the waves are characterized as *transverse*.

2.5. Electromagnetic Waves and Poynting's Vector. Although electromagnetic waves are transverse, close analogies with the motion of a vibrating rope must not be expected. In the case of the former there are no "particles" which vibrate, nor must there *necessarily* be a material medium in which the wave is propagated. If this seems difficult to believe, we may, on the one hand, accept the pragmatic viewpoint that although the phenomenon is not fully understood, the assumptions are justified by the results of experiment. On the other hand, we may attach no particular physical significance to the electromagnetic field, looking upon it merely as a mathematical device by means of which we may calculate the transfer of radiation through space. The latter interpretation is an example of the abstract viewpoint which is receiving ever increasing acceptance in contemporary physics.

Some comprehension of the physics underlying the subject may be obtained from a consideration of two rather simple experiments which led Maxwell in 1864 to predict mathematically the existence of electromagnetic waves.

Kirchhoff's law for steady, direct currents states that there must be a continuous flow of electrons throughout the entire circuit. If the current is varying with time and a capacitor is included in the circuit, this is not necessarily true. The situation is illustrated in Fig. 2.3. The alternating voltage causes the charges to flow on and off the plates of the capacitor C.

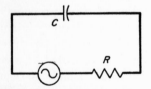

FIG. 2.3. A changing electric field produces a displacement current in C.

If the space between the plates is a vacuum, it is clear that for moderate voltages, at any rate, no charges will move across this region. Yet a magnetic field may be observed, not only in the neighborhood of the wires, but also within the evacuated space. Since an actual flow of electrons is always accompanied by a magnetic field, we may say that so far as the magnetic effect is concerned, the changing electric field produced by the alternate charging and discharging of the capacitor is equivalent to an electric current, which Maxwell called a *displacement current*. Although its presence may be detected by the accompanying magnetic field, it has none of the other properties of a conduction current. The concept of displacement current now enables us to make a statement of far-reaching importance, namely, that any closed path, consisting of any combination of conductors, dielectrics, or evacuated spaces, may form a continuous electric circuit. In effect, it is a statement that electric currents are continuous in space.

If, for any reason, there is a change in the strength of an electric field a magnetic field must also be present. The existence of the latter is independent of the nature of the surrounding space; it may be observed in a vacuum as well as in a material medium. The phenomenon forms the experimental basis of Maxwell's first law which, most briefly stated, is: a changing electric field is accompanied by a magnetic field.

Familiar to all who have studied elementary physics is the experiment in which a magnet, thrust into a loop of wire, induces by its changing magnetic field a voltage in that wire. This voltage is proportional to the rate of change of flux and is equal to the product of the average electric field and the length of the circuit. If the loop is closed the electrons are set in motion, the magnitude of the current depending on the resistance of the circuit. Even if the resistance were to become infinite, as if no wire were present, the electric field set up by the varying magnetic flux would still exist. The voltage around any closed path, be it described in a material medium or in free space, is given by the rate of change of magnetic flux. On the basis of this reasoning Maxwell's second law may be stated: a changing magnetic field is accompanied by an electric field.

Let us assume that at a given time and at a given point in space there exists a rapidly changing electric field. According to Maxwell's first law, there must also exist a magnetic field. The variations in the latter, by Maxwell's second law, must in turn produce an electric field, and so on. It then follows from Maxwell's two laws that there will be an interchange of energy between the electric and magnetic fields analogous to the interchange of potential and kinetic energy in a sound wave. If the rate of variation is sufficiently high, significant amounts of energy will be propagated outward into space. Since each of the fields may be said to be created from the other, it follows that they contain equal amounts of energy. Jointly they are called the electromagnetic field.

Although a wave generated at an antenna may be spherical, only a small portion is intercepted by the receiving antenna at a relatively great distance. For all practical purposes it may be treated as a plane wave. Under these circumstances the electric and magnetic fields oscillate in planes which are at right angles to each other and perpendicular to the direction of propagation of the wave. If, in the plane of the paper, the electric field is vertical, the magnetic field is horizontal (Fig. 2.4). The positive maximum, for example, occurs at the same time for both fields. Thus it may be stated that for radio waves the electric and magnetic radiation fields are in time phase and in space quadrature (Fig. 2.5). The electric field will be denoted by ε; the magnetic field, by $\mathcal{H}$. (Bold face type will be used when it is desired to emphasize the vector nature of a quantity.)

Plane transverse waves, in which the varying electric and magnetic vectors are perpendicular to the direction of wave propagation, may exist in free space and in the region surrounding open-wire and coaxial forms of transmission lines. With this type of wave, called a transverse electromag-

FIG. 2.4. Relative directions of the electric and magnetic fields and the Poynting vector.

netic (TEM) wave, we shall be primarily concerned. However, it should be pointed out that although the ε- and $\mathcal{H}$-vectors are always mutually perpendicular, when a wave is propagated in a hollow tube having no inner conductor, either ε or $\mathcal{H}$ must have a component in the direction of wave propagation. These waves are customarily named after their transverse component. They will be discussed as transverse magnetic (TM) and transverse electric (TE) waves under *Waveguides*.

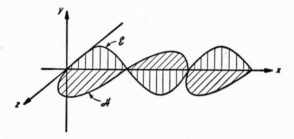

FIG. 2.5. Conventional diagram of the distribution of the electric and magnetic fields in a plane wave.

In order to determine the direction of wave propagation, rotate the ε-vector through 90° into the $\mathcal{H}$-vector; the wave, i.e., the energy will be propagated in the direction in which a right-handed screw will advance. In Fig. 2.4 such a rotation, denoted mathematically by $\varepsilon \times \mathcal{H}$, shows that the direction of wave propagation is *into* the paper, as indicated by the vector **P**. This vector is most appropriately called the *Poynting vector* in honor of the English physicist who discovered the theorem.

Furthermore, the product $\varepsilon \times \mathcal{H}$, with the proper choice of units, will give the time rate at which electromagnetic energy is propagated into space. Let ε be measured in volts per meter and $\mathcal{H}$ in amperes per meter.

Their product will give watts per square meter, that is, power per unit area, which is equivalent to the *intensity* of the radiation. The Poynting vector will show the direction in which the energy is propagated.

The rate of dissipation of electrical energy in a resistor is determined in a similar manner. Here the power is given by the product of the voltage V and the current I. From the viewpoint of electron flow, power in watts equals volts times amperes. From the viewpoint of energy transfer by the electromagnetic field, intensity in watts per square meter equals volts per meter times amperes per meter.

2.6. Long and Short Lines. That electromagnetic waves may be propagated along wires, or rather in the medium surrounding them, may be understood from a consideration of the following experiment. Let there be a long tube, filled with air, which is closed with a driving piston at one end and a thin diaphragm at the other (Fig. 2.6). When the piston is moved back and forth *slowly* the pressure is *substantially* the same in all

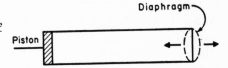

FIG. 2.6. Tube for demonstration of compressional waves in air.

parts of the tube, the diaphragm moving *in phase* with the piston. For example, when the piston moves to the right, the diaphragm also moves to the right. If, however, the frequency with which the piston moves back and forth is increased, there will be an appreciable lag at the distant end, since time is required for pressure changes to be transmitted along the tube to the diaphragm. The frequency may be such that when the piston is moving to the right the diaphragm may be moving to the left. In technical language the diaphragm is said to be 180° out of phase with the piston. For the lowest frequency at which this relation exists the length of the tube is 180° or a half-wavelength.

The velocity of the wave in the tube is determined by the pressure and density of the gas within it. Under specified conditions this velocity is constant. The frequency is determined by the rate at which the observer wishes to oscillate the piston with a motion which may be made at least approximately simple harmonic. From Eq. (2.2) the wavelength may be calculated.

Notice that when the wavelength is very large compared with the length of the tube, the magnitudes of the pressure and the particle velocity at a given time are nearly independent of the position along the tube. If, however, the length of the tube is large, compared with the wavelength, the pressure will not be the same in different parts of the tube and the particle velocity will vary in magnitude and direction.

The phenomena described above are analogous to those which exist in the case where a transmission line is supplied by an a-c generator. We may think of current and voltage maxima progressing along the wires, or magnetic and electric fields propagating energy in the neighborhood of the line at the rate of 3×10^8 meters per sec, much the same as waves of particle velocity and pressure travel along the air-filled tube. The phase relation between the generator and the end of the line will evidently be determined by the relative magnitudes of the length of the transmission line and the frequency. In other words, is the line long or short? The question is easily answered by considering a few numerical examples.

For a power line, let $f = 60$ cycles per sec. Thus,

$$\lambda = (3 \times 10^8 \text{ meters/sec})/(60 \text{ cycles/sec}) = 5 \times 10^6 \text{ meters} \doteq 3100 \text{ miles.}$$

This is a case in which the wavelength is much greater than the length of the line. No single power line is even approximately 3000 miles long. It is a case analogous to moving the piston very slowly in the air-filled tube. At any instant the voltage or current is everywhere substantially the same. Even if the frequency is several times 60 cycles per sec, the wavelength is still large in comparison with the length of actual power lines. No troublesome problems with respect to phase are likely to arise at power frequencies.

Let us examine the situation at other frequencies. Near the middle of the standard broadcast band, say 1000 kc, the wavelength is 300 meters or about 1000 ft. For television Channel 11, 200 Mc, the wavelength is only 1.5 meters or approximately 5 ft. In the case of a radar magnetron oscillator, 10,000 Mc, the wavelength is reduced to 3 cm, only a little more than an inch. At the two higher frequencies it is clear that the wavelengths are not large in comparison with the length of a practical transmission line. For example, at the TV frequency a line about 10 ft long, or for the radar frequency a line less than 3 in. long would be equivalent to two wavelengths. The generator will go through two complete oscillations before the first maximum, say, reaches the end of the line. The fact that current or voltage is not substantially the same at all points along the line is of considerable importance.

We may think of electric and magnetic fields in the immediate neighborhood of the wires traveling down the line along with voltages and currents. We may say that electromagnetic energy is conveyed in these *fields,* as in acoustics sound energy is transferred by the air in a speaking tube. In the case of wires the point of view selected may be one of *convenience* but, in our present state of knowledge, for the transmission of electrical energy through space, consideration of the fields becomes practically *necessary.*

2.7. The Infinite Line. At the beginning of this chapter we spoke of an infinitely long row of spheres. Perhaps we should have emphasized a similar qualification regarding the tube closed at the ends by a piston and a diaphragm, the oscillating rope, and the transmission line fed by an a-c generator. Such an assumption may seem to lack practicality. But if any of these devices is actually terminated, a new situation is introduced. The incident wave will, in general, be partly reflected and there will exist the more complex case of two waves traveling in opposite directions. The assumption of an infinite medium simplifies, rather than complicates, the situation.

In an adequate discussion of any of the foregoing examples we must take into account both the incident and reflected waves. The displacement, velocity, and acceleration, or their electrical counterparts, in accordance with the principle of superposition, are the resultants of the effects produced by the two waves (Sec. 5.1). A consideration of this problem, which is of primary importance, will be taken up next.

PROBLEMS

2.1. The length of the fundamental antenna for best television reception is approximately a half-wavelength. Find the dimensions of this antenna in feet for (a) Channel 4, $f = 67$ Mc, and (b) Channel 12, $f = 205$ Mc.

2.2. WHDH, $f = 850$ kc, uses a special transmission line to suppress its second harmonic frequency. What is the frequency of the second harmonic? Does it lie within the AM broadcast band?

2.3. The amplitude of a wave is 12 in. and its wavelength is 12 ft. A given particle is observed at its maximum positive displacement. *How far* will this particle travel in one-eighth period? How far will the wave travel in the same time? Diagram.

2.4. A wave with an amplitude of 10 cm and a wavelength of 60 cm has a displacement of $+ 8.2$ cm, which is decreasing at $x = 0$ when $t = 0$. (a) What is the displacement at $x = 12$ cm when $t = 0$? (b) What will be the displacements of the two particles when $t = T/3$? Diagram.

2.5. Compare the number of waves on a transmission line 100 ft long for KGO, $f = 810$ kc, and KGO–TV, $f = 175$ Mc.

2.6. Electric field strength $\mathcal{E}$ may be expressed in newtons per coulomb. Show this to be equivalent to volts per meter.

2.7. Magnetic field strength $\mathcal{H}$ may be expressed in newtons per weber. Show this to be equivalent to amperes per meter.

2.8. A plane electromagnetic wave in free space has an electric field with a maximum value of 2 mv per meter and a magnetic field with a maximum value of 5.3 microamperes per meter. Find (a) the value of Poynting's vector, (b) the impedance of free space. Assume that the fields are sinusoidal.

2.9. Show that $\mathcal{H} \times \mathcal{E}$ is not equivalent to $\mathcal{E} \times \mathcal{H}$.

2.10. How much energy is there in a cubic meter of space where the Poynting vector has a value of 20 microwatts per square meter?

Chapter 3

STANDING WAVES AND TRANSMISSION LINES

3.1. Reflection from a Rigid Boundary. We shall first consider the waves formed on a string or rope. Let one end of the string be attached to a wall which, for all practical purposes, may be considered rigid. When the incident wave reaches the wall it will be reflected. Since the wall is rigid, it is clear that the rope can show no displacement there *at any time*. Speaking mathematically, at the boundary y must equal zero for *all* values of t. Two identical waves can cancel each other only if they are 180° out of phase at the point in question. This, of course, is their phase difference at the boundary but not necessarily at all points along the string.

One method of representing the reflected wave after a phase change of 180° is shown in Fig. 3.1. Extend the incident wave, as it appears at a given time, beyond the boundary. Then cut out a half-wavelength and send the wave in the reverse direction, starting, of course, at the boundary. The resultant wave is obtained by adding the displacements algebraically point by point.

Fig. 3.1 shows the incident, reflected, and resultant waves for the following values of t: 0, $T/8$, $T/4$, $3T/8$, and $T/2$. The reader should draw the waves for values of t between $T/2$ and T. Notice the special features of this family of curves. There is *always* a point of zero displacement at the rigid boundary—we call it a *node*. Furthermore, at distances equal to integral multiples of $\lambda/2$ from the boundary there are also nodes. The segments of the string between adjacent nodes are called *loops*. A point halfway between nodes is called an *antinode*. The displacements of points on the loops vary between positive and negative values at a given time as shown in Fig. 3.2. The first segment at the left has a positive displacement and its neighbor to the right a negative displacement at $t = 0$. A half-period later, at $t = T/2$, these displacements have changed signs. At an intermediate time all the points on the first segment have moved down, and all points on the second segment, upward, with resulting zero displacement all along the string, as shown for the time $t = T/4$ in Fig. 3.1. If the amplitude of the

28

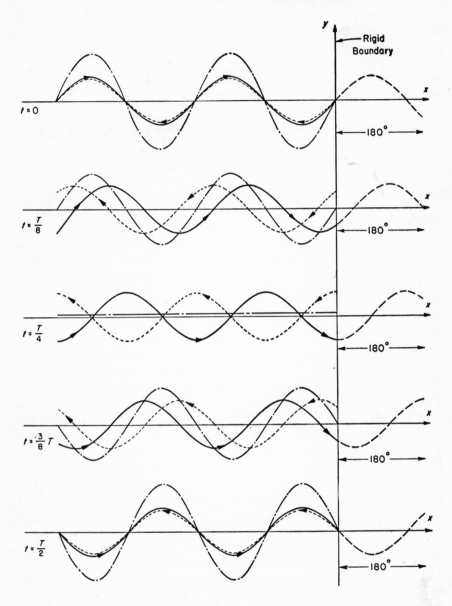

FIG. 3.1. Reflection of waves from a rigid boundary.
———— Incident wave   — — — Extended incident wave
······ Reflected wave   —·— Resultant wave

incident wave is A and there is no loss on reflection, as will be the case for a truly rigid boundary, the displacement at the antinodes will vary between $+ 2A$ and $- 2A$. In adjacent loops, at a given time, the string is moving in opposite directions. When the frequency is 20 cycles per sec or more, the string appears as if it were divided into segments. This effect is called persistence of vision.

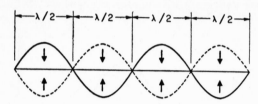

FIG. 3.2. Nodes and antinodes.
———— Resultant wave at $t = 0$
— — — — Resultant wave at $t = T/2$

In the case of the infinitely long string (Sec. 2.7) a given aspect of the waveform, say the maximum positive displacement, travels at a constant speed determined by the tension in the string and its mass per unit length. For this reason it is called a *traveling* wave. When there is a rigid boundary at which reflection occurs there is no progression of any aspect of the waveform. Instead there are nodes and loops which maintain invariant positions on the string. For this reason, we speak of a *standing* or *stationary* wave.

3.2. Reflection from a Nonrigid Boundary. The end of the string need not be attached to a rigid boundary; it may be perfectly free. In practice this condition may be realized approximately by hanging the string or rope vertically with its lower end unattached. In this case there will be no change of phase on reflection and there will be an antinode at the boundary. A method of representing the reflected wave, under these circumstances, is shown in Fig. 3.3 for values of t equal to 0, $T/8$, and $T/4$. As before, extend the incident wave, as it appears at a given time, beyond the boundary. Since there is no phase change, send the wave directly back at the boundary. The result is the same as if the incident wave and its extension were drawn on transparent paper which is then folded back upon a crease along the boundary. The resultant wave is of course obtained by adding the displacements.

By drawing the curves for values of t between $T/4$ and T, it will be seen that a series of standing waves is also obtained for this type of boundary. However, at the free end of the string, i.e., at the nonrigid boundary, there will be an antinode instead of a node.   This constitutes the essential difference between reflections from these two types of boundaries.

3.3. Reflection of Voltage and Current Waves.   We shall now pass over to the more pertinent cases of standing waves of voltage and current on transmission lines.   Even though the line is lossless, if it is long in comparison with the wavelength, the magnitudes of voltage and current as read on voltmeters and ammeters will not be everywhere the same.   Since the

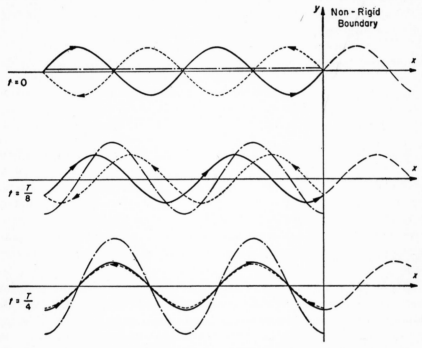

FIG. 3.3.   Reflection of waves from a nonrigid boundary.
——————— Incident wave   ————— Extended incident wave
• • • • • • Reflected wave   —·—· Resultant wave

line must be terminated in some way, we shall expect to find the current and voltage distributions as the resultants of this pair of incident and reflected waves.   Our discussion at first will be confined to the rather simple cases of three specific terminations—an open circuit, a short circuit, and a characteristic impedance.

At this point it may be remarked that there is a special method of terminating a line so that all the energy is absorbed at the load and none is reflected.   This may be accomplished by terminating the line by its *characteristic impedance* (sometimes called *surge* impedance), a quantity which may be calculated from the inductance, capacitance, resistance, and conductance per unit length of line. Their relative magnitudes are usually such that at radio frequencies a transmission line has the properties of a pure resistance. If there is no reflection there will be no standing waves, a situation which is equivalent to an infinitely long line.

Before considering specific cases let us point out that the standing wave configuration on a transmission line is always determined by the *way in which the line is terminated*.

All discussions will be based on the assumption that the line is lossless. This is an idealized situation; it can be approximated in practice by using tubes plated with silver, since that metal is the best conductor of electricity. At high frequencies the current is not distributed uniformly throughout the conductor; it may be considered as flowing almost exclusively in a thin layer at the surface, a phenomenon known as the *skin effect*. Since the effective cross section of the conductor is thereby decreased, the resistance is greater than the direct current value.   In general, the current tends to concentrate on the surface of the conductor nearest to the field producing it.   In the case of wires, which are surrounded by the field, the current tends to seek the outside of the conductors.   The exciting field in coaxial cables, however, is in the region between the two conductors.   The current, therefore, will be concentrated on the outer wall of the central wire and on the inner wall of the metallic sheath.

Consider either an open-circuited or a short-circuited transmission line. Recall that power, the rate at which energy is transmitted, is given by the product of voltage and current.   If either of these factors is zero, there is no power.   If a line or cable is open-circuited at the distant end, the termination can absorb no power because the current through it must be zero. *All* the energy that reaches the distant end must be reflected to the sending end.   Likewise, if a line or cable is short-circuited no power is absorbed, for no voltage can exist across the termination. *All* the energy reaching the distant end must be reflected.

Parenthetically, it may be of interest to compare transmission lines to inductors and capacitors.   In that part of elementary physics dealing with alternating currents it is shown that inductors and capacitors absorb energy from the source during one part of the cycle and return energy to the source during another part of the cycle.   The limitations imposed upon the current by these elements are known as reactances, which are related to the power factor of the circuit.   It may be pointed out that this characteristic of accepting power from the source and later returning power to it shows that transmission lines may act as inductors and capacitors.   At low frequencies the length of these lines would make their use for this purpose very awkward.   At high frequencies, on the other hand, the short lengths of lines and cables make them very convenient to use. For example, at 3000 Mc an appreciable range of inductive and capacitive reactances may be provided by a line less than 2 in. long, which compares very favorably with the dimensions of conventional type elements. To avoid misunderstanding it should be pointed out that at the higher frequencies the use of short lengths of transmission lines as reactive components is not merely convenient but also necessary, because it is physically impracticable to construct lumped inductances and capacitances which can be used at these frequencies.

3.4. The Open-Circuited Line. We shall now consider the specific case of an open-circuited transmission line, two wavelengths long—similar to the string in Fig. 3.1. The reflected current wave will be like the reflected wave shown in that diagram, i.e., there will be a phase reversal of 180°. This must be true, for the electrons arriving at an open circuit reverse their direction of flow or, equivalently, the magnetic field undergoes a phase reversal. The net result is a current node at the end of the line with additional nodes spaced at half-wavelength intervals.

For the voltage, however, the case is different. When this wave comes to the end of the open line it merely flows back in the same manner it would have gone forward. The electric field extends from the positive charges on one wire to the negative charges on the other wire and, since the charges cannot flow across the open termination, the sign of the voltage wave is not changed at the boundary. But the direction of travel is changed and the wave moves backward. The situation is analogous to the reflection of waves on a string at a nonrigid boundary (cf. Fig. 3.3). The net result is a voltage antinode at the end of the line with additional antinodes at half-wavelength intervals.

Alternating currents and voltages along the line may be measured by ammeters and voltmeters designed to respond to the high frequencies involved. These meters are usually calibrated to read rms values of sinusoidal

FIG. 3.4. Standing waves of voltage and current on an open-circuited transmission line.
——————— Voltage   — — — — Current

current and voltage, which are related to the maximum values by the expressions, $V = V_m/\sqrt{2}$ and $I = I_m/\sqrt{2}$ (Sec. 1.7). Now, these meters are incapable of distinguishing the phase of the voltage or current they record; only the magnitudes of the rms values, as in 60-cycle measurements, are recorded. Hence it is customary to represent voltage and current waves on transmission lines as in Fig. 3.4.

If a voltmeter or ammeter is moved along the line it will read alternately rms maxima and zero—with, of course, intermediate values. Successive maxima will be spaced a half-wavelength apart. In actual practice a voltmeter will not read zero at the nodes because a physical transmission line only approximates the idealized line which we have assumed. The arrangement by which the wavelength is determined from the location of maxima and minima with a voltmeter is called a *Lecher wire* system.

3.5. The Short-Circuited Line. Next, let us consider the case of the short-circuited line. At the instant of reflection there is no phase shift of 180° in the current. The reason is that the termination provides a path for the electrons; the direction of travel only is changed. This case is equivalent to a reflection at a nonrigid boundary; there will be a current antinode at the end of the line (cf. Fig. 3.3).

When a voltage wave reaches the end of a short-circuited line its resultant value must be zero, for no potential difference can exist across a termination of zero resistance or impedance. The charges, between which the electric lines of force extend, pass from one wire to the other through the short circuit and at the instant of reflection the voltage is reversed. This is equivalent to a phase change of 180°, i.e., a reflection at a rigid boundary (cf. Fig. 3.1). Hence there is a voltage node at the end of the line.

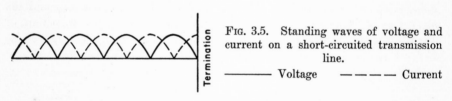

FIG. 3.5. Standing waves of voltage and current on a short-circuited transmission line.

———— Voltage   — — — — Current

The voltage and current distributions along a short-circuited line, presented according to meter readings, are shown in Fig. 3.5. Compare the results with the open circuit in Fig. 3.4.

A somewhat spectacular demonstration of voltage distributions may be made with a short fluorescent tube such as is used in study lamps. The tube is placed across the wires and moved along the line. At a voltage antinode the tube will glow brilliantly but it will be extinguished when a voltage node is approached.

3.6. Energy in the Electromagnetic Field. As already stated, we shall find it convenient to think of voltage and current fluctuations as variations in the electric and magnetic fields, respectively, in the space surrounding the wires. To repeat, the latter serve as guides to the fields and confine them, for all practical purposes, to the region in the immediate neighborhood of the wires. That energy does exist in this space may be readily shown with the aid of the fluorescent tube used to indicate voltage distributions. The lamp may be made to glow by holding it a short distance above or in the space between the wires, but not touching them. A transmission line, confining as it does the energy of the electromagnetic field to the immediate neighborhood, is not an effective device when the objective is radiation of energy into space. The required modification will be taken up when we consider the design of an antenna.

It has been stated that the energy of the electromagnetic field is propagated in free space at the rate of 3×10^8 meters per sec. Many transmission lines are constructed of coaxial cable, which consists of a central metallic conductor, say a wire, embedded in a cylinder of some highly insulated material, such as polystyrene, which, in turn, is covered with metallic braid. The field is therefore propagated within the insulator where the velocity of the wave energy is less than its velocity in free space. This fact must be taken into account by multiplying the free-space velocity by a factor which depends on the material of the insulator and which is known as the *velocity factor*. Its value is always less than unity, for 3×10^8 meters per sec is the highest speed at which energy can be transmitted.

3.7. Applications of Quarter- and Half-Wavelength Lines. To one whose experience has been limited to low frequency phenomena, transmission lines at the higher frequencies often exhibit some rather surprising characteristics. Suppose, for example, we have a line of quarter-wavelength shorted at the end. As we have seen, the voltage and current distributions will be as given in Fig. 3.6. Now, recall that impedance $Z = V/I$. Look-

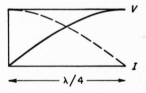

FIG. 3.6.   Shorted quarter-wave stub.

ing in at the right end of the line the approaching energy "sees" a high impedance, i.e., a high voltage and a nearly zero current. This is equivalent to the somewhat paradoxical statement that "a short looks like an open." If a voltage-current diagram is drawn for an open quarter-wave line, it will be seen that the impedance is very low. A quarter-wave line "inverts" the load.

If the shorted line is a half-wave in length, the propagated energy sees a low impedance, for the voltage is practically zero and the current is a maximum (Fig. 3.7). Clearly, in this case "a short looks like a short." Similarly, for a half-wave open line it may be seen that the impedance is very high. In these cases, however, it should be noticed that the input and terminal voltages are of opposite polarities.

If a two-wire transmission line needs a support, a satisfactory insulating material would ordinarily be used. However, at high frequencies two metal tubes, each a quarter-wavelength long, fastened to a *metal* base,

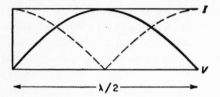

Fig. 3.7. Shorted half-wave stub.

will serve the purpose admirably (Fig. 3.8). When the energy reaches the points of support it sees a high impedance, i.e., the short looks like an open and no energy is transmitted to the stub. Of course, this is the case only if the stub is a quarter-wavelength for the frequency of the oscillator. Otherwise, energy will pass from the line to the stub.

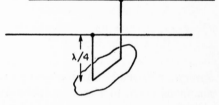

Fig. 3.8. Two-wire transmission line with quarter-wave insulating stub.

The principle involved in the shorted quarter-wavelength transmission line, or stub, may form the basis for a device used to suppress an unwanted second harmonic of a broadcasting oscillator. Let us assume that the transmission line shown in Fig. 3.8 forms the connection between the oscillator and the antenna. The attached quarter-wavelength stub provides a high impedance for the station's carrier frequency and its energy is transmitted undiminished to the antenna. The second harmonic has double the frequency of the carrier. From the relation among velocity, frequency, and wavelength, we see that a quarter-wavelength for the carrier is a half-wavelength for the second harmonic. The stub therefore presents a low impedance to the latter and none of its energy passes to the antenna for radiation into space. Furthermore, the stub will be an effective suppressor for all even-numbered harmonics.

A balanced transmission line has a pair of equally spaced identical conductors, such that their impedances to ground are the same. The equal and opposite currents in the wires are accompanied by magnetic fields which substantially cancel each other and minimize radiation. If the line is connected to a center-fed antenna each half will receive the same current. At the higher frequencies a coaxial cable, which is not a balanced line, is often employed. The outer conductor of the cable is connected to ground; the inner has a relatively high impedance to ground. The problem of transforming from an unbalanced to a balanced system may be solved by making use of the properties of a quarter-wave line.

In Fig. 3.9 the coaxial cable is connected to the center of the antenna at A and B. (The antenna is not shown in the diagram.) At high frequencies the current I_A flows on the outer surface of the inner conductor and I_B on the inner surface of the outer conductor. Both currents are equal. When I_B reaches the point B it will divide, part going to one half of the

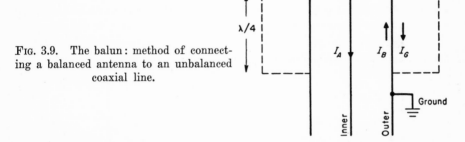

FIG. 3.9. The balun: method of connecting a balanced antenna to an unbalanced coaxial line.

antenna and the remainder along the *outside* of the outer conductor. The magnitude of I_G depends on the impedance to ground by the path along the outside of the conductor.

If a cylindrical shield (indicated by broken lines in the diagram), a quarter-wave long and concentric with the cable, is bonded to the outer conductor at the lower end and left open on the end next to the antenna, a shorted quarter-wave section is provided. The impedance of this section as seen from the antenna end is very high and, even though the outer conductor is grounded, there will be a high impedance between B and ground, thus making I_G negligible and balancing the currents in the two halves of the antenna.   The same arrangement may be used where A and B represent the connections to a two-wire balanced line. Since this device produces a *bal*anced line from an *un*balanced line, it is called a *balun*. Colloquially, it is often referred to as a *bazooka*.

In radar sets the transmitter and receiver are adjacent to each other and both use the same antenna. Since the power transmitted in a single pulse may be of the order of megawatts, it is essential to protect the receiver during the intervals of transmission.   In contrast, the energy of the echo pulse is small; all should go to the receiver and none be absorbed by the transmitter. Some device is necessary whereby the receiver is disconnected from the line during transmission and the transmitter is disconnected during reception. The former is called a *transmit-receive* (*T-R*) box; the latter an *anti T-R* box. Both devices make use of the inversion properties of quarter-wavelength lines.

When the signal is transmitted the high voltage pulse produces an arcing over at both spark gaps. Since these arcs are essentially short circuits, the two quarter-wave lines terminated by the gaps present high impedances to the signal which travels directly to the antenna without entering the receiver (Fig. 3.10).

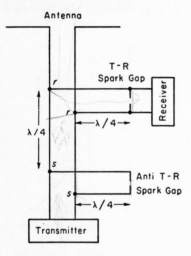

FIG. 3.10. *T-R* and anti *T-R* boxes, illustrating the use of quarter-wave lines as receiver protective devices in radar sets.

The lower voltage of the echo pulse is insufficient to fire either of the spark gaps. At the terminals *ss* the open anti T-R line appears as a short circuit. At the terminals *rr,* a quarter-wavelength along the line, this short circuit appears as an open circuit which presents a high impedance to the incoming signal. The transmitter is thus effectively disconnected, and the receiver, which is matched to the line, absorbs all the energy from the returning pulse.

In order to produce required radiation patterns the same transmitter may be used to operate two antennas with a phase difference of 180° between their currents. Since the phase shift is proportional to the wavelength, the objective may be attained by adding a half-wavelength to one of the transmission lines.

In some cases a circuit produces a voltage waveform of the desired shape and amplitude, but with the wrong polarity. For example, a positive square pulse may be developed where a negative one is required. At low frequencies the phase may be inverted by using a one-to-one ratio transformer in which the secondary voltage is 180° out of phase with the primary. At higher frequencies the same result may be obtained by using a half-wave line. For frequencies at which the substitution becomes practical, reference may be made to Sec. 2.6.

Other applications of quarter- and half-wavelength lines will be discussed as the occasion warrants.

3.8. The Transmission Line as a Reactor. In Fig. 3.6 and 3.7 it is shown that the impedance observed when looking into a short-circuited line depends upon the dimensions of the line, measured in units of wavelengths. At the termination the voltage is zero and the current a maximum. Hence, as shown in the upper part of Fig. 3.11, the former may be repre-

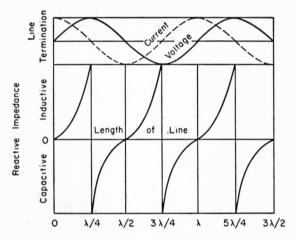

FIG. 3.11. Input impedance of a short-circuited lossless transmission line as a function of the electrical length.

sented by a sine; the latter, by a cosine curve. The lower part of the diagram shows the variations in the impedance, *looking toward the left*, as the line is extended from zero to three half-wavelengths. The values of the impedance are found by dividing the voltage by the current at each point along the line. Notice that these values agree with the impedances obtained for quarter- and half-wavelength sections in Fig. 3.6 and 3.7, and that all values are repeated at half-wavelength intervals.

In this representation of impedances it should be easy to recognize the familiar tangent curve. An analytical proof, however, may be of value. If the actual length of the line is represented by x, its extension in terms of wavelength is given by x/λ. As shown in Sec. 2.3, one wavelength is equivalent to 360° or 2π radians. If, for example, $x = \lambda/4$, $x/\lambda = [\lambda/4/\lambda] \cdot 360° = 90°$ or $\pi/2$ radians. The length of a line may be expressed in *electrical degrees* as $x/\lambda \cdot 360°$ or $2\pi \cdot x/\lambda$. Since, for the shorted line, the voltage and current are represented by sine and cosine curves, respectively, we may write for any given value of x

$$\left.\begin{array}{l} V = V_m \cdot \sin 2\pi x/\lambda \\ I = I_m \cdot \cos 2\pi x/\lambda \end{array}\right\} \tag{3.1}$$

where the subscript m refers to the maximum values which occur at the antinodes.

The impedance at any point on the line is given by the ratio of the voltage to the current at that point.

$$Z = \frac{V}{I} = \frac{V_m \cdot \sin 2\pi x/\lambda}{I_m \cdot \cos 2\pi x/\lambda} = Z_c \cdot \tan 2\pi x/\lambda \tag{3.2}$$

where Z_c is the characteristic impedance of the line. Notice that the ratio V_m/I_m does not represent the maximum impedance, which in the idealized case is, of course, infinite; but, as will be shown later (Sec. 3.11), it has a constant finite value equivalent to the characteristic impedance.

Since a shorted line can absorb no energy, its impedance must be a pure reactance, i.e., the elements in the circuit must be inductive or capacitive (Sec. 3.3). If we follow the convention of representing the inductive reactance as positive and the capacitive as negative, we may determine from an inspection of Fig. 3.11 the type of reactance at any point on the line. Between 0 and $\lambda/4$ both current and voltage are positive; therefore, their ratio, the reactance, is inductive. Between $\lambda/4$ and $\lambda/2$ the voltage is positive and the current is negative; the reactance is capacitive.

Remembering that for an open line the voltage is a maximum and the current zero at the termination, the reader should construct a diagram similar to Fig. 3.11 for this type of line. Since the voltage is represented by a cosine, and the current by a *minus* sine curve, the variations in impedance follow a cotangent relation, expressed by

$$Z = - Z_c \cdot \cot 2\pi x/\lambda \tag{3.3}$$

3.9. Characteristic Impedance: Lumped Parameters. In Sec. 3.3 it was stated that if a transmission line were terminated by a pure resistance, known as its characteristic impedance, all the energy would be absorbed at the load and standing waves would be eliminated from the line. Since this case is equivalent to an infinitely long line, a discussion of how it may be realized in practice is now in order.

Let us begin by considering the case of a line made up of T sections, one of which is shown in Fig. 3.12. In order to simplify the analysis at the beginning, it will be assumed that all elements in the line are resistive.

The resistance at the input on the left may be measured with a Wheatstone bridge. If the right-hand terminals are shorted, the value will be

$$R_s = R_1/2 + R_1R_2/(R_1 + 2R_2) \qquad (3.4)$$

a result which may be easily verified from the principles of elementary physics.

If the right-hand terminals are left open, the resistance will be

$$R_0 = R_1/2 + R_2 \qquad (3.5)$$

We shall denote the *geometric mean* of R_s and R_0 by the symbol R_c. Then

$$R_c = \sqrt{R_s \cdot R_0} = \sqrt{R_1R_2 + R_1{}^2/4} \qquad (3.6)$$

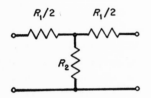

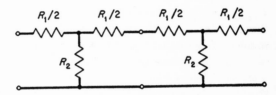

FIG. 3.12. *T* section.   FIG. 3.13.   Two *T* sections.

If we next consider two sections of the line (Fig. 3.13), measuring input resistance on short circuit and open circuit, we obtain, after a certain amount of algebraic manipulation, the following values:

$$R_s = \frac{(R_1 + 2R_2)(R_1{}^2 + 4R_1R_2)}{2(R_1{}^2 + 4R_1R_2 + 2R_2{}^2)} \qquad (3.7)$$

$$R_0 = \frac{R_1{}^2 + 4R_1R_2 + 2R_2{}^2}{2(R_1 + 2R_2)} \qquad (3.8)$$

$$R_c = \sqrt{R_s \cdot R_0} = \sqrt{R_1R_2 + R_1{}^2/4} \qquad (3.9)$$

Notice that the values of R_c in Eq. (3.6) and (3.9) are identical for a circuit of either one or two T sections. By physical reasoning or by mathematical induction it may be seen that the same value of R_c will be obtained, no matter how many T sections are used. Hence R_c may be taken as a value characteristic of a line made up of an infinite number of T sections. For this reason it is called the characteristic resistance of the line. The more general term, designed to include reactances as well as resistances, is, of course, *characteristic impedance*.

It will now be shown that if one section of the line is terminated by a resistance equivalent to the characteristic impedance as in Fig. 3.14, the input impedance will also appear as R_c. In order to prove the statement let it be assumed that R_c is the input impedance. Then,

$$R_c = \frac{R_1}{2} + \frac{(R_1/2 + R_c)R_2}{R_1/2 + R_c + R_2} \tag{3.10}$$

The solution of this equation for R_c will give a value identical with that obtained in Eq. (3.6) or (3.9).

If more T sections are added to the transmission line and the output terminated by R_c, it will be found, at the expense of much algebra, that the input impedance always has the value R_c. In other words, for any finite

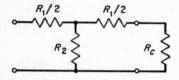

FIG. 3.14. T section terminated by its characteristic impedance.

number of sections terminated by R_c, the input impedance will have the same value as that for an infinite line. A transmission line, therefore, may be made to "look like" an infinite line by terminating it with its characteristic impedance Z_c, which symbol will hereafter replace R_c.

3.10. Characteristic Impedance: Uniformly Distributed Parameters. A transmission line composed of, say, two parallel wires has impedances distributed along its entire length. For the sake of simplicity in the treatment above these impedances were assumed, somewhat improperly, to be concentrated, or "lumped" on the line. The correct analysis requires that the line be cut into infinitesimal lengths and the method, although not necessarily the mathematical technique, of the calculus used.

In Fig. 3.12 or Fig. 3.13 it may be seen, by substituting Z for R, that Z_1 is the series impedance and Z_2 the shunt impedance of the finite section of the line. It is assumed that *conductance*, the reciprocal of resistance, is a familiar concept. We now introduce an analogous term, called *admittance* Y, which is the reciprocal of impedance, i.e., $Y = 1/Z$. For the impedance and admittance per unit length of line, say per foot, the small letters, z and y, respectively, will be used. If the length of line to be considered is very small, its value may be designated by Δx, where the symbol Δ is not a multiplying factor, but is prefixed to the x solely for the purpose of designating an infinitesimal length. Then, $Z_1 = z \cdot \Delta x$ and $Y_2 = 1/Z_2 = y \cdot \Delta x$. Remembering the change in notation and substituting these values in Eq. (3.6) or (3.9), we have the relation,

$$Z_c = \sqrt{\frac{Z_1}{Y_2} + \frac{Z_1^2}{4}} = \sqrt{\frac{z \cdot \Delta x}{y \cdot \Delta x} + \frac{z^2 \cdot (\Delta x)^2}{4}} = \sqrt{\frac{z}{y} + \frac{z^2 \cdot (\Delta x)^2}{4}} \tag{3.11}$$

Now, let Δx approach zero; the value of Z_c becomes

$$Z_c = \sqrt{\frac{z}{y}}\bigg|_{\Delta x \to 0} \tag{3.12}$$

where z and y are the series impedance and the shunt admittance, respectively, per unit length of line.

Now, let us *suppose* that the series impedance and the shunt admittance per unit length have the values Z_1 and $Y_2 = 1/Z_2$, i.e., identical with those given, in terms of R, in the original examples. Then Eq. (3.12) becomes

$$Z_c = \sqrt{Z_1/Y_2} = \sqrt{Z_1/(1/Z_2)} = \sqrt{Z_1 Z_2} \tag{3.13}$$

If this exact expression for distributed constants is compared with the approximate equations (3.6) and (3.9), using lumped constants, it is found that the latter has the additional term $Z_1^2/4$ under the radical.

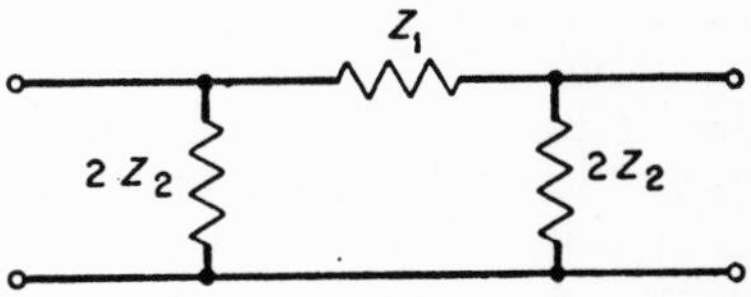

Fig. 3.15. π section.

Fig. 3.15 shows a π section in which the series impedance and the shunt admittance are the same as in Fig. 3.12. The parameters, be it noticed, are differently distributed in the two types of sections. By employing the methods used above, it may be shown that the characteristic impedance is

$$Z_c = \frac{Z_1 Z_2}{\sqrt{Z_1 Z_2 + Z_1^2/4}} \tag{3.14}$$

When, however, we pass to the limit—$\Delta x \to 0$—the result is $Z_c = \sqrt{z/y}$, which is the same as Eq. (3.12). For lumped impedances the solutions are not unique, their form depending on the type of section used. Upon passing to the limit, which is the case for distributed impedances, all results are identical.

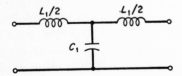

Fig. 3.16.   Section of transmission line at radio frequencies.

At radio frequencies the resistance losses are negligible and a section of the line may be considered as made up of inductances in series and capacitances in parallel. For illustrative purposes, a section with lumped parameters is shown in Fig. 3.16. In an actual line the parameters are assumed to be distributed and the characteristic impedance is given by the geometric mean of the series and shunt impedances which are purely reactive. The former is $2\pi f L_1$ and the latter is $1/2\pi f C_1$, where L_1 and C_1 refer to the inductance and capacitance per unit length. Eq. (3.12) now becomes

$$Z_c = \sqrt{L_1/C_1} \tag{3.15}$$

a result which, on the above assumptions, is seen to be independent of frequency. By expressing L_1 in henrys per meter and C_1 in farads per meter the value of Z_c may be found in ohms.

By using an impedance bridge the characteristic impedance of a lossless line may be determined as follows: Measure the capacitance of a given length of transmission line with the output terminals open-circuited. Short the output terminals of the same line and measure the inductance. Compute Z_c from Eq. (3.15).

3.11. Standing Wave Ratio. Since a line terminated by its characteristic impedance simulates an infinite line, no energy is reflected and there are no standing waves. There are, of course, incident traveling waves of voltage and current. A fluorescent lamp (Sec. 3.5) moved along a lossless two-wire line with a Z_c-termination will glow with substantially uniform intensity. A voltmeter connected across the line at any point will read a constant rms value of the potential difference. The ratio of the effective voltage to the effective current gives the characteristic impedance of the line. Since the maximum values of these quantities are proportional to their effective values, $V_m/I_m = Z_c$, which is in accordance with the statement made in Sec. 3.8.

When a transmission line is used as a guide or conveyor of energy the essential reason for terminating it by its characteristic impedance is the elimination of standing waves. Primarily, all the energy will be absorbed at the load and none will be reflected in the line. Localized heating, "hot spots," at the current antinodes will be avoided and insulation difficulties minimized. If, for example, coaxial cable is used, the insulation must be able to withstand the maximum voltage between the two conductors. Where standing waves exist, this potential difference at the antinodes may be considerably greater than the incident peak voltage, thus causing a breakdown of the dielectric. When such a rupture occurs, it will be found to have taken place near the center of a voltage loop.

The terminations of a transmission line are not confined to those which result in complete reflection or absorption of energy. In practice the energy is partly absorbed and partly reflected, with the result that the maxima are always less and the minima greater than the values assumed in the idealized cases of complete reflection. A lossless line terminated by its characteristic impedance shows no variations in voltage or current along its entire length and is, therefore, called a *flat line*. The ratio of the maximum to the minimum voltage (or current) is an important property of the line known as its *standing wave ratio* (*SWR*). It is a measure of the mismatch between the line and the load. A perfectly flat line would have a standing wave ratio of unity; experimentally, a value of 1.03 would be excellent.

The voltage standing wave ratio is often written *VSWR* in order to distinguish it from the power standing wave ratio. The latter is obtained when the readings of the measuring instrument are proportional to the square of the voltage. The square root of the power ratio is the voltage ratio. In this book *SWR* will always be used to indicate the voltage ratio.

In Sec. 3.8 it was shown that the input impedance of a transmission line on which standing waves exist may be varied considerably by altering its electrical length. This may be accomplished either by keeping the frequency constant and changing the physical length of the line or by retaining the same line and using a different frequency. When the standing wave ratio is large, small variations in the frequency of the oscillator change the electrical length of the line and may alter the input impedance so that the transfer of energy is reduced appreciably. A flat line, however, is terminated by its characteristic impedance which in radio circuits is practically independent of frequency. In the absence of standing waves, the input impedance is substantially constant and the transfer of energy is unchanged.

There is also a reciprocal effect. Since the transmission line is essentially a part of the oscillator's circuit, the frequency of the oscillator is affected by changes in the impedance of the line. If the latter has a large standing wave ratio, small changes in the frequency of the oscillator at first produce large variations in the input impedance of the line, as stated above. The new impedance, in turn, becomes a component of the oscillating circuit and, if the change is sufficiently great, the oscillator may be "pulled" from its resonant or natural frequency. Although the effect is reduced by minimizing the standing wave ratio on the line, this procedure alone does not constitute a solution to all problems. In the operation of magnetrons, for example, a flat line is incompatible with maximum frequency stability and the best compromise must be selected.

If a load of unknown impedance, not Z_c, terminates the line, standing waves will appear. The voltage ratio, maximum to minimum, is measured and found to be, say 3. The load impedance is either $3Z_c$ or $Z_c/3$. To resolve the doubt, measure the voltage at the load. If it is a maximum, the load has the larger impedance. The reliability of this method is based on the assumption that the resistive component of the load's impedance is large compared to its reactive component.

3.12. Measurement of Standing Wave Ratio. In order to determine the standing wave ratio it is necessary to measure the maximum and minimum values of either current or voltage. Measurement of the latter is the usual practice. In accordance with the fundamental principle that a measuring device should not alter the quantity being measured, the voltmeter must have a high impedance in order not to draw appreciable current from the line. The method to be described here has been selected because it is illustrative of the principles discussed in this chapter.

A quarter-wave stub, provided with sliding contacts for moving it along an open-wire transmission line, is shorted through a low impedance, high frequency ammeter A which may be of the thermocouple type (Fig. 3.17).

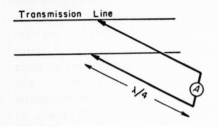

FIG. 3.17. Measurement of SWR with stub voltmeter on open-wire line.

If the impedance of the ammeter is very low the stub presents a high impedance to the line. The voltage across the stub is

$$V = V_m \cdot \sin\ 2\pi x/\lambda$$

from Eq. (3.1.) V_m may be set equal to $I_m Z_c$, following Eq. (3.2). Then,

$$V = I_m Z_c \cdot \sin\ 2\pi x/\lambda$$

which, for a quarter-wave line, reduces to $V = I_m Z_c$. Hence the voltage is the product of the ammeter reading and the characteristic impedance of the stub, which may be chosen to have the same value as that of the line. The value of I_m is to be taken as the reflected current at the stub termination. As the stub is moved along the line, variations will occur in I_m, with the highest values at the voltage antinodes. The frequency, of course, must be sufficiently high so that the length of the stub does not become inconveniently long.

For coaxial lines the fundamental principles of the instrument for measuring the standing wave ratio are the same, but a slotted section must be provided for the insertion of a probe. The length of the slot should be greater than a half-wavelength. One end of the shorted quarter-wavelength stub is placed in contact with the outer conductor of the cable; the other is inserted in the slot to serve as a pick-up device (Fig. 3.18). It should not be in contact with the inner conductor, but the depth of insertion as the probe is moved along the slot should remain constant.

It may be of interest to view the probe as a receiving antenna placed parallel to the radial electric field within the cable. The voltage developed is proportional to the strength of this field, the maxima occurring at the voltage antinodes. The slot, which is parallel to the current in the outer conductor, has a negligible effect on the electromagnetic field within the cable.

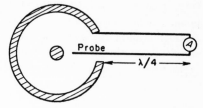

FIG. 3.18.   Measurement of SWR with stub voltmeter in coaxial cable.

3.13. Terminated Lines.   It has been shown that there are no standing waves on a lossless line terminated by its characteristic impedance. The ratio of voltage to current is everywhere the same and the input impedance $Z_s = Z_c$ for any length of line. All the energy is absorbed at the load.

It has been further shown that an open- or short-circuited line has the characteristics of a pure reactance. The value of the input impedance varies periodically with the electrical length of the line (Sec. 3.8). None of the energy is absorbed at the termination.

Clearly these are special cases. The line may be terminated by any combination of resistances and reactances. In general, the energy is partly absorbed and partly reflected, and there are standing waves on the line.

Let us first consider a line terminated by a pure resistance Z_R which is not equal to the characteristic impedance. A certain fraction of the incident energy will be dissipated in the load, the relative amount being greater the more nearly the value of Z_R approaches Z_c. The magnitudes of the reflected voltage and current are less than their incident counterparts. There will be no double maxima or zero minima, as in the cases of the open- and short-circuited lines, but the phase relations will be similar. When $Z_R > Z_c$, the case is analogous to that of the open-circuited line. At the termination there is a voltage maximum and a current minimum, the incident and reflected components being in phase and out of phase, respectively. Maxima and minima of voltage and current, with magnitudes modified by the relative values of Z_R and Z_c, will be found in the same positions as those on the open-circuited line. For example, if $Z_R/Z_c = 3$, the voltage at the load will be a maximum having a value three times as large as the minimum voltage, which is a quarter-wavelength from the termination. The standing wave ratio is, of course, three.

If $Z_R/Z_c = 1/3$, the SWR will be the same, but the voltage at the load will be a minimum. The standing wave configuration will be similar to that on a shorted line.

When a transmission line is not terminated by its characteristic impedance, the input impedance Z_s depends on the length of the line. In general, Z_s will be partly resistive and partly reactive. It may, therefore, be represented by a resistance and a reactance in series, or in parallel, the choice being determined solely by convenience. In order to avoid misunderstanding, it should be mentioned that the numerical values of the components will differ according to the type of equivalent circuit chosen.

The results for two special cases of line length can be obtained very simply from the theory already presented. In Sec. 3.8 it was shown that, in the ideal case, the reactance of a quarter- or half-wave line, shorted or open, is zero. At these lengths the line itself will appear as a pure resistance, sometimes pictured as a series resonant or a parallel resonant circuit. It is characteristic of a half-wave line, or any integral multiple thereof, that it "repeats" the load. If the termination is Z_R, the input impedance will also be Z_R at each half-wavelength from the load and it will be independent of the characteristic impedance of the line.

A quarter-wave line, or any *odd* multiple thereof, "inverts" the load. A high impedance looks like a low impedance and vice versa. If we assume that $Z_R > Z_c$, the relatively high impedance of the former will appear as a low impedance a quarter-wavelength from the load. The value of Z_s is low and that of Z_R is high. The characteristic impedance of the line therefore has a value which lies between Z_s and Z_R, and which turns out to be their geometric mean, i.e., $Z_c = \sqrt{Z_s Z_R}$. Hence the input impedance at odd multiples of a quarter-wavelength is Z_c^2/Z_R. For example, let $Z_c = 300$ ohms and the length of the line be $\lambda/4$. If $Z_R = 900$ ohms, $Z_s = (300)^2/900 = 100$ ohms. If $Z_R = 100$ ohms, $Z_s = (300)^2/100 = 900$ ohms.

For line lengths which are not integral multiples of a quarter-wavelength and which are terminated by a resistance, the input impedance will have resistive and reactive components. Various situations are illustrated in Fig. 3.19, where a series circuit has been chosen arbitrarily to represent the input impedance in all cases. Notice that R_R has been used in place of Z_R to emphasize the purely resistive nature of the termination. When $R_R < Z_c$, the input impedance has the general characteristics of a shorted line; when $R_R > Z_c$, it resembles that of an open line.

It should be noted that the resistive and reactive components of the input impedance do not, in general, have the values of the load resistance and the reactance of the line. They must be calculated from the appropriate equations derived from transmission line theory. For example, if an eighth-wave section of a 300-ohm line is terminated by a resistive load of 100 ohms, the resistive and reactive components are found to be, respectively, 180 and 240 ohms.   Therefore, $Z_s = \sqrt{R^2 + X^2} = 300$ ohms.   Although Z_s has the same numerical value as Z_c, the situation is not physically equivalent to terminating the line with a resistive load of 300 ohms.

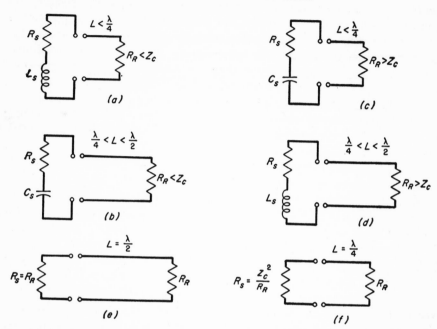

FIG. 3.19.   In each of the six cases the circuit at the left shows the equivalent input impedance Z_s of a transmission line terminated by a pure resistance R_R. The equivalent Z_s may also be represented by a resistance and a reactance in parallel, if convenient.   The terminations (a) and (b) have the general characteristics of a shorted line; (c) and (d), of an open line.   When $L = \lambda/2$ the load is repeated (e); when $L = \lambda/4$ it is inverted (f).

Let us next consider a line terminated by a purely inductive reactance. Recalling that a shorted section, less than a quarter-wavelength, has an inductive reactance, we may substitute an appropriate length for the lumped parameter.   The inductively terminated line is thus electrically equivalent to a somewhat longer short-circuited line as in Fig. 3.20(a).   The phase relations of voltages and currents will, however, be modified.   The position of maximum voltage and minimum current is located, not a quarter-wavelength from the end of the line, but at a point nearer the termination.

If the line is terminated capacitively, it is equivalent to a somewhat longer open-circuited line (Fig. 3.20b).   The position of maximum current and minimum voltage is closer than a quarter-wavelength to the end of the line. In each of these cases, since the load is assumed to be purely reactive, no energy is absorbed: the standing wave maxima of voltage and current are twice the incident values and the minima are zero.

Finally, we shall consider a line terminated by an impedance which has both resistive and reactive components. The effective length of the line is increased by an amount which depends upon the relative magnitudes of the two components. As might be expected, the standing wave configuration has the qualitative features of both reactive and resistive terminations.

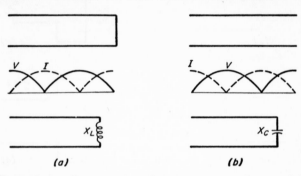

FIG. 3.20. Transmission lines terminated by a pure reactance. (a) The inductively terminated line is electrically equivalent to a longer short-circuited line. (b) The capacitively terminated line is electrically equivalent to a longer open-circuited line.

When the reactance is inductive, the position of maximum voltage and minimum current, with a somewhat different shift, is still less than a quarter-wavelength from the end of the line. A similar relation holds for the point of maximum current and minimum voltage when the reactance is capacitive. The resistive component, however, absorbs some of the energy: the maxima are less than twice the incident values and the minima are greater than zero.

3.14. Matching Stubs. A transmission line is often terminated by an antenna. In order to eliminate standing waves and insure the transfer of maximum energy, the line should be matched to the load. On open-wire lines this is done most conveniently with the use of stubs, adjustable in position and variable in length. Either open- or short-circuited sections satisfy the requirements although, from considerations of rigidity, the latter are usually employed.

Let us assume that we have a lossless line terminated by a resistance $R_R > Z_c$ (Fig. 3.21). The input impedance depends on the length of the line and will, in general, have both resistive and reactive components. At the load the input impedance is R_R; at a distance a quarter-wavelength to the left, it is Z_c^2/R_R. These are maximum and minimum values of Z_s and are purely resistive. Clearly there is some point on the line between these two extremes for which the resistive component of Z_s is Z_c. There is also a reactive component which in this case is capacitive. This follows from the assumption that $R_R > Z_c$, thus producing the general characteristics of a line with an open termination, the reactance of which, between 0 and $\lambda/4$, is capacitive. If a match is to be made at this point, a stub which has an inductive reactance is ideally suited to neutralize the reactive component of the input impedance.

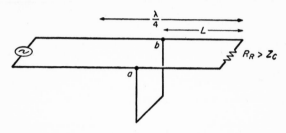

FIG. 3.21. Impedance matching with a single movable stub. At ab the resistive component of Z_s equals Z_c (a pure resistance). The reactive component (a capacitance) is neutralized by the inductance of the stub. The line is flat to the left of ab.

Let us assume that at a distance L from the load the resistive component of the input impedance is equal to Z_c. A shorted stub less than a quarter-wave in length has a purely inductive reactance. If this stub, with the same characteristic impedance as the line and cut to a length such that its reactance cancels that of the input impedance, is connected in parallel, as shown in Fig. 3.21, the line to the left sees its characteristic impedance and is therefore matched to the load. The stub is mounted at right angles to the line in order that the coupling between them may be reduced. Since the stub is in parallel with the line, the computations are usually made in terms of admittance (Sec. 3.10).

If $R_R < Z_c$, the matching may be accomplished by attaching an open stub, which has a purely capacitive reactance, at a point less than a quarter-wavelength from the end of the line.

Usually it is best to locate a stub as near as possible to the load in order that the line may be flat over a greater length. If necessary, however, the stub may be placed farther from the load. In the region between a quarter- and a half-wavelength from the termination a second point at which the resistive component equals Z_c may be found. Here the reactive component of the input impedance will have changed sign. An open stub must be replaced by a shorted section and vice versa. If the stub is to be located still farther from the load, it is merely necessary to remember that the input impedance repeats itself every half-wavelength.

Conditions may arise where the use of a single movable stub is impracticable, e.g., in the case of a coaxial cable. Under these circumstances two stubs, both fixed in position, but variable in length, are used.

Details of the methods by which complex impedances may be calculated and stub matching accomplished are not included in the plan of this book. Calculations may be made, of course, from the fundamental equations of transmission line theory. Also two graphical devices, the rectangular-coordinate circle diagram and the Smith chart, should be mentioned. Although using different methods of presentation, both eliminate the necessity of repeated calculations and both supply the same information. In practice, the final stage for the best adjustment in stub matching is accomplished by trial and error.

PROBLEMS

3.1. On an *open-circuited* lossless transmission line 540° in length, the *incident* voltage wave at $t = 0$ is shown in Fig. 3.22. Assume *incident* voltage and current are in phase. Draw carefully on quadrille paper diagrams showing

(a) The reflected voltage wave at $t = 0$.
(b) The incident and reflected voltage waves at $t = T/4$.
(c) The incident and reflected current waves at $t = 0$.
(d) The incident and reflected current waves at $t = T/4$.

Fig. 3.22. Incident voltage wave for Problems 3.1 and 3.2.

If the actual length of the line is 6 ft, what is the wavelength? What is the approximate frequency of the oscillator? At what points, measured from the termination of the line, will a voltmeter read substantially zero?

3.2. Repeat Problem 3.1 for a *short-circuited* line.

3.3. A voltmeter placed across a parallel open-wire transmission line reads practically zero at equal distances of 30 cm along the line. What is the wavelength of the voltage waves? The approximate frequency of the oscillator?

3.4. A polyethylene insulated coaxial cable is substituted for the two-wire line in Problem 3.3. The velocity factor for this cable is 0.66. What is the wavelength of the voltage wave? The approximate frequency of the oscillator?

3.5. In Problem 3.3 the oscillator supplies a sinusoidal peak-to-peak voltage of 282 volts, as observed with a cathode-ray oscilloscope. What will a voltmeter read when connected across the line at a voltage antinode? If the line is now terminated by its characteristic impedance, what will the voltmeter read?

3.6. Two lines are composed, respectively, of T and π sections of pure resistance. The series resistances are 10 ohms per section and the shunt resistances are 200 ohms per section for each. Draw diagrams for single sections and label with numerical values. Calculate characteristic impedances on the basis that the resistances are (a) lumped, (b) distributed.

3.7. A line with the *lumped* parameters of Problem 3.6 is composed of 10 *T* sections, matched to a generator with an emf of 3 volts, and terminated by its characteristic impedance. Find the current at the sending end of the line. As the current passes through each section an equal *proportion,* not an equal amount, is drawn off in that section. Find the current at the receiving end of the line.

3.8. A transmission line has a characteristic impedance of 300 ohms and is operated at a frequency of 200 Mc. What is the shortest length of line necessary to obtain (a) an inductance of 0.1 microhenry, (b) a capacitance of 1 micromicrofarad, for a shorted line?

3.9. Solve Problem 3.8 using an open-circuited line.

3.10. A lossless transmission line with a characteristic impedance of 300 ohms is connected to a resistive load of 100 ohms. The frequency is 300 Mc and when the line is 15 cm long the input impedance (combined resistive and reactive components) is 386 ohms. What is the input impedance when the length of the line is (a) 25 cm, (b) 50 cm, (c) 65 cm? Explain.

3.11. A lossless line with a characteristic impedance of 200 ohms is one wavelength long and is terminated by a resistive load of 100 ohms. The voltage across the load is 500 volts. Find the maximum and minimum values of voltage and current and their positions on the line. Diagrams.

3.12. A lossless line with a characteristic impedance of 300 ohms is 30 cm long and is operated at a frequency of 150 Mc. (a) What inductance (microhenrys) should be connected to the end of the line to make the input impedance infinite? (b) What capacitance (micro-microfarads) should be connected to the end of the line to make the input impedance zero? Diagrams.

3.13. A transmission line with a characteristic impedance of 300 ohms is matched by a quarter-wave section to an antenna with a resistive load of 75 ohms. (a) What is the characteristic impedance of the matching section? (b) If the power delivered to the load is 1 kilowatt, find the current and voltage at (1) the input of the line, (2) the input of the matching section, (3) the load. Neglect all losses in the line and matching section. Diagram.

Chapter 4

REFLECTION AND REFRACTION

4.1. Range of Electromagnetic Waves. The range of electromagnetic waves is enormous. It extends from the negligibly radiating 25-cycle a-c generated in power plants to the gamma rays from radioactive substances with frequencies of the order of 10^{22} cycles per sec. All these radiations have the same velocity, 3×10^8 meters per sec, in free space.

Radiation is produced by oscillating systems which are essentially electrical in nature. For the lower frequencies we ordinarily have a man-made electrical circuit of some sort, with inductance and capacitance which, we recall, correspond to the inertia and the reciprocal of elasticity in mechanically oscillating systems. For the higher frequencies the oscillator is contained within the structure of the atom. Energy changes in the so-called planetary electrons or in the rotation and vibration of molecules produce the infrared, visible, ultraviolet, and X-ray radiations; changes in the nucleus are responsible for the gamma rays.

The classification of electromagnetic radiations is usually made according to frequency or wavelength. However, waves of certain frequency ranges can be produced and detected in a number of physically different ways, as was shown by Nichols and Tear (1917). Infrared waves were produced from the heat radiations of molecules and were detected by optical or quasi-optical devices. Radio waves with frequencies of the same order of magnitude were generated by using oscillators of very small dimensions. Actually, there was an overlapping of wavelengths, the longest infrared waves being 0.42 mm and the shortest radio waves, 0.22 mm.

An arbitrary classification of radio frequencies made by the Federal Communications Commission (FCC) for assignment to different types of radio service is given in Table 4.1.

It is reasonable to expect similarities in the behavior of the different types of electromagnetic waves. When Hertz first produced radio waves in 1887, he made systematic experiments to show that the behavior of these waves, which had been predicted by Maxwell, was similar to light waves. Hertz

54

TABLE 4.1. FCC CLASSIFICATION OF RADIO FREQUENCIES

Frequency, Mc	Description	Abbreviation
0.01–0.03	Very low frequency	VLF
0.03–0.3	Low frequency	LF
0.3–3	Medium frequency	MF
3–30	High frequency	HF
30–300	Very high frequency	VHF
300–3000	Ultra high frequency	UHF
3,000–30,000	Super high frequency	SHF
30,000–300,000	Extremely high frequency	EHF

found that electromagnetic waves have the properties of *all* waves, namely, reflection, refraction, diffraction, and interference. Furthermore, he showed that electromagnetic waves must be transverse, for they also exhibit the property of polarization which is characterized by the direction of the electric field (Sec. 6.1).

4.2. The Law of Reflection. Sometimes it is an advantage to consider rays instead of waves. Now, the word *ray* is a technical term, meaning usually a line drawn perpendicular to the wavefront. (For exceptions, see Sec. 6.2.) Fig. 4.1, in which the waveform for the electric field component

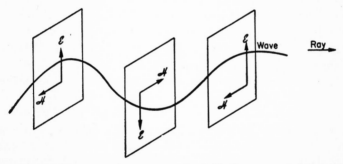

FIG. 4.1. Spatial relations among the field, the wave, and the ray.

only is drawn, shows the spatial relations between a plane electromagnetic wave and its ray. For some purposes, drawing a ray is equivalent to assuming that the radiation travels in straight lines.

When radiation is incident upon a boundary separating two mediums, it will, in general, be partly reflected and partly transmitted. The direction of the ray is specified by the angle which the ray makes with the normal, i.e., the perpendicular to the surface.

The law of reflection states that the angle of incidence is equal to the angle of reflection and that both lie in the same plane. The direction of the reflected ray may be found by erecting a perpendicular at the point on the surface where the incident ray strikes it, and then drawing the reflected ray such that the angle of reflection is equal to the angle of incidence. For a plane surface this is easily seen in Fig. 4.2. In the case of a spherical surface the normal is the radius or an extension thereof (Fig. 4.3).

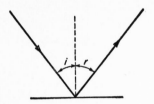

FIG. 4.2. Reflection at a plane surface.

4.3. Parabolic Reflecting Surfaces. An important surface, for our purposes, is the paraboloid of revolution, which is the surface generated by rotating a parabola *AGH* about its axis *GD* (Fig. 4.4). Such a surface is found in the interior of an automobile headlamp. The geometry of the parabola is such that if any straight line *FP* is drawn from the focus *F* to a point *P* on the parabola, and a line *PB* is drawn from this same point, parallel to the axis, each line makes the same angle with a perpendicular *PN* erected at the given point. In the headlamp the bulb is located practically at the focus and the reflected light emerges in nearly parallel rays.

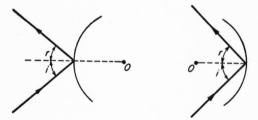

FIG. 4.3. Reflection at spherical surfaces.

In the propagation of high frequency electromagnetic waves it is often desirable to beam the radiation in a given direction. A half-wave antenna is placed at the focus of a paraboloidal reflector or "dish," and the radiation is propagated in a direction substantially parallel to the axis. Since the antenna has a finite length, all the radiation does not originate at the exact focus of the paraboloid. To illustrate, let the antenna be placed vertically with its center at *F*. Only from this point will the radiation be reflected in a direction parallel to the axis of the paraboloid. As a result of the contributions from other points, the reflected beam tends to be somewhat divergent. Fortunately the radiation pattern of the half-wave antenna introduces a corrective factor. As shown in Fig. 8.9, the maximum field strength is propagated from the center of the antenna at right angles to its length. The reflected beam is therefore sharper than the geometry of the paraboloid indicates. Nevertheless, in order to minimize the spreading of the beam it is necessary that the length of the antenna be small in comparison with the diameter of the reflector. In the middle of the broadcast band, for example, where a half-wavelength is of the order of 500 ft, this

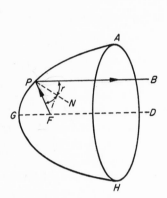

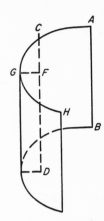

FIG. 4.4. The paraboloid of revolution.   FIG. 4.5. The parabolic cylinder.

would be impractical. If, however, the antenna is of the order of 10 cm and the aperture of the reflector perhaps a dozen wavelengths, the device may be conveniently used.

Sometimes a hemispherical mirror is mounted in front of the antenna so that radiation leaving it in the forward direction will be directed back on the main surface and hence into the beam. Designers of this type of directional antenna, however, have reported that a flat reflecting surface is often as satisfactory as the hemispherical mirror. In the section on parasitic arrays (Sec. 9.5) it will be shown that a straight conductor, somewhat longer than the antenna, may be placed parallel to and ahead of it to minimize the forward direct radiation.

The paraboloid of revolution should not be confused with the parabolic cylinder. A cylindrical surface is a surface generated by a moving straight line which constantly intersects a fixed curve and remains parallel to a fixed straight line. In the familiar right circular cylinder the fixed curve is a circle and the fixed straight line is the axis of the figure which passes through the center of the circle. In the parabolic cylinder the fixed curve is a parabola AGH, the moving straight line is AB, and the fixed straight line is the axis of the figure CD which passes through the focus F (Fig. 4.5).

The restrictions imposed upon the parabolic cylinder are less severe than those for the paraboloid. The former, for example, needs to be only a half-wavelength long. Furthermore, although both types may be built of properly shaped wires to avoid the windage of solid structures the construction is easier in the case of the parabolic cylinder.

4.4. Electrical Images. A consideration of the image formed by a plane reflecting surface will prove to be of some importance in the later study of antennas. By the construction of ray diagrams which involve only the law of reflection, it may be seen that the image formed by a plane mirror has the following pertinent characteristics: (a) it is located as far behind the reflecting surface as the object is in front of it, (b) it is the same size as the object, (c) it is perverted, i.e., a right hand becomes a left hand. These characteristics do not apply, without modification, to curved reflectors.

Consider a positive charge q placed above an infinite plane conducting surface which is at zero potential. In practice this plane may be the surface of the earth which is assumed to be flat and perfectly conducting in the idealized case. The negative charges induced on the conducting surface must be equal to q in magnitude and distributed so that every point on the plane is at zero potential. Instead of finding the distribution of charge on the plane, we shall attack the problem from a different standpoint.

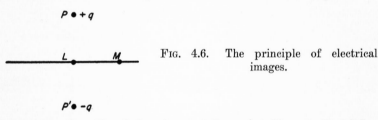

Fig. 4.6. The principle of electrical images.

On the opposite side of the plane, at the point P', such that $PL = P'L$, let there be a charge $-q$ (Fig. 4.6). This charge is said to be the *electrical image* of $+q$, a term suggested by its optical analog. We shall show that both the charge and its image and the charge placed above a grounded infinitely plane conducting surface have a plane of zero potential in the same geometrical position.

The potential V at a point is defined as the work done on a unit positive charge in bringing it from infinity to the point in question. As shown in books on general physics, it is expressed by $V = q/kr$, where r is the distance between the point and the charge q, and k depends on the medium and the system of units. If M is any point on the plane, its potential is

$$V = \frac{+q}{k(PM)} + \frac{-q}{k(P'M)} = 0 \qquad (4.1)$$

It is thus seen that if the conducting plane were removed and the charge $-q$ placed at P', every point on the plane would be at zero potential.

The boundary condition, that the potential along the plane be zero, is satisfied in each case. In advanced texts on electricity it is proved that if two seemingly different problems have the same boundary values of the potential, the solution in the *region of physical interest* is indeed unique. That is, the potential is identical at equivalent points in the *P*-region, corresponding to the space above the earth, whether the negative charge is concentrated at *P'* or is distributed over the conducting plane. In the latter case, however, there is no electric field within the *P'*-region in which the potential is everywhere zero.

Now, suppose we have a horizontal half-wave antenna located at a distance *h* above the surface of the earth. This antenna will radiate in different directions. Some of the radiations will go directly into space; others will be reflected from the surface of the earth. We are interested in the combined effect of these two types of radiation at a distant point where a receiving antenna may be located. We shall find that our problem may be simplified by making use of the concept of electrical images. Assume that an image antenna is located at a distance *h* below the surface of the earth. If, at a given instant, the polarity of the real antenna is that shown in Fig. 4.7, the polarity of its image will be that shown in the same diagram.

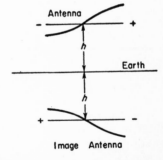

FIG. 4.7. Horizontal half-wave antenna and its image.

(The instantaneous polarity of the voltage which, in a half-wave antenna, has a node at the center and antinodes at the ends, is indicated by the segments of the sine curve drawn above or below the straight line representing the antenna.) With this assumption, we may proceed to find the relative field strength, in a given direction, as the resultant of the combined effects produced by the antenna and its image. Since the method involves the concept of interference, an explanation of the procedure will be postponed until Sec. 5.5 is reached.

A dihedral corner reflector consists of two intersecting reflecting planes. Assuming that the reflecting sheets are perfectly conducting and of infinite extent, the method of images can be applied to the analysis of corner-reflector antennas having values for angles $\theta = 180°/n$, where *n* is a positive integer. If $\theta = 90°$, the reflector may be replaced by three images with the positions and polarities shown in Fig. 4.8 without changing the distribution of the electric field in the quadrant at the right. In the optical case, the eye sees the "positive" image as the result of successive reflections by each plane. Since perversion takes place at each reflection, this image appears exactly like the object. If $\theta = 180°$, we have the case of the flat earth discussed above. If 180° is not an integral multiple of θ, the method cannot be used, although acceptable results may be obtained by interpolation. For

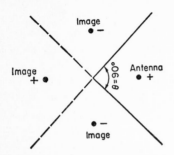

Fig. 4.8.   Dihedral corner reflector of 90° and its images.

example, a satisfactory pattern for $\theta = 75°$ may be obtained from $\theta = 60°$ and $\theta = 90°$. Although the analysis calls for infinite reflectors, the dimensions may be reduced to the order of a single wavelength without greatly impairing the performance. When desirable, the metal sheets may be replaced by wires parallel to the antenna and spaced about one-tenth of a wavelength apart.

4.5. Ghost Images. In urban areas reflections of radio waves may occur at the surfaces of buildings. The dimensions of these structures may be relatively large compared to the wavelengths employed in television, particularly in the ultra-high frequency band. Thus conditions for appreciable reflections of the signal may exist. If so, there may be two images on the viewing screen, one from the direct, the other from the reflected wave. The difference between the two paths may be such that the two images are separated by an appreciable amount.

The unwanted image is called a "ghost." If the horizontal separation between the desired image and its ghost is measured and the positions of the transmitter and the receiver are known, the location of the reflecting surface which produces the ghost may be found.

Television broadcasting in the United States employs a system whereby a single picture is composed of 525 horizontal lines which are scanned in 1/30 sec. The period for a single line is therefore $(1/30 \text{ sec})/525 = 63.5 \times 10^{-6}$ sec or 63.5 microseconds. However, an interval of time, during which the signal is blanked, must be allowed for the electron beam to fly back to its starting point on the left. This process requires about one-sixth of the period, thus making the horizontal interval approximately 53 microseconds.

During this interval the electromagnetic wave travels a distance of $d = (186 \times 10^3 \text{ mi/sec})(53 \times 10^{-6} \text{ sec})(5.28 \times 10^3 \text{ ft/mi}) = 5.2 \times 10^4 \text{ ft}$. If Δ is the difference between the direct and reflected paths which produces a horizontal displacement s between the image and its ghost on a television screen of width w, we may set up the proportion

$$\Delta/d = s/w \qquad\qquad (4.2)$$

from which the value of Δ may be calculated.

The quantity Δ, of course, is merely the difference in the paths of the two waves, a value which, in itself, gives us no definite information as to the location of the reflecting surface. In order to solve the problem we need a map which includes the locations of the transmitter T and the receiver R. The locus of the points of reflection for which the difference in path is a constant is an ellipse. Let T and R be located at the foci of the conic. The definition of an ellipse states that it is the locus of a point such that the sum of its distances from two fixed points, called the foci, is a constant. If P and

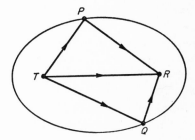

FIG. 4.9. An ellipse of reflection is used to locate the source of a television ghost image.

Q are two arbitrary points on the curve (Fig. 4.9), it follows from the definition that

$$TP + PR = TQ + QR$$

If the reflecting source is on the ellipse the path of the reflected wave will be a constant. The path of the direct wave is clearly the constant TR. If the reflection is at, say, Q, $TQ + QR - TR = \Delta$. The value of Δ may be computed from Eq. (4.2).

In order to draw the ellipse stick two pins in the map, one at T and the other at R. Place a loop of string over the pins and adjust its length to equal $2(TR) + \Delta$. Then insert a pencil in the loop and describe the ellipse. The map will show that the reflecting surface is a large building or other object which lies on the ellipse.

In the case of a stationary object, the ghost is eliminated by using some form of directive antenna. When reflection takes place from the surface of a moving object, such as an airplane, appreciable interference occurs only when the object is relatively near the receiver. The value of Δ is small and the effect is temporary, being designated as a "flutter" rather than a ghost. Because of the changing position of the plane no directive antenna can remedy the trouble, but it may be minimized by appropriate circuits within the receiver.

4.6. Refraction: Snell's Law. It has been stated that the velocity of electromagnetic waves of *all* frequencies is 3×10^8 meters per sec in free space. In a material medium the velocity is different from its free-space value and is dependent on the frequency of the radiation. For example, when light is transmitted by a glass prism, the differences in the velocities of the waves to which the eye is sensitive produce the beautiful color phenomenon known as the spectrum.

It is necessary for us to consider what is meant by wave velocity. In Sec. 2.3 it was pointed out that the wave velocity measures the rate at which a certain configuration or phase, say the maximum positive displacement, is propagated. For this reason it is often called phase velocity. In general, it is not the same as the group velocity which is the rate at which the energy flows through the medium. An illustration may be drawn from water waves. When a stone is dropped into a smooth pond a group of circular waves or ripples is sent out. An individual wave travels faster and dies out more rapidly than the group as a whole. The wave form has one velocity and the wave group, which represents the energy flow, has another. When all waves travel with the same speed, as is the case with electromagnetic waves in a vacuum or sound waves in air, it is unnecessary to make this distinction. When electromagnetic waves are used to transmit a signal by transferring energy through a material medium, a *range* of frequencies, the extent of which depends on the information to be conveyed, is necessary. Since the velocity of these waves varies with their frequency, the resultant waveform, in a manner similar to the group in water waves, is constantly changing. The group velocity is different from the wave velocity.

Although the wave velocity may be greater or less than the group velocity, it is a fundamental principle of physics that no signal can be transmitted with a speed greater than the velocity of light. Hence the group velocity can never be greater than 3×10^8 meters per sec.

When electromagnetic radiation passes from one medium to another, the direction of the waves, in general, is changed. A quantitative relation was obtained by Snell as early as 1621. If i is the angle of incidence and r the angle of refraction

$$\sin i / \sin r = \text{constant}$$

This relation in itself tells us nothing as to the medium in which the velocity is greater. If the mediums are air and water, it may be shown on the basis of a wave theory that the velocity is greater in air. Using a particle theory based on Newtonian mechanics the converse may be proved. Confirmation of the wave theory seemed assured when Foucault (1850) showed experimentally that light travels faster in air than in water.

The proof of Snell's law on the basis of wave theory is developed from Huygens' principle and may be found in texts on general physics. If i is the angle in a vacuum and r is the angle in the medium,

$$\frac{\sin i}{\sin r} = \frac{c}{v} = \mu \qquad (4.3)$$

where c (the universal symbol) is the velocity of electromagnetic waves in free space and v is the wave velocity in the medium. The symbol μ, defined as the ratio c/v, is called the *index of refraction*, or the *refractive index*, of the medium. When we say that the refractive index for yellow light is 1.5, the statement means that the wave velocity of this type of electromagnetic radiation is 1.5 times as great in free space as it is in glass. The reciprocal $(1/\mu)$ of the refractive index is the *velocity factor*. If the value of the latter for polyethylene, used as an insulator in some types of coaxial cable is 0.66, its refractive index is 1.52.

The velocity of an electromagnetic wave changes whenever the electric and magnetic properties of the medium in which it is traveling are altered. The *frequency*, however, *does not change*. Hence the wavelength must increase or diminish in accordance with the relation

$$v = f\lambda$$

For example, the wavelength in polyethylene is about two-thirds of the value in free space or, practically, in air.

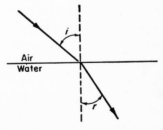

FIG. 4.10. Snell's law.

Next, let us review briefly the method of determining the refractive index when light, say, passes from air into water. Unless the incident ray is perpendicular to the boundary (zero angle of incidence), the direction of the ray is changed, being bent toward the normal when it passes into the medium where its wave speed is less (Fig. 4.10). Snell's law may be written

$$\frac{c}{v_1} \cdot \sin i = \frac{c}{v_2} \cdot \sin r$$

$$\mu_1 \cdot \sin i = \mu_2 \cdot \sin r$$

(4.4)

where the subscripts 1 and 2 refer to air and water, respectively. As in the law of reflection, the incident and refracted rays lie in the same plane.

In general, when light passes from one medium to another it is both reflected and refracted. Let us consider the case where a ray of light passes from a medium of higher to a medium of lower refractive index, say from water ($\mu_2 = \frac{4}{3}$) into air ($\mu_1 = 1$). If the light is incident normally (Ray 1 in Fig. 4.11) upon the interface of the two mediums, about

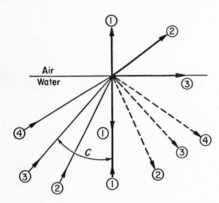

Fig. 4.11. Critical angle and total reflection.

2 per cent of the incident radiation will be reflected, the remainder being transmitted to the air. If the angle of incidence is increased (Ray 2), a larger percentage of the energy will be reflected. When the angle defined by Ray 3 is reached (or more precisely, exceeded by an infinitesimal amount), all the light is reflected. If this angle, called the *critical angle C*, is exceeded, no light will pass from the water to the air (Ray 4).

From Snell's law (recall that the incident angle is now in the water),

$$\mu_2 \cdot \sin i = \mu_1 \cdot \sin r$$

The value of sin r, while always greater than sin i, cannot exceed unity. For the critical ray, $i = C$, and we may write

$$\sin C = \frac{\mu_1}{\mu_2}$$

(4.5)

Since in this case the index for air may be taken as approximately unity, the relation in elementary physics is usually written: the sine of the critical angle is the reciprocal of the refractive index for the given medium. (For water, sin $C = \frac{3}{4}$, $C = 48.5°$.) It should be realized, however, that the statement refers to a special case ($\mu \doteq 1$ for air) and cannot be used generally.

When radio waves pass from a vacuum into a region containing free electrons, the ray is bent away from the normal, showing that the refractive index of the second medium is less than unity. This is essentially the case when radio waves are propagated into the ionosphere, a series of layers with varying electron densities in the upper atmosphere (Chapter 7). When the angle of incidence exceeds its critical value, the radio wave will be returned to the earth by total reflection. Although the wave velocity in the ionosphere is greater than in free space, the speed with which the signal travels, i.e., the group velocity, must be less than c. The refractive index represents the ratio of the wave velocities in free space and in the medium. The group velocity is the rate at which the signal travels from the transmitter to the receiver. The amount by which the group velocity differs from the wave velocity depends on the wavelength in the medium and the rate at which the wave velocity changes with the wavelength.

4.7. Optical Refraction in the Atmosphere. As stated above, the refractive index of air, in certain cases, may be taken as unity, although the average value is about 1.0003. If the word *air* is considered synonymous with the atmosphere, its refractive index will vary with its state and composition. The principal factors involved are: density; temperature; proportions of chemical elements present; existence of water vapor; and number of free electrons available, particularly in the upper regions known as the ionosphere. (The last will be discussed in detail in Chapter 7.)

Fig. 4.12. Refraction of the sun's rays by the earth's atmosphere.

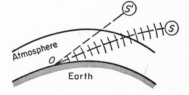

In dealing with radio waves we shall be primarily interested in those cases where the radiation travels paths along which the refractive index does not undergo a sudden alteration, as it does when light passes from air into glass but, instead, experiences a gradual, continuous change. Two examples of optical phenomena which may be observed in everyday life will illustrate the physical principles involved.

The first is concerned with the apparent position of the sun or other heavenly body. Consider a plane wavefront of light entering the earth's atmosphere from the sun S (Fig. 4.12). Since the density of the atmosphere is greatest at the earth's surface and decreases with increasing elevation, the lower part of the wavefront travels in air of greater density than the upper portion. An increase in density is equivalent to a higher refractive index or a lower velocity. (The speed of light in air near the earth's surface is about 50 miles per sec less than in a vacuum.) The lower portion of the wavefront travels more slowly causing the direction of the wave to change as it moves through the atmosphere. As a result the sun's rays follow a *curved* path. However, it has become second nature with us to assume that it is straight. Accordingly an observer *O* on the surface of the earth believes that he sees the light traveling in a direction tangent to the rays which reach his eye, apparently from *S'*, and perceives that the sun is nearer to the zenith (a point directly overhead) than it actually is. Because of this apparent lifting effect, the result of atmospheric refraction, the sun is seen for a few minutes before sunrise and after sunset. All navigators, who employ a sextant to determine their latitude, know that they must apply a correction for atmospheric refraction to the readings of their instruments, except of course in the special case where the sun is directly overhead.

The second well-known optical phenomenon which occurs as the result of refraction is the *mirage*. It is observed in regions where the air near the surface of the earth has a lower density than that above. This is a condition often found over an area which strongly radiates the heat received from the sun. Although usually associated with the desert, a mirage may commonly be seen when riding along a black surfaced highway. As the temperature of the pavement rises, the air directly above it becomes warmer than the air at a higher level. The changes in refractive index are such that the observer sees the light from the sky as if it came from an

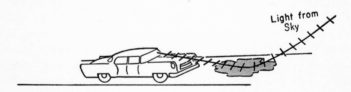

Fɪɢ. 4.13. A highway mirage.

area of the road ahead of the car (Fig. 4.13). The refracted sky light is perceived as a patch of water on the highway, the effect being especially striking if there is a slight upward slope in the road ahead.

4.8. Radio Refraction in the Atmosphere. We shall now see how some of the foregoing principles may be applied to radio waves in their propagation through the atmosphere. Let us recall that the air surrounding the earth may be divided into three main parts. (1) The *troposphere,* extending 7 or 8 miles above the earth's surface, is the region in which changing weather conditions take place. Its nonuniform characteristics have an important effect on the behavior of electromagnetic waves of certain frequencies. (2) The *stratosphere,* seldom affected by ordinary weather conditions, may be said to extend, for our purposes, roughly 20 miles beyond the troposphere. The effect of this intermediate layer on radio wave propagation is negligible. (3) The *ionosphere,* lying above the stratosphere, consists of a series of electrified layers which are responsible for the return of radio waves of certain frequencies to the earth. Its properties demand careful study and will be considered in detail in Chapter 7.

At this point an explanation of certain necessary terminology will be given. All electromagnetic radiation reflected or refracted back to the earth from the ionosphere is universally designated as the *sky wave.* It is used for nearly all long-distance radio communication and until fairly recently it was seldom dependable beyond 30 Mc. Some writers define the *ground wave* in effect as all radiation except the sky wave. Others break down the classification of radiation not involving the ionosphere into a *ground wave* and a *tropospheric wave.*

The former, used principally at broadcast and lower frequencies, is thus a surface wave in actual contact with the ground and travels along its surface. The tropospheric wave may consist of several components. One, called the *direct* wave, travels directly from the transmitter to the receiver; another, the *ground-reflected* wave, reaches the latter after a reflection from the surface of the earth. Also included are waves which are received as the result of rather abrupt variations in the refractive index of the troposphere and by diffraction (bending) around obstacles. (Sometimes the direct and ground-reflected waves are considered to be constituents of the ground wave.) Ordinarily the tropospheric wave accounts for transmission in the VHF and higher frequency bands which include television and radar.

One aspect of the tropospheric wave at the higher frequencies is *line-of-sight* propagation. The problem is essentially that of finding the distance from the top of the transmitting antenna to the horizon and, with the aid of Fig. 4.14, may be solved by applying certain well-known theorems of plane geometry.

Let $AB = h$, the height of the antenna. $AH = d$ is the distance from the top of the antenna to the horizon. $OH = OB = R$ is the radius of the earth. AH is tangent to the spherical surface of the earth and is therefore perpendicular to its radius OH. The triangle AHO is a right triangle to which the Pythagorean theorem may be applied.

$$(R + h)^2 = R^2 + d^2 \tag{4.6}$$

Solving for d,

$$d = \sqrt{2Rh + h^2} \tag{4.7}$$

Since h^2 is small *in comparison with* $2Rh$, the former may be neglected and the line-of-sight range given by

$$d = \sqrt{2Rh} \qquad (4.8)$$

In order to see the relative magnitude of the error involved in this approximation, consider a numerical example. Let the antenna be located on an elevation such that $h = 1$ mile and let the radius of the earth $R = 4000$ miles.

$$2Rh = 8000; \; h^2 = 1$$

The relative or percentage error is 1/8000 or 1/80 of 1 per cent. Since the expression for d appears under the radical sign, the percentage error is halved, thus making the error in the range only 1/160 of 1 per cent, a quantity which is entirely negligible.

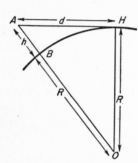

Fig. 4.14. The line-of-sight horizon.

In the foregoing discussion we have tentatively assumed that the receiving antenna was at ground level. When it is elevated, as is usual, its line-of-sight distance may also be calculated by the method of Eq. (4.8). The two values are added to obtain the total range.

Since changes in the physical characteristics of the troposphere (density, temperature, water vapor content) with height above the earth produce variations in the refractive index, the statement that the ray travels in a straight line is not strictly true. Although these variations are dependent on weather conditions, the assumption is usually made that the rate of change of refractive index with height above the earth is uniform. A region of the troposphere where the temperature gradient is 2C° per 1000 ft is called a *standard atmosphere*. Under these conditions the ray travels in a curved path with a radius approximately four times that of the earth. This curvature of path permits the direct ray to reach a point somewhat beyond the horizon of the straight-line path (Fig. 4.15).

It is clear that if the earth were flatter, i.e., had a larger radius of curvature, the horizon would be extended. The idea, therefore, suggests itself that the effect of refraction may be accounted for by giving the earth a fictitious radius, somewhat greater than its actual value, and assuming propagation in a straight line. For a standard atmosphere it turns out that this *effective radius* is 4/3 the measured value. This method of treating atmospheric refraction such that straight-line instead of curved paths may be drawn is an example of the "convenience" point of view introduced at the beginning of the first chapter. (Here it may be remarked that in order to simplify certain types of computations, the reverse procedure of using curved rays above a flat earth is also employed.)

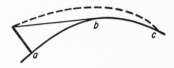

FIG. 4.15. The extension of line-of-sight by tropospheric refraction. For an antenna located at *a*, *b* is the visual horizon and *c* is the radio horizon.

Under standard conditions the horizon is extended over the line-of-sight distance by an appreciable amount (see Problem 4.13). Under nonstandard conditions the effect may be considerably greater. Two conditions which contribute to an increase in the velocity of electromagnetic waves in air are lower density and higher temperature. Clearly, if both conditions exist simultaneously, enough refraction may be produced to return radio waves to the earth at a considerable distance beyond the line-of-sight horizon. It is well known, however, that as we ascend into the air its density becomes less but its temperature also becomes lower.

We shall now consider what may take place on a summer day when there is an abundance of sunshine (Fig. 4.16). Since the air absorbs only a small part of the solar radiation, the energy received by the ground causes

FIG. 4.16. Day and night refraction of a radio wave by the troposphere.

it to rise to a relatively high temperature during the day. After sunset both the ground and the air become cooler, but the temperature change in the latter takes place at a much slower rate. As a consequence we have a state of *temperature inversion*, i.e., the temperature of the air increases with increasing height above the earth. Conditions are now favorable for the refraction of radio waves in the troposphere and signals may be received at points which are well beyond the line-of-sight horizon.

4.9. Dynamic Inversion. There are of course various meteorological conditions which contribute to a state of temperature inversion. Of particular interest is *dynamic inversion* which is associated with the enormous volumes of air which travel, roughly, from west to east across the United States. These air masses move with speeds determined by the pressure gradient, although from time to time their motion may be arrested. During such periods there is a protracted season of uniform weather—usually fair.

Let us suppose that a cold air mass, moving rapidly, overtakes a warm air mass. The former, having a greater density, remains closer to the ground and the warm air is pushed upward. The boundary between the two is relatively sharp, considering the nature of the mediums and, while the motion is relatively slow, it may be assumed that they are two separate gases with different refractive indices. As shown in Fig. 4.17, the line of

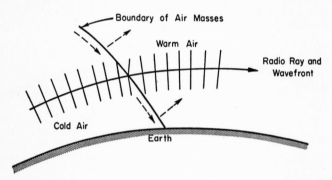

Fig. 4.17. Tropospheric refraction. Warm air pushed upward by cold air mass. Broken arrows show directions in which air moves.

separation makes an angle with the ground. We now have a condition of dynamic temperature inversion such that electromagnetic waves of the higher frequencies are refracted toward the earth.

Fig. 4.18 shows the case where the cold air is overtaken by a mass of warm air, the refraction of the wave being similar to Fig. 4.17. These two figures show the wave traveling from the colder to the warmer mass. If the diagrams are redrawn, reversing the direction of wave propagation, it will be found that the refraction is such that the wave is also directed toward the surface of the earth. The conditions for extended favorable temperature distributions occur more frequently in summer when the air masses tend to move more slowly than they do in winter.

In order to apply the phenomena of dynamic inversion to problems of transmission and reception, recourse should be had to the meteorological charts published by the Weather Bureau. These maps show conditions of pressure and temperature at a given time over the entire country. With the use of weather charts for successive days, reasonably satisfactory predictions may be made regarding conditions suitable for the bending of high frequency waves in the troposphere. Many amateurs have obtained interesting results at 50 Mc and above, ranges of over 200 miles having been reported. Note, however, that satisfactory reception can be expected only for waves which leave the ground at relatively small angles. Furthermore, since the phenomenon depends on weather conditions, it can be relied upon just as much as the weather itself—no more and no less.

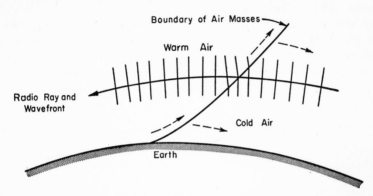

FIG. 4.18. Tropospheric refraction. Warm air overrides cold air mass. Broken arrows show directions in which air moves.

Tropospheric refraction, together with diffraction, to be discussed in the next chapter, plays an important role in television reception in the so-called "fringe" areas, but, of course, it is not dependable. Line-of-sight and diffraction ranges are, in general, constant and dependable.

4.10. Atmospheric Ducts. It is, of course, the *gradient*, i.e., the rate of change of the refractive index with the height, that is principally responsible for the bending of radio waves in the troposphere. If there is a relatively abrupt change in the index, it may be convenient to classify the phenomenon as reflection. Since the water vapor content of the atmosphere has a considerable effect on its electrical properties, even more than temperature, a rapid decrease in humidity with increasing height provides the conditions for reflection and refraction.

If nearly constant deviations from standard conditions persist in time and provide a rather sharp change in refractive index at one or two levels above the earth, a *duct* is formed in which the waves may be *trapped* or *superrefracted*. If the lower side is the earth, the stratum is called a *surface* duct; otherwise, an *elevated* duct.

In Fig. 4.19 let T be a transmitting antenna located within a surface duct.   The energy radiated at various angles is represented by rays proceeding from the antenna.   The angles of incidence which the rays a and b make with the normal to the upper surface of the duct are less than the critical angle and the energy is refracted into the space above.   On the other hand, the incident angles for rays c, d, and e are greater than the critical angle.   Accordingly they are reflected and the radiation is guided along the duct as indicated.   In this way the range of the propagated signals is increased far beyond the line-of-sight, provided both transmitting and receiving antennas are located within the duct.   For example, an airplane flying in an elevated duct may receive exceptionally good signals the strength of which diminishes rapidly when the plane changes altitude.

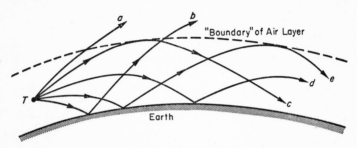

FIG. 4.19.   Radio wave propagation in a surface duct.

Ducts may be reasonably stable over the ocean, particularly in the tropics, but over land they are always of short duration.   Their disappearance is usually coincident with a change in the weather.   Ducts are common in Southern California, where they extend considerably the range of television transmission; and in certain areas of the Pacific, where their effect on the interpretation of the range of radar signals led to a detailed study of the phenomenon.   Their thickness varies over a wide range, from a few feet to a thousand feet.

The propagation of waves in a duct may be compared to a waveguide, which is the subject matter of a later chapter.   In passing, it may be remarked that for both devices there is a critical frequency below which transmission will not occur.   For example, in a rectangular waveguide the half-wavelengths must not be larger than the distance between parallel conductors.   In this respect the guide behaves like a high-pass filter.   A duct may also be compared to a dielectric waveguide which has no metallic boundaries, the waves being propagated partly through the dielectric (the duct) and partly through the surrounding space.   In the preceding section it was pointed out that satisfactory refraction effects are restricted to waves which are projected at small angles with the horizon.   For this reason the thickness of the duct must be large in wavelengths and propagation within it is likely to be confined to the higher frequencies.

PROBLEMS

4.1. The wavelength of visible light is measured in angstroms (1 A = 10^{-10} meter). Find the frequency in Mc of yellow sodium light which has a wavelength of 5890 A.

4.2. A short pulse of radiation is sent out by a radar set, is reflected from the surface of an airplane and is returned to the receiver 500 microseconds after transmission. How far away is the plane?

4.3. Assume that we have a point source and wish to produce a plane wavefront by means of a sheet reflector. In Fig. 4.20 the distance from the source F

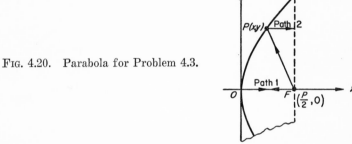

Fig. 4.20.   Parabola for Problem 4.3.

to the plane wavefront (the vertical broken line) via Path 1 or Path 2 must be equal. Show that the equation for the surface contour is a parabola.

4.4. Let a point source be placed at one focus of an elliptical reflector. Draw a diagram showing a pair of incident and reflected rays. Discuss the result.

4.5. Repeat Problem 4.4 for a hyperbolic reflector and compare the results.

4.6. Copy Fig. 4.7. Following the method used there, draw similar diagrams for (a) half-wave vertical antenna, (b) full-wave horizontal antenna, (c) full-wave vertical antenna. Compare the results.

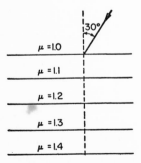

Fig. 4.21.   Multilayered liquid with variations in refractive index, for Problem 4.10.

4.7. Construct the images for a dihedral corner reflector of 60°.

4.8. A television receiver is located 5 miles from the transmitter. A ghost image is displaced from the main image by 0.5 in. on a screen 20 in. wide. Construct the ellipse on which reflecting objects must lie in order to produce the ghost. Find the major and minor axes of the conic and write its equation. Assume the origin to be at the center of the ellipse.

4.9. In Fig. 4.11 let glass (refractive index, 1.50) and water replace water and air, respectively. Compute the critical angle in glass.

4.10. Light travels from a vacuum into a multilayered liquid with variations in refractive index as shown in Fig. 4.21. Construct the ray as it progresses through the layers. Draw each layer 1 in. thick and record the angles to the nearest 0.5°.

4.11. Assume that the radiation from a television antenna travels in a straight line. What will be the range d in miles for a transmitting antenna with a height h of 528 ft? Radius of the earth: 4000 miles. Use the geometry of Fig. 4.14 in the solution.

4.12. The effective range of the television station in Problem 4.11 can be extended in two ways: (a) by increasing the height of the transmitting antenna, (b) by keeping the transmitting antenna at the same height and raising the receiving antenna above the earth's surface. Solve the problem for both cases, for a range of 40 miles, and discuss the results. Diagrams.

4.13. By what percentage is the horizon extended over the line-of-sight range if the effective radius of the earth is based on the assumed standard atmosphere?

Chapter 5

INTERFERENCE AND DIFFRACTION

5.1. Principle of Superposition. The principle of superposition has many applications in various branches of physics. Insofar as it applies to the subject matter to be discussed here, this principle states that the effect resulting from the simultaneous action of any number of causes is the sum of the effects due to the causes taken separately. Each cause produces its own effect, without regard to the presence or absence of the others.

In mechanics we may have two perpendicular forces acting simultaneously on a body. The first displaces the body 5 ft upward; the second, 12 ft to the right (Fig. 5.1). Each force independently produces its own dis-

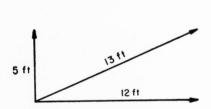

Fig. 5.1. Superposition of two displacements.

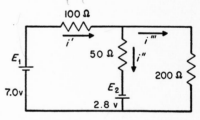

Fig. 5.2. Superposition of two currents.

placement. The resultant effect is the *vector sum* of the two displacements, as shown in the diagram.

The following problem shows how the principle of superposition may be applied to a simple direct-current network (Fig. 5.2). The resultant current in each branch is the *algebraic sum* of the currents produced by the individual batteries acting separately. Applying the laws governing series-parallel circuits, with the battery E_2 removed, the currents are found to be $i_1' = 50$ ma, $i_1'' = 40$ ma, and $i_1''' = 10$ ma. (The subscript 1 indicates that these currents are produced by E_1 alone in the network.) Similarly, when E_1 is removed, the currents produced by E_2 are $i_2' = 16$ ma, $i_2'' = 24$ ma, and $i_2''' = 8$ ma. All these currents, with the exception of i_2''', are in

75

a clockwise direction. Their algebraic sums, indicated by the absence of a subscript, are given by $i' = 66$ ma, $i'' = 64$ ma, and $i''' = 2$ ma.

Let us next consider the superposition of two waves which are identical in every respect, except for possible phase differences. If their displacements are added algebraically, point by point, the resultant will be greater or less than the corresponding displacements of the individual waves, as determined by the existing phase difference. If this phase difference is zero, all the displacements will be double those for a single wave. If it is 180°, there will be complete cancellation.

5.2. Young's Experiment. Fig. 5.3 shows the essentials of a well-known experiment designed to show the effects of reinforcement and cancellation in the case of light waves. A source of monochromatic light (*),

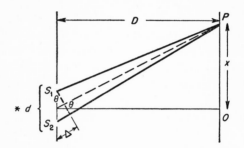

FIG. 5.3. Young's experiment.

e.g., a sodium lamp, is placed behind an opaque screen in which two narrow slits S_1 and S_2 are cut. A single primary source is necessary in order that the light waves from the two secondary sources (slits) shall instantaneously be in phase, a restriction which we shall not find necessary to impose when the radiators are antennas. At a distance D is a second screen on which the resultant intensity of the radiation may be observed.

At O there will be reinforcement. Since both waves start in phase and travel the same distance, they will arrive at their destination in phase. At some point P, in the direction θ, there will, in general, be a difference in phase, owing to the fact that each of these waves has traversed a different distance. Let the difference in path, $S_2P - S_1P = \Delta$. (The meaning of this symbol will be extended in Sec. 5.5.) If Δ is $1/2\ \lambda$, $3/2\ \lambda$, $5/2\ \lambda \ldots$, the two waves will be out of phase by an angle equivalent to 180°. Hence there will be darkness. If Δ is 0, λ, 2λ, $3\lambda \ldots$, there will be maximum brightness. In reality there is no loss of energy, for the radiation in the bright regions is much more intense than it would be if the illumination were uniform. We have, essentially, a pair of antennas, fed in phase, which beam their radiation in certain preferred directions.

Briefly, the mathematical analysis is as follows. From the diagram, the relations

$$\sin \theta = \Delta/d \text{ and } \tan \theta = x/D$$

may be obtained. Since $\tan \theta = \sin \theta/\cos \theta$, we may write

$$\sin \theta = (x/D) \cos \theta$$

Upon substitution,

$$\Delta/d = (x/D) \cos \theta$$

If the point P is relatively distant, the angle θ will be small and the value of $\cos \theta$ may be taken as unity. Solving for x, we obtain

$$x = \Delta \cdot D/d$$

For darkness or maximum brightness the path difference must be equal to an integral number of half-wavelengths, i.e., $\Delta = n\lambda/2$. If n is odd (1, 3, 5 . . .), there is darkness (*destructive interference*); if n is even (0, 2, 4 . . .), there is maximum brightness (*constructive interference*). The distance x, which locates the point P with respect to O, may be determined from the expression

$$x = (n\lambda/2) \cdot (D/d) \tag{5.1}$$

This experiment, with modifications, was performed by Thomas Young (*circa* 1805); it was perhaps the first planned demonstration of the existence of electromagnetic waves—although, of course, they were not so designated at that time. The average wavelength of the radiation was about 6×10^{-7} meter. Hence the frequency was $(3 \times 10^8 \text{ meters per sec})/(6 \times 10^{-7} \text{ m}) = 5 \times 10^{14}$ cycles, which is equivalent to 500 mega-megacycles.

The bright and dark fringes described above may be observed conveniently by holding the plate or screen, in which the two slits are cut, close to the eye and viewing a lamp with a single straight filament. The distance between the slits should be less than a millimeter and the lamp should be at least 2 meters away. In order to obtain approximately monochromatic light, which is necessary if sharp images are to be viewed, a piece of colored glass is placed in front of the lamp. For a selected wavelength of light, slits very close together give widely spaced fringes and vice versa. For a given slit separation, red light, because of its greater wavelength, produces wider fringes than blue light. Used in this way, the slit system is analogous to a pair of receiving antennas which intercept electromagnetic radiation from a distant linear source. A plot of the variations in light intensity is thus comparable to the power pattern of an antenna. This will be discussed later.

5.3. Hyperbolic Navigation.   We shall now discuss a method by which the principles involved in Young's experiment may be applied to the use of radio waves in navigation.   In Fig. 5.3 let P represent a point where the first maximum beyond the central bright image is observed.   The difference in path between S_1P and S_2P is one wavelength.   If the observing screen were moved, the point for which this same Δ exists would vary with respect to the central image.   In Sec. 5.2 the assumption that the angle θ is small leads to the conclusion that x is proportional to D.   This is equivalent to stating that the locus of P is a straight line.

Since P is any point for which the difference in distances from two fixed points S_1 and S_2 is a constant, the line is actually a segment of a hyperbola.   By choosing different values for the path difference a series of hyperbolas with S_1 and S_2 as foci may be constructed.

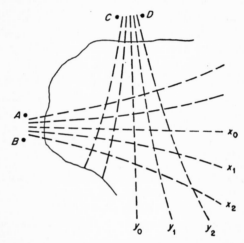

FIG. 5.4.   The interference of radio waves forms the basis of hyperbolic navigation.

Let two radio stations A and B (Fig. 5.4) located on shore a known distance apart replace the slits S_1 and S_2.   Pulses of radio frequency waves transmitted by A and B are received by ships or aircraft whose positions are to be ascertained.   The detecting apparatus, however, does not distinguish phase differences as in the optical case.   There is merely a difference in the time at which the two signals are received.   Their velocity being constant, this time difference is equivalent to a space distance.

If A and B send out pulses in unison, a ship anywhere along the line x_0 receives the two pulses at the same time because both signals travel the same distance.   A ship on the line x_1 receives the two pulses separated by an interval of time corresponding to the appropriate difference in path.   On each branch of the family of hyperbolas associated with the stations A and B, different time intervals are recorded.

One set of transmitters, A and B, serves to locate the ship somewhere along the line, say x_1. If there is a second pair of stations C and D, a position of the ship somewhere on one of their hyperbolas can be determined. Let this line be y_1. Their intersection fixes the ship's position, which is read from charts crossed by families of hyperbolas instead of the familiar lines of latitude and longitude.

The difference in time is measured by observing the pulses on the screen of a cathode-ray oscilloscope. Since both pulses appear alike, they must be distinguished. In practice, therefore, the two stations of a given pair, called the master and the slave, transmit their signals separated by a time delay instead of simultaneously. An interval may be determined with an error of less than a microsecond, which is equivalent to fixing the position of the ship to within a thousand feet.

In the United States, hyperbolic navigation is called *loran,* a contraction of *long-range* *n*avigation. Standard loran, operating in a frequency band of 1700 to 2000 kc, uses the ground wave in the daytime and the sky wave at night. During the day, signals transmitted over the ocean have a range of about 700 miles; at night the distance may be increased to 1500 miles. The poor conductivity of land limits the daytime range over this type of terrain to about 200 miles. Using the same frequencies, SS (sky-wave synchronized) loran, originally developed for the guidance of night bombers, employs the sky wave exclusively. Low frequency loran (100 to 200 kc) was developed to·extend the ground-wave range and to increase the reliability of sky-wave operation in the polar regions.

5.4. Interference of Radio Waves. In optics Young's experiment illustrates the point that interference effects are, in general, observable to an appreciable extent only when the dimensions of obstacles or openings are comparable to the wavelengths involved. As the use of radio waves with shorter wavelengths becomes more common, increased attention to interference phenomena typical of light waves becomes necessary.

Path differences in relation to wavelengths must be considered. The average wavelength of the radiation transmitted from television stations in the VHF band is of the order of 10 ft. Signals from a transmitter may reach the receiver by reflection from buildings or the terrain, in addition to the direct path. Under these circumstances the path difference may easily be of the order of magnitude of a wavelength.

Let us suppose that the receiving antenna accepts from the transmitting antenna signals which have arrived over two paths (Fig. 5.5). The first along d_1 is obtained directly. The other along $d_2 + d_3$ is obtained after reflection from a building. If the difference in paths $(d_2 + d_3) - d_1$ equals an integral number of wavelengths, the received signal is strengthened; if an odd number of half-wavelengths, the signal may be too weak to produce a satisfactory image on the screen.

If conditions are such that there is a phase change of 180° on reflection, it must be taken into account by adding a half-wavelength to the reflected path. This, of course, is equivalent to changing the condition for cancellation, insofar as the geometric path is concerned, into a condition for rein-

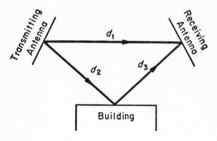

FIG. 5.5. Interference of television waves.

forcement. Clearly, methods must be devised to cancel an unwanted reflected signal. Just as a transmitting antenna can be made directive, e.g., the parabolic reflector (Sec. 4.3), so can a receiving antenna. Some of the methods used to accomplish this desirable effect will be discussed later (Sec. 9.5).

5.5. Ground Reflection Factors. Now that the concept of electrical images and the fundamentals of interference have been discussed, we are prepared to study the combined effects of reflection and interference for the case of an antenna mounted a specified distance above the surface of an ideally conducting earth. Although the discussion will be confined to horizontal antennas, it may be readily extended to those of the vertical type.

Let a horizontal half-wave antenna, with instantaneous positive polarity at one end, be located a distance h above the earth (Fig. 5.6). Its image, an equal distance below the earth, will have opposite polarity. Let a signal be transmitted to a distant receiver in a direction designated by the angle θ. The signal will be modified by the existing phase difference between the direct and the reflected ray. It is further assumed that the strength of the signal received by the direct path is unity. For an ideal earth, the reflected signal will have the same value. The resultant signal, modified by phase relations, may then have any value between 0 and 2.

Following the method of electrical images, we shall assume that the earth is removed and that the radiation depends only on the emission from two line sources, the antenna and its image. The signal received along the image path will lag the direct signal by $180° + 2h \sin \theta$, where $2h$ must eventually be expressed in electrical degrees. The lag of 180°, to be denoted in general by φ, occurs because the ends of the real and the image antennas have opposite polarities at a given time. The second term is the result of the fact that the wave from the image antenna must travel a distance $2h$ sin θ farther than the direct wave. If we take $h = \lambda/4$, $2h = \lambda/2$ or 180°. The image wave, therefore, lags the direct wave by a phase angle, $\Delta = 180°$ $+ 180°$ sin θ. Notice that the meaning of Δ, as given in Sec. 5.2, has been extended so as to include the difference in the phasing of the antennas as well as the path difference. This procedure is justified as the latter may be

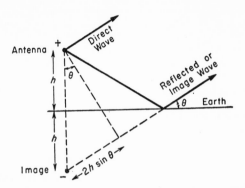

FIG. 5.6.　Diagram showing how the wave from an image antenna is equivalent to the wave reflected from the earth.

expressed in degrees. For any given direction, the phase angle between the two rays must be calculated and the phasors combined to form the resultant R.

Before deriving a general expression which may be used for all values of Δ, we shall discuss two special cases in which the resultant can be obtained from physical considerations. Parallel to the surface of the earth, $\theta = 0°$, the radiation must be zero, for the direct and the reflected waves are originally 180° out of phase and they travel the same distance to the receiver. In the vertical direction, $\theta = 90°$, the resultant radiation will be doubled. *Assume* that the phase of the real antenna at a given time is 180°; at the same instant the phase of its image is 0°. When the wave from the latter reaches the antenna a half-period later—it must travel a distance of one-half wavelength—the phase of the real antenna has become 360°, and the two waves are in phase.

In attacking the problem of a general expression for the resultant, we first recall that the magnitudes of the direct and reflected phasors are to be taken as unity. Further, we recall that a *lag* of Δ is equivalent to a *lead* of $360° - \Delta$. For example, a lag of 270° may be expressed as a lead of 90°.

Since we are interested only in the *magnitude* of the resultant we shall use Δ as the angle of lag or lead, as convenience suits.

Let the direct and image phasors, each with a magnitude of unity, and with a phase difference Δ between them, be added in the usual manner as shown in Fig. 5.7. From the construction, ABC is an isosceles triangle and Δ is the exterior angle opposite the two equal interior angles. Since Δ is equal to the sum of these angles, each must have the magnitude $\Delta/2$. The

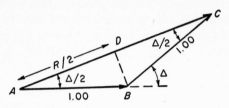

FIG. 5.7. Diagram illustrating the relation between the resultant and phase angle for two phasors of equal magnitude.

phasor AC is the resultant R. Drawing the perpendicular bisector BD makes $AD = R/2$. In the right triangle ADB, $\cos \Delta/2 = (R/2)/1.00$. Hence,

$$R = 2 \cdot \cos \Delta/2 \qquad (5.2)$$

The *relative* magnitude of the resultant is equal to twice the cosine of half the phase angle (which may be either a lag or a lead).

Table 5.1 presents data for the effect of ground reflection from a half-wave horizontal antenna a quarter-wavelength above the surface of the

TABLE 5.1. DATA ON GROUND REFLECTION

θ	$\sin \theta$	$180° \sin \theta$	$180° + 180° \sin \theta$	Δ	$R = 2 \cdot \cos \Delta/2$
0°	0.000	0°	180°	180°	0.00
5	0.087	16	196	164	0.28
10	0.174	31	211	149	0.52
15	0.259	47	227	133	0.77
20	0.342	62	242	118	1.03
30	0.500	90	270	90	1.41
40	0.643	116	296	64	1.70
50	0.766	138	318	42	1.87
60	0.866	156	336	24	1.96
70	0.940	169	349	11	1.98
80	0.985	177	357	3	1.99
90	1.000	180	360	0	2.00

earth. A plot of these data is *not* an antenna radiation pattern. It is a presentation of the factors by which the free-space pattern must be modified in order to take account of the reflection by the earth. Since no reflection takes place below the surface of the earth, the values of θ range from 0° to 180°. Values of R are computed for angles between 0° and 90° only, and the pattern is completed from considerations of symmetry.

Notice that $\Delta \leqq 180°$; therefore $\Delta/2 \leqq 90°$, and cos $\Delta/2$ may be obtained immediately from the tables. In the solutions of problems, all computations should be tabulated in a format similar to the illustrative example. By a judicious use of the slide rule the number of columns may be made smaller. Carry the sines to three decimal places only. Compute all angles to the nearest degree and the resultant to two decimal places. Further refinement is a mere waste of time.

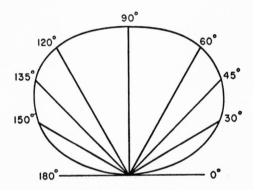

Fig. 5.8. Ground reflection pattern for horizontal antenna located a quarter-wavelength above the surface of the earth.

Admittedly the plotting of ground reflection patterns by the above method may become somewhat laborious. Yet it must be done if an accurate graph is required. There may be occasions, however, when a simple sketch will answer the purpose. Fortunately a rather convenient method is available.

For a null ($R = 0$) and for a maximum lobe ($R = 2$), Δ must equal an integral number of half-wavelengths, which may be expressed in degrees.

$$\Delta = \varphi + 2h \cdot \sin \theta = n \cdot 180° \qquad (5.3)$$

If φ and $2h$ are expressed in degrees, sin θ may be conveniently written as a function of n.

$$\sin \theta = \frac{n \cdot 180° - \varphi}{2h} \qquad (5.4)$$

The values of θ for which n is odd locate the nulls; the values of θ for which n is even locate the maximum lobes. Negative values of the sine are excluded because there is no reflection below ground.

The following examples will make the procedure clear. First, consider the case presented by the data in Table 5.1.

$$\Delta = 180° + 180° \cdot \sin \theta = n \cdot 180°$$

$$\sin \theta = n - 1$$

Admissible values of n are 1 and 2. For the former, $\sin \theta = 0$; for the latter, $\sin \theta = 1$. Hence there are nulls at $0°$ and $180°$, and a maximum lobe at $90°$, as shown in Fig. 5.8.

In Problem 5.5,

$$\Delta = 180° + 360° \cdot \sin \theta = n \cdot 180°$$

$$\sin \theta = \frac{n-1}{2}$$

Tabulating the results, we have

n	$\sin \theta$	θ	
1	0.0	$0°, 180°$	Nulls
2	0.5	$30°, 150°$	Maximum lobes
3	1.0	$90°$	Null

A sketch prepared from these data will be found to agree with the pattern obtained by the more accurate method.

If the antenna and its image are in phase, as is the case for certain vertical antennas, φ is set equal to zero and the procedure is the same as given above.

While this method will give all the *nulls* and *maximum lobes,* it will not reveal the existence of minor lobes or minima where the reflection factor is neither 2 nor 0 (see Problem 5.10). The reason is clear: setting $\Delta = n \cdot 180°$ is equivalent to including only those cases where the two waves are *completely* in or out of phase.

5.6. Diffraction. At the beginning it was stated that convenience often dictates the point of view assumed in describing physical phenomena. In optics, for example, it is convenient to divide the subject into two broad classifications, geometrical optics (rays) and physical optics (waves). Since light is a form of electromagnetic energy, some illustrations may be drawn from that branch of physics.

Suppose we have light incident upon a cylinder. From the standpoint of ray optics, there should be a rectangular shadow with sharply defined edges behind the object, and full intensity beyond the boundary of the shadow.

This prediction is not fulfilled, particularly if the diameter of the cylinder is rather small, in the ordinary sense of the word. Suppose the object is a wire or a needle. If the light is propagated in the form of waves they should undergo bending or *diffraction*. Just outside the geometrical shadow there should be alternate bright and dark bands as a result of reinforcements and partial cancellations of the waves, the effect being qualitatively similar to the one observed in Young's interference experiment. Furthermore, inside the geometrical shadow another series of bands should be formed. The pattern is, indeed, easily observed. Evidently, we must resort to wave optics in order to obtain a satisfactory description of the phenomenon.

Other similar experiments may be performed. Bright and dark bands are observed just beyond the edge of the geometrical shadow of a razor blade. Within the shadow the intensity of the light falls off rapidly but not discontinuously. If a coin with a *smooth* edge or a ball bearing is illuminated by a point source of light there will be a bright spot in the center of the shadow.

Objections may be offered that the phenomena described above are not usually observed. In reply, it may be pointed out that diffraction effects become apparent only when the source of light is of very small dimensions or when the dimensions of obstacles and openings are somewhat comparable to the wavelengths of the radiation. The diffraction of sound waves is easily observed, that is, one may "hear around a corner" because the wavelengths of many ordinary sounds are of the order of a few feet. Light waves have wavelengths which are of the order of a few hundred thousandths of an inch. Hence optical diffraction effects are observable only under special conditions.

Long radio waves may be expected to show diffraction with respect to most obstacles. In the standard broadcast band, for example, the average wavelength is of the order of a thousand feet. With increasing use of higher frequencies, i.e., shorter wavelengths, the diffraction becomes less noticeable and conditions of rectilinear propagation are approached. As previously stated, in the VHF spectrum of television the wavelength is of the order of 10 ft. However, in this band diffraction at the earth's horizon is by no means negligible, for it accounts for an increase of several miles beyond the range computed for line-of-sight reception. This increase, for a given frequency, it will be remembered, is independent of atmospheric conditions and can always be relied upon.

Unfortunately the rigorous solution for the diffraction of radio waves around the earth is exceedingly complicated. The solution for an ideal sphere is in the form of an infinite series, with such a slow rate of convergence that it is ill-adapted to numerical computation. This difficulty has now been lessened by recent advancements which have been concerned with better methods of approximation whereby numerical answers can be obtained more readily.

It has been shown (Sec. 4.8) that the reception of electromagnetic radiation, particularly beyond the visual horizon, is subject to variations in the refractive index of the troposphere. The phenomenon of diffraction extends the field a definite amount, for a given wavelength, beyond this horizon. Essentially, refraction increases the effective radius of the earth by pushing the horizon farther out. Now if refraction only is considered there should be a distance at which the field strength drops more or less suddenly to zero, this distance being determined by the existing pattern of refractive indices in the troposphere. Such is not the case. We must conclude that refraction and diffraction assist one another. Refraction sets up a new horizon for the transmitting antenna; diffraction extends the field beyond this boundary into what in optics would be called the shadow region. It is very diffcult, however, to obtain a quantitative check on the magnitudes of the two effects, because of the variable nature of the refraction and because of the irregular nature of the existing terrain which differs markedly from the ideally spherical earth on which the diffraction theory is based.

5.7. Fresnel Zones. A wavefront is a surface on which every point is vibrating in the same phase. According to *Huygens' principle,* all points on a wavefront may be considered as sources of secondary spherical wavelets, the envelope of which is the new wavefront. Fig. 5.9 illustrates the

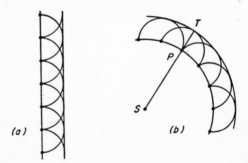

Fig. 5.9. Huygens' principle. Propagation of (*a*) plane and (*b*) spherical waves.

propagation of plane and spherical waves. In elementary physics where Huygens' principle is used to establish the laws of reflection and refraction, it is assumed that the wavelets are effective only at the points of tangency to the enveloping surface. This assumption enables us to define a ray as a line drawn perpendicular to the wavefront, e.g., *SPT* in the diagram. In diffraction, where geometric optics is not valid, it is necessary to assume that the wavelet is effective over the entire forward hemisphere, but not equally in all directions.

We now proceed to consider the diffraction produced by a limited portion of a plane wave, i.e., a spherical wave which has its origin in a distant source. By Huygens' principle, every point on the plane wavefront in Fig. 5.10 is the origin of secondary wavelets. We wish to find their resultant effect at the point P.

Let M_0 be the foot of the perpendicular drawn from P to the wavefront. With M_0 as a center, draw circles such that the first M_1 is a half-wavelength farther from P than the center M_0, the second M_2 is two half-wavelengths, etc. The path of the wave from any ring or zone is thus increased by a half-wavelength over the zone immediately within it.

Let $PM_0 = b$ and the radius of the first zone $M_0M_1 = r_1$. By the Pythagorean theorem

$$(b + \lambda/2)^2 - b^2 = r_1^2$$

If we assume that λ is small compared to b we may neglect $\lambda^2/4$ (see Sec. 4.8). The radius of the first zone is

$$r_1 = \sqrt{b\lambda}$$

In like manner it may be shown that the radii of the other circles are

$$r_2 = \sqrt{2b\lambda}, \quad r_3 = \sqrt{3b\lambda}, \cdots \quad r_n = \sqrt{nb\lambda}$$

Since the area of a circle is πr^2, the areas of the circular zones are $\pi b\lambda$, $2\pi b\lambda, \ldots n\pi b\lambda$.

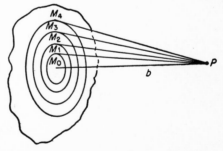

FIG. 5.10. Division of plane wavefront into Fresnel half-period zones.

The difference betweeen the areas of two successive circles is the area of the ring included between them. If the approximation given above is valid, the area of the central circular zone or that of each enclosing ring is $\pi b\lambda$. More precisely, each succeeding ring has a slightly greater area.

The effect on the electric (or magnetic) field strength which each zone, called a *Fresnel half-period zone,* produces at P is directly proportional to its area and inversely proportional to its distance from P. If these were the only factors they would just compensate for each other, such that adjacent zones would produce equal and opposite effects at P. That is, the radiation from each zone would be equal in magnitude to, and out of phase with, the radiation from its immediate neighbor.

The magnitude of the secondary wavelets, however, is not the same in all forward directions. As a consequence of the increasing obliquity, the amplitude of the radiation from successive zones tends to decrease slowly, and then more rapidly. Since the amplitude is proportional to the area of the zone, we may say that the effective area of the zones becomes smaller as we go out from the first. Furthermore, the difference between the areas of two successive zones becomes less as their number is increased.

The contributions of adjacent zones being 180° out of phase with one another, the resultant effect of each pair is approximately zero. If the wavefront contains an integral number of zones, it turns out that the resultant field at P is half the sum or half the difference of the amplitudes of the first and last zones, depending on whether the number is odd or even. When the dimensions of a wavefront are large compared to the wavelength, thereby exposing a large number of zones, the obliquity factor reduces the contribution from the last zone to practically zero. Hence the resultant of the electric field at P, due to the entire wavefront, is only one-half the contribution of the first zone. The intensity, which is proportional to $\mathcal{E}^2$, is therefore only one-fourth that produced by the innermost zone.

Let us now insert in the plane of the wavefront an opaque screen with a circular aperture containing only a few half-period zones. If the number of zones is odd, they cancel in pairs and the intensity at P is a maximum, being substantially that produced by the first zone alone. If the area includes an even number of zones, cancellation is nearly complete and the intensity at P is almost zero.

The same effect may be obtained by keeping the radius of the aperture fixed and moving the point P along the perpendicular b. The area of a circular zone is $n\pi b\lambda$. If b is increased the number of zones included in an aperture of constant area is diminished. Let us assume that P is originally in a position such that three zones are included. A maximum effect is observed at the point. If the distance is increased so that the aperture embraces two zones, there is a minimum at P. When the distance is increased sufficiently, the first zone completely fills the opening and a maximum reappears. Thus the field along the axis passes through a series of maxima and minima.

The statements given above regarding the electric field and the intensity of the radiation are true only for points along the axis. Off the axis the effects of the zones vary in a less simple manner. For a circular opening P is surrounded by a series of bright and dark diffraction rings.

In the case of light waves the results are easily verified by experiment. Monochromatic light from a distant point source is passed through a small circular opening and the diffraction pattern is viewed with an eyepiece. As the distance between the ocular and the screen is varied, the center of the field becomes alternately bright and dark.

5.8. Fresnel and Fraunhofer Diffraction. When the point for which the entire aperture coincides with the first Fresnel zone is reached, there are no additional fluctuations in the intensity at the point P. At this distance, however, the contribution from the edge of the aperture reaches P 180° out of phase with that from the center. If the distance is further increased, the phase difference at P between the contributions from central and peripheral regions (we are now dividing the aperture into subzones) is diminished. At an infinite distance from the aperture lines drawn from the effective wavefront are parallel. The radiation from all points, originally in phase and having equal amplitudes, travels the same distance and combines in phase to produce a maximum at P.

Infinity, of course, is a concept, not a number. In practice, we need to seek a distance b beyond which there will be no observable change in the diffraction pattern. In a crude way, the situation is analogous to that which obtains in the use of a camera. If, when the instrument is focused for 100 ft, the images of all objects beyond that distance are equally sharp, 100 ft is a working value for infinity.

Rigorously, the distance from the aperture at which the lines referred to above become parallel is infinite. The wider the aperture or the shorter the wavelength, the greater is the minimum distance at which the approximation becomes valid. Hence the critical distance is not a specific number of feet or meters. For the accuracy required in most measurements it is often specified as $2a^2/\lambda$, where a is the diameter of the aperture. Calculations show that field measurements made at distances greater than this value yield results which differ from the theoretical value by only 1 per cent.

Positions of P which are relatively near the aperture are within the Fresnel region where the field or intensity distribution is known as a *Fresnel diffraction pattern*. As the distance from the aperture is increased the patterns undergo a series of transitions. At sufficiently great distances where lines drawn from all points on the aperture to the point in question may be considered substantially parallel, the distributions are unchanged for all greater distances. This is the Fraunhofer region in which a *Fraunhofer pattern* is obtained. Physically there is no difference in the nature of the two types of diffraction. At a given distance from the aperture the Fraunhofer region may be entered by decreasing the dimension of the opening or by using radiation of lower frequency.

Although a circular aperture has been used in illustrating the foregoing principles, a rectangular opening may be employed. The patterns are qualitatively the same, but differ in quantitative details because of the difference in the shape of the aperture. In optics the aperture is often a slit upon which a beam of light is incident. An equivalent arrangement in radio may be a rectangular horn antenna or an array of half-wave antennas carrying equal currents and backed by a reflector. As will be shown later, the free-space radiation pattern of an antenna is one of its important characteristics. In the Fresnel region the shape of the curve depends on the distance from the radiator. Measurements should therefore be made in the Fraunhofer region where the *form* of the pattern is independent of distance.

An example of Fraunhofer diffraction by a single slit, having a width a equal to twice the wavelength, is shown in Fig. 5.11. The intensity at a given distance from the slit is plotted as a function of the angle θ with respect to the normal direction. The obliquity factor is neglected. Both

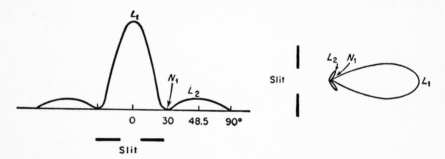

Fɪɢ. 5.11. Fraunhofer diffraction for a single slit: $a = 2\lambda$. The intensity is plotted as a function of the angle, using (a) rectangular and (b) polar coordinates.

rectangular and polar coordinate systems are used. The position and number of the nulls and minor lobes and the width of the major lobe are determined by the ratio of a to λ. If a is much less than λ, the waves spread out in the plane of the paper as if from a point source and the polar diagram is very nearly a semicircle. If $a = \lambda$ there is just one major lobe. For values of a greater than λ, the energy is largely concentrated in a narrow major lobe with much smaller amounts in the minor lobes. As the ratio a/λ becomes larger, which is the usual situation in optics, the major lobe appears narrower and the number of side lobes increases. A linear array of antennas, which occupies a flat area of rectangular shape, may be treated as Huygens' sources from which a highly directive pattern in the Fraunhofer zone may be obtained.

5.9. Diffraction by a Straight Edge. The wavefront of a given radiation is usually assumed to be plane, spherical, or cylindrical. In any case it may be divided into half-period zones or strips. The field at any point is the resultant of the contributions from the effective areas. If there are obstacles or apertures in the path, the limitations which they impose on the wavefront must be taken into account.

Radio waves may encounter hills, ridges, and other obstacles or they may pass through openings between objects of various sorts. If it is assumed that the edges of the obstacles or apertures are approximately straight, only one basic problem is involved. We shall therefore discuss the diffraction around a straight edge.

When the wavefront is cylindrical as in the case where the radiation passes through a slit or past an obstacle having a straight edge, the front is divided into half-period strips, the areas of which are by no means even approximately equal. The area of the first strip, that nearest P_0 in Fig. 5.12 (a), is the largest. As we go out along the wavefront, the areas of the other strips decrease rapidly. The radiation from each strip is, of course, out of phase with its immediate neighbor.

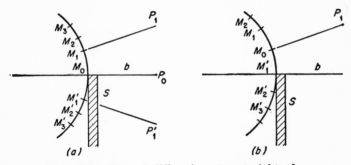

Fig. 5.12. Fresnel diffraction at a straight edge.

Consider the straight edge S which intercepts the radiation of the cylindrical wavefront. At P_0 only half of the strips are uncovered. At this point the field strength, which is the sum of the contributions from these strips, is one-half that of the unobstructed wave. The intensity at the edge of the geometrical shadow is therefore one-fourth the value which would be obtained if the obstacle were removed.

Next consider a point P_1 which lies in the direction M_1P_1. The center of the first half-strip must now lie on a line connecting P_1 with the center of curvature of the wave as in Fig. 5.12 (b). This is equivalent to uncovering not only all of the strips above M_0, but also the first one below it. Since this strip has a relatively large area and is in phase with the first strip above it, there will be a considerable addition to the field strength at P_1, the value being more than twice that at P_0.

As the point of observation is moved farther from the edge of the geometric shadow, more zones below M_0 are uncovered. Because of the existing phase relations among these zones the amplitude of the field strength will fluctuate, passing through successive maxima and minima.

When we pass into the region of the geometric shadow all the radiation is not canceled.   Let the point selected be P_1', as far below P_0 as P_1 is above it.   In the diagram M_1 must be moved down to M_0, thereby diminishing the number of effective zones.   The field strength is thus reduced at the observational point.   However, moving farther into the shadow does not produce the fluctuations observed on the other side of the edge.   The areas of the effective strips decrease rapidly and continuously and the resultant amplitude takes on successively smaller values.

The intensity pattern may be obtained from the field pattern, which is shown in Fig. 5.13, by plotting the values of ε^2 against the corresponding distances from the edge.   Notice that the fluctuations outside the shadow become less pronounced as the distance increases.   The mean value about which they oscillate is the magnitude of the field (or the intensity if ε^2 is plotted) of the unobstructed wave.

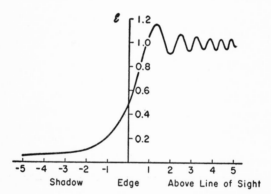

FIG. 5.13.   Relative field strength: Diffraction by a straight edge.

The above theory may be applied with moderate success to the diffraction of radio waves beyond a ridge.   The distances from the transmitter and the receiver to the ridge must be large compared with the height of the obstruction which, in turn, must be large compared with the wavelength.   Unless the ground is moderately rough, reflection must be taken into account.   (If necessary this can be done by assigning an image to both the transmitting and receiving antennas.)

The reception obtained when a ridge is interposed between a fixed transmitting antenna T and a receiving antenna located at R_0, R_1, or R_1', may be explained with the aid of Fig. 5.14.   When the latter is placed at R_0 so that the line of sight just grazes the ridge, the signal strength is only one-half the free-space value.   As the antenna is moved upward, the signal strength oscillates about its free-space value. If R_1 is the position at which the highest maximum of the straight-edge diffraction pattern is intercepted, the signal becomes appreciably stronger (about 17 per cent) than the free-space value. This fact is sometimes advantageous in selecting a site for the receiving antenna. At R_1', below the line of sight, reception is still possible, the strength of the signal depending on the number of Fresnel zones uncovered.

Fɪɢ. 5.14.   Diffraction of radio waves by a ridge.

As previously noted, the magnitude of diffraction effects increases with an increase in wavelength, other factors remaining unchanged. The phenomena are therefore more apparent in the lower frequency bands. Analogously the diffraction of sound is an everyday experience, whereas the diffraction of light is observed only under special circumstances.

Although the theory based upon the use of Fresnel zones has a number of shortcomings, it often provides us with relatively simple solutions to diffraction problems in optics and radio. The reader should bear in mind that situations may arise for which a more elaborate theory is required.

5.10. Resolving Power.   A printed picture or halftone in a newspaper is composed of a large number of black dots on a white background. When the picture is viewed at the usual reading distance these dots blend into one another and form a continuous image. The greater the number of dots per unit area, the more detail there is in the picture. No additional information is obtained by using a magnifying lens, for the lens merely enlarges the images of the dots.

An ideal image would have to correspond exactly to the object, line for line and point for point. Even with a perfect lens this would be impossible. A lens is ordinarily a circular aperture which forms images of all the points composing an object. As we have seen, the images produced by a circular aperture are not points but small illuminated disks surrounded by dark and bright rings. The larger the diameter of the lens and the smaller the wavelength of the light the smaller will be the dimensions of the diffraction pattern, but owing to the wave nature of light, this pattern can never be completely eliminated. The extent to which a lens can reduce the size of the diffraction pattern may be taken as a measure of its *resolving power*.

The stars are so far away that their images as formed by the objective lens or mirror of an astronomical telescope are not magnified. They appear as small patches of light.   One of the important functions of a telescope is the separation of the images of two stars which subtend a small angle at the earth.   These images are diffraction patterns, small bright disks surrounded by dark and bright concentric rings.   It is only with the central disks that we are concerned, for the intensities of the rings are very weak. If the angular separation of the stars is small, the central portions of their diffraction images may overlap and it may not be possible to separate or resolve them.   Increasing the magnifying power of the eyepiece will not bring out any further detail which does not already exist in the image formed by the objective.   The circular diffraction patterns are analogous to the dots in a halftone.

All observers will not agree on how far the patterns may overlap and yet be distinguished as two separate images.   Some arbitrary standard of judgment must therefore be established.   Let the centers of the two diffraction patterns be represented by P_1 and P_2, with the resultant intensity distribution over their central disks as indicated in Fig. 5.15(a).   Here it

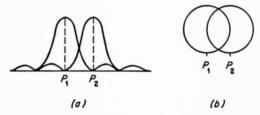

(a)   (b)

FIG. 5.15.   Diffraction images of two point sources just resolved: Rayleigh's criterion.

is shown that the central maximum of one pattern coincides with the first minimum of the other.   The relation is a simple one and the change in intensity is easily visible to the eye.   Accordingly most users of optical instruments have adopted Rayleigh's criterion: two point sources may be just resolved if the central maximum of each diffraction pattern falls on the first minimum of the other.

The rule may also be stated: two point sources are distinguished as separate when their central diffraction images do not overlap by more than the radius of one disk (Fig. 5.15(b)).

A telescope having a high resolving power will separate the images of two point objects which subtend a small angle at the instrument.   When the magnitude of this angle, as determined by Rayleigh's criterion, is used as a figure of merit, it is properly designated as the *minimum angle of resolution*.

The resolving power of a telescope is directly proportional to the diameter of the objective lens or mirror and inversely proportional to the wavelength of the radiation. Astronomical telescopes have large diameters for two reasons: (a) to increase their resolving power by decreasing the size of their diffraction patterns, (b) to increase their light-gathering power by increasing the area which they present to the incident radiation. The Palomar Mountain telescope which has a diameter of 200 in. has twice the resolving power of the 100-in. reflector on Mount Wilson. Since the area is proportional to the square of the diameter, the larger instrument has four times the light-gathering power of the smaller.

The same general principles are applicable to radio telescopes. These instruments are antennas designed to receive signals of radio frequencies originating in outer space. Although a wide variety of antennas is in use, it will be sufficient for the present discussion to describe a radio telescope as a parabolic reflector with an antenna of adjustable length at the focus. Structures of large dimensions are necessary in order to gather sufficient radiation and to provide adequate resolving power. As a consequence of the longer wavelengths characteristic of the radio spectrum and the constructional limitations imposed on the magnitude of the reflector, the resolving power of the best radio telescopes seems destined to fall far below that of their optical counterparts. The poor resolution of a single antenna may be improved, however, by using a radio interferometer which is essentially a combination of two antennas separated by an appropriate distance and connected to a single receiver. Although the underlying principles are those of Young's experiment, other factors make it advantageous to defer the explanation (see Sec. 10.8).

With regard to the wavelength of the radiation, there is little man can do to increase the resolving power of his instruments in either radio or optical astronomy. In radar, however, the observed signals are the echoes of the transmitted radiation, the frequency of which is determined by the inductance and capacitance of the oscillating circuit. By decreasing the wavelength the angular resolution required for the separation of targets in fire control can be substantially improved.

PROBLEMS

NOTE: Granville's Plotting Paper Tablet for Polar Coordinates (Yale Cooperative Corporation, New Haven, Conn.) is recommended for the plotting of ground reflection and free-space field patterns in Chapters 5, 8, and 9.

5.1. Draw two sine waves having the same amplitude and wavelength, but with a phase difference of 60°. Find the resultant wave graphically by the method of superposition. What is the amplitude of the resultant? Its frequency?

5.2. Obtain the square waveform of Fig. 1.5 by the method of superposition.

5.3. In Young's experiment what is the maximum allowable value of θ if $\cos \theta$ is not to differ from unity by more than 1 per cent?

5.4. In Fig. 5.3 a thin piece of glass, 4.2×10^{-4} cm thick and with a refractive index of 1.50, is placed against the slit S_1 on the right-hand side. The light has a wavelength of 6×10^{-5} cm in air. Show that there will be darkness at O.

5.5. Plot the reflection factors for the effect of ground reflection from a horizontal half-wave antenna one-half wavelength above the surface of the earth. Use $0°, 5°, 10°, 15°, 20°, 30°, 40°, 50°, 60°, 70°, 80°, 90°$ for computations and complete the pattern from considerations of symmetry. Plot on polar coordinate paper. Use the blank space below the graph to tabulate all values.

5.6. Same as Problem 5.5, using a horizontal half-wave antenna, three-fourths wavelength above the surface of the earth.

5.7. Same as Problem 5.5, using a vertical half-wave antenna, with its center one-half wavelength above the surface of the earth.

5.8. Same as Problem 5.5, using a vertical half-wave antenna, with its center three-fourths wavelength above the surface of the earth.

5.9. Using the method of nulls and maximum lobes, sketch the ground reflection patterns for the antennas in Problems 5.5 to 5.8. Compare these patterns with those obtained from point-by-point plotting.

5.10. Using both the method of nulls and maximum lobes and the method of point-by-point plotting, obtain the ground reflection pattern for a horizontal half-wave antenna 5/8 wavelength above the surface of the earth. Compare results.

5.11. Sketch the ground reflection patterns for both horizontal and vertical antennas one wavelength long, with their centers three-fourths wavelength above the earth. The solution may be conveniently obtained from the results of Problems 4.6 and 5.9.

5.12. Prove that the phase difference between the wave from the center of a circular aperture and the wave from the periphery is $\pi/8$ at the minimum distance for Fraunhofer diffraction, that is, $b = 2a^2/\lambda$. Assume that a is large compared to λ.

5.13. The two headlights of an automobile are 4.5 ft apart. Assuming that the eye can just resolve two objects which subtend 1 minute of arc, what is the maximum distance at which the two lamps may be distinguished?

5.14. Construct a few lines typical of a loran map by selecting two points, A and B, 6 cm apart and drawing a series of lines such that every point on a given line is Δ cm farther from A than from B. Let $\Delta = 0, 1, 2, 3$ cm.

5.15. A small antenna is placed at the focus of a parabolic metal reflector. Show that the intensity of the radiation is greatest if the focal distance is a quarter-wavelength.

Chapter 6

POLARIZATION

6.1. Nature of Polarization. As stated in Sec. 4.1, Hertz, the discoverer of radio waves, demonstrated their undulatory character by the phenomena of interference and diffraction. He revealed their transverse nature by showing that they could also be polarized. The term *polarization* merely indicates a quality which exhibits contrasted properties in different parts or directions. For example, a bar of magnetized iron or steel may be said to be polarized.

For a mechanical wave the effect may be pictured by further consideration of the vibration of a rope (Sec. 2.4). Let the vibrations take place in a plane perpendicular to the length of the rope at an angle of, say 45° with the horizontal. The vibrations may thus be resolved into equal vertical and horizontal components. If the rope is unobstructed, the waves will travel freely along its entire length; but, if the rope is passed through a vertical slit, the horizontal component will be eliminated beyond this point. The proceeding wave is said to be vertically polarized. If a horizontal slit is now placed beyond the vertical, all vibrations will be extinguished. Since the word polarization implies a lack of symmetry about the axis of wave propagation, it should be clear that transverse, but not longitudinal, waves can be polarized.

In the case of electromagnetic waves the fact that the vibrations of the electric and magnetic fields are in mutually perpendicular directions requires that an arbitrary choice be made for the direction of polarization. By general agreement this is taken as the direction of the *electric vector*. Hence a linear antenna is polarized in the direction of its axis.

6.2. Polarization of Light Waves. Many illustrations of polarization may be found in optics. In Fig. 6.1 the light is to be regarded as a wave propagated to the right, the electric vibrations being equal in all directions and lying in a plane perpendicular to the paper. The light is said to be unpolarized. Certain crystals, of which the semiprecious gem, tourmaline, is an example, have the property of transmitting only those components of

97

the electric field which are parallel to the crystal axis, a direction shown as a broken line in the diagram.

The light transmitted by the first crystal P consists of vibrations in a vertical direction only, as indicated by the double-headed arrows. This light is appropriately designated as *linearly polarized*. The second crystal A, set at right angles to P, extinguishes the light completely, for there are no components parallel to its crystal, or optic, axis. If A is parallel to P, vertically polarized light will pass through A. At intermediate positions of the latter vertically polarized light will also be transmitted, but its in-

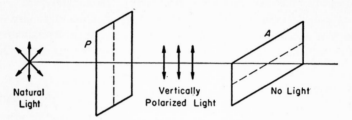

FIG. 6.1. Polarizing action of a tourmaline.

tensity will be diminished. The electric vector of the linearly polarized light may be resolved into two components, one parallel and the other perpendicular to the axis of A. The former is transmitted while the latter is completely absorbed. Plate P is called the *polarizer* and plate A, the *analyzer*. A crystal such as tourmaline which polarizes by absorption is known as a *dichroic* substance.

Perhaps the best known dichroic material is polaroid. Originally needlelike crystals of sulfate of iodo-quinine were aligned parallel to one another in a base of cellulose film and protected by thin covers of glass or transparent plastic, a process which has been subsequently simplified and improved. Polaroid has a number of advantages, the most important of which are: (1) it is relatively free from color effects prevalent in some natural crystals; (2) it may be fabricated in large sheets; (3) it is relatively inexpensive. As many of the practical uses of polaroid are well known, they need not be enumerated here.

When natural light is incident on a transparent surface, such as a glass plate, the reflected and refracted lights are, in general, partially polarized. The extent to which the waves are polarized in a given plane depends upon the angle of incidence, the frequency of the radiation, and the refractive index of the material. Only at one particular angle, called the polarizing or Brewster angle, is the reflected light completely plane polarized, with the electric vector perpendicular to the plane of incidence. For glass of refractive index 1.54 and yellow light ($f = 590$ mega-megacycles), this angle is 57° and the relative intensity about 8 per cent of the original. The refracted light is therefore more intense, but only partially polarized. The percentage of energy reflected depends upon the characteristic impedances of the two mediums. When light incident on a perfect dielectric at the Brewster angle is polarized with the electric field parallel to the plane of incidence, there is an impedance match between the two mediums and all the radiation is refracted.

Another type of crystal possesses the property of double refraction, the single incident beam being split into two parts within the crystal. The best known examples are calcite (Iceland spar), quartz, and mica.

Let a beam of natural unpolarized light be incident normally upon an end face of a calcite crystal (Fig. 6.2). The beam O, which passes through without deviation, is polarized with its electric vector perpendicular to the

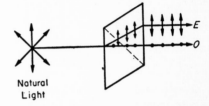

FIG. 6.2.   Polarization and double refraction in calcite.

plane of the paper and is called the *ordinary* ray. The beam E, which is deviated despite its perpendicular incidence, is polarized in the plane of the paper and is called the *extraordinary* ray. Both emergent beams, however, are parallel. If the crystal is rotated the extraordinary image will revolve about its stationary companion. If a sheet of polaroid is placed in the issuing beams and then rotated the two images will alternately appear and disappear.

The directions of the rays are different because of a difference in the velocities of the waves within the crystal. The velocity of the ordinary wave is constant for a given wavelength. Hence its path is determined in accordance with Snell's law (Sec. 4.6). The extraordinary wave travels with a speed depending on its direction. If it is parallel to the optic axis, denoted by a broken line in the diagram, the wave will travel with the same velocity as the ordinary wave and the two images will coincide. In any other direction the speed of the extraordinary ray will be greater, the maximum value occurring when the ray is at right angles to the crystal axis. Hence the E ray does not obey Snell's law, the ratio of the sines of the angles of incidence and refraction varying with the angle of incidence.

Huygens' principle (Sec. 5.7) may be applied to the phenomenon of double refraction in calcite. Since two waves traverse the crystal, each point on the incident wavefront must be the source of two secondary wavelets. The velocity of the O wave being equal in all directions, the corresponding wavelet is spherical. On the other hand, since the velocity of the E wave varies with the direction, the associated wavelet is represented by an ellipsoid of revolution. In view of the fact that the two velocities are equal in a direction parallel to the optic axis, the O and E wavelets touch at the points where they are intersected by the optic axis.

Let S represent a point source of light in a calcite crystal as shown in Fig. 6.3. If the figure is rotated about the optic axis $O.A.$, a sphere will be generated as the wave surface for the O wave and an ellipsoid of revolution as the wave surface for the E wave. The velocity of the latter varies

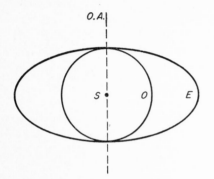

FIG. 6.3. Cross section of wave surfaces for O and E wavelets in calcite.

as the length of the radius drawn from S to the surface of the ellipsoid. The directions of the refracted wavefronts within the crystal depend on the angle of the incident radiation and the orientation of the optic axis. These wavefronts are always tangent to the O or E wavelets, as the case may be. Although the O ray is always perpendicular to its wavefront, this relation does not in general hold for the E ray.

The velocity of the ellipsoidal waves in calcite is greater than that of the spherical waves except in the direction of the optic axis. In other types of crystals, e.g., quartz, the reverse is true. The appropriate wave surfaces may be represented by drawing the ellipsoid within the sphere.

6.3. Polarization of Radio Waves. Polarization of radio waves was demonstrated by Hertz (1887) in his original experiments which verified their existence as predicted by Maxwell (1864). The essentials of the oscillator are shown at the left in Fig. 6.4. Two metal plates are joined to a spark gap which, in turn, is connected to an induction coil. When the potential difference between the terminals of the gap reaches a sufficiently high value, the air becomes conducting and a discharge takes place. The values of the circuit constants, resistance, inductance, and capacitance, are chosen so that the discharge is oscillatory (Sec. 1.3). The frequency was of the order of 50 Mc, with a corresponding wavelength of 6 meters. The diagram shows the rods of the oscillator to be coincident with the y-axis. The $\mathcal{E}$-vector and the $\mathcal{H}$-vector are therefore parallel to the y- and z-axis, respectively. The waves are vertically polarized and the direction of energy flow is, by Poynting's theorem (Sec. 2.5), parallel to the x-axis.

As a detector Hertz used a circle of wire with a very narrow gap of adjustable length, where sparks could be observed when the radiation was incident in a suitable manner. If the plane of the detector were parallel to the xy- or the yz-plane, as shown in positions A and B, there was a

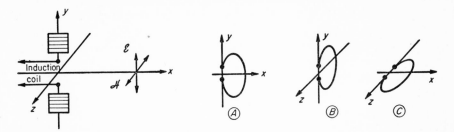

FIG. 6.4. Essentials of Hertz's apparatus and the polarization of radio waves.

response. The effect may be explained by observing that the gap, in each case, is parallel to the electric vector which causes the electrons to oscillate and build up a high potential difference sufficient to produce a discharge. From another viewpoint it may be said that the magnetic field at right angles to the gap links with the loop of the detector and thus builds up the necessary potential difference. But if the detector is in the xz-plane, position C, the gap is normal to the electric vector and its plane is parallel to the magnetic vector. Therefore there will be no response. The similarity between these observations and the transmission or extinction of a beam of plane polarized light by a properly oriented polaroid should be noticed.

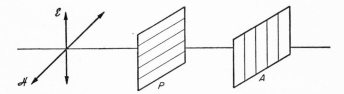

FIG. 6.5. Radio analog of crossed polaroids.

The radio analog of crossed tourmalines or polaroids may be demonstrated with the apparatus shown schematically in Fig. 6.5. Equally spaced wires are stretched on two wooden frames forming a kind of grating. When one frame is used and the wires are parallel to the $\mathcal{E}$-vector, position A, a detector placed at the right will fail to respond. Since currents are set up in the wires, part of the energy will be absorbed, while the remainder will be reflected as from a metal sheet. As the frame is rotated about an axis parallel to the direction of wave propagation, the response of the detector will increase until the maximum signal is received when the wires are aligned as in position P. If the two frames, oriented as shown in the diagram, are used, linearly polarized waves will exist between P and A, but to the right no radiation whatever can be detected.

Radio antennas are usually polarized horizontally or vertically, depending on the type of service. In some cases the polarization is regulated by civil law. For example, horizontal polarization is required in frequency modulated broadcasting and in television. In general, at low and medium frequencies vertical polarization is used because the earth acts as a conductor at frequencies below, say 5 Mc, and tends to short out the horizontal component. At higher frequencies the ground takes on the characteristics of a dielectric. Since the earth is necessarily an imperfect dielectric, vertically polarized waves incident at the Brewster angle are not completely absorbed but the reflected component is a minimum under these circumstances. The advantages and disadvantages of the two kinds of polarization will be discussed in considering different types of antennas.

6.4. Elliptical Polarization.   Hitherto we have confined our discussion to vibrations of the electric vector along a straight line, a type of polarization called linear. We now describe a more general kind, *elliptical* polarization. Let a beam of linearly polarized light, obtained by passing ordinary light through a sheet of polaroid, be incident upon a thin slab of calcite

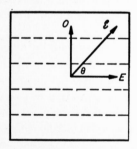

FIG. 6.6.   Resolution of linearly polarized light into two components in passing through a crystal of calcite.

cut with faces parallel to the optic axis. Assume that the vibrations of the electric vector make an angle θ with the axis. The crystal will separate the light into its O and E components (Fig. 6.6). The latter will travel faster, along the same path as the O wave and perpendicular to the plane of the vectors.

Since the two waves have the same frequency but different speeds their wavelengths will be different. In a crystal of thickness d there will be more O waves because they travel more slowly and their wavelength is shorter (Sec. 4.6). The O and E waves in their progress through the slab gradually get out of step with a phase difference of Δ, which increases proportionately to the thickness of the crystal. Of course, Δ may be expressed in terms of an angle or the wavelength in air. Thus we have the equivalent of two simple harmonic motions of the same frequency at right angles. In Sec. 1.6 it was shown that the resultant path is an ellipse, with the straight line and the circle as special cases. The light emerges from the crystal under these conditions in a state of elliptical polarization.

When the thickness of the crystal is such as to produce a phase difference of 90° the crystalline slab is called a *quarter-wave plate*. For the special case of $\theta = 45°$, the O and E waves are equal in amplitude and the emergent light is said to be *circularly* polarized. If this light is analyzed by a polaroid whose transmission plane PP' makes an angle φ with, say the

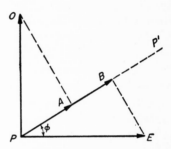

Fig. 6.7. Resolution of the O and E vectors for circularly polarized light incident on a polaroid analyzer.

E vibrations, only the components PA and PB which are parallel to PP' are transmitted (Fig. 6.7). Letting $\mathcal{E}_0$ be the common amplitude of the O and E vibrations, $PA = \mathcal{E}_0 \sin \varphi$ and $PB = \mathcal{E}_0 \cos \varphi$. These components differ in phase by 90° and therefore their sum is $\sqrt{\mathcal{E}_0{}^2 \sin^2 \varphi + \mathcal{E}_0{}^2 \cos^2 \varphi} = \mathcal{E}_0$. A rotation of the polaroid produces no change in the intensity of the transmitted light for the resultant electric vector is always the same. In this respect circularly polarized light resembles unpolarized light.

To distinguish between the two let the light under examination be passed through a quarter-wave plate. Circularly polarized light may be considered as made up of two equal linear vibrations at right angles to each other and having a phase difference of 90°. The quarter-wave plate introduces an additional phase change of 90° such that the components of the emergent vibrations differ by 0° or 180°. In either case the resultant vibrations are linear (Fig. 1.7). The light, when examined by a rotating polaroid, will pass through alternate maxima and minima of intensity. Unpolarized light after traversing the quarter-wave plate will not be plane polarized. Consequently, no changes in intensity will be observed as the polaroid is rotated.

In elliptical polarization the resultant electric or magnetic field never passes through zero because its horizontal and vertical components do not become zero at the same time. (We neglect the special cases when the phase angle is 0° or 180°.) The field rotates in the plane of the wavefront at a rate equal to the frequency of the wave and, except for circular polarization, with varying amplitude.

The electromagnetic nature of light and radio waves leads us to expect many similarities of behavior. For example, the electric field at an appreciable distance from a half-wave antenna or dipole is polarized in a direction parallel to the axis of the radiator. If the currents in two such antennas, one horizontal and the other vertical, are equal and out of phase by 90°, the resultant field is circularly polarized.

Observations of radio waves from the sun show that they are often circularly polarized. A device, similar to a quarter-wave plate in optics, has been developed to study these waves and will be described in Sec. 11.13.

Electromagnetic waves which traverse a medium capable of separating them into fast and slow components will be elliptically polarized. The ionosphere is such a medium for radio waves. The manner in which they are elliptically polarized will be discussed in Sec. 7.11.

PROBLEMS

6.1. In Fig. 6.4 the detector, originally at position A, is rotated about the x-axis until its plane makes an angle of 60° with the y-axis. What is the relative *intensity* of the signal in the new position?

6.2. If ordinary light is incident on a plate of glass at the Brewster angle the reflected and refracted rays are just 90° apart. Prove that the tangent of the polarizing angle is equal to the refractive index of the glass. Diagram.

6.3. The critical angle for a given sample of glass is 40°. What is the polarizing angle?

6.4. The refractive indices of calcite for the fast and slow axes are 1.49 and 1.66, respectively, when the wavelength of the light in air is 6×10^{-5} cm. What is the minimum thickness d of a crystal which will convert linear into circularly polarized light?

Chapter 7

THE IONOSPHERE

7.1. Ionization. The strength of a radio signal obtained from a receiver depends on the voltage supplied to it by the antenna. This voltage, in turn, depends on the magnitude of the electric (or magnetic) field where the antenna is located. The field strength in free space varies inversely as the distance from the transmitter, a relation which often must be considerably modified in accordance with the nature of the terrain over which the wave travels.

Early in the history of radio it was found that signals were received at much greater distances than could be accounted for, even on the basis of an ideally conducting earth, especially at night and in the winter. There were, however, intermediate regions where no signal at all could be received. Furthermore, to complicate the situation, beyond this so-called skip distance the signals appeared to be arriving from above.

All the phenomena associated with this type of long-distance wave propagation may be adequately described by assuming the existence of a region of conducting material in the upper atmosphere of the earth. Variations in conductivity at different heights make it convenient to divide the region into somewhat ill-defined layers. Abundant in positively charged particles and free electrons—the latter are more important for our consideration—these layers are found at heights of about 50 to 450 km above the earth's surface. This is the region known as the *ionosphere*.

Let us first recall the general structure of the atom which for our immediate purpose may be depicted as a positive nucleus around which one or more negative electrons revolve in circular or elliptical orbits. It is now well known that this so-called planetary model of the atom is at variance with the results of experiment, but it is the best *picture* that we have. Nearly all the mass of the atom is concentrated in the nucleus. The mass of an electron at rest or moving with a speed which is small compared with the velocity of light is 9.1×10^{-31} kg. For the lightest of all the chemical elements, ordinary hydrogen, there is only one electron, the ratio of its mass to that of the nucleus being about 1/1840. Thus in any atom the inertia—that property of matter which resists change of motion—of the nucleus is, in round numbers, at least 2000 times as great as that of the electron.

The nucleus and the electrons associated with it are bound together by that property of electricity which requires that unlike charges attract each other. The number of electrons associated with a nucleus varies with the chemical elements, extending from *one* in the case of hydrogen to 102 for nobelium. When the atom is in its neutral state, the positive charge of the nucleus is exactly equal to the combined negative charges of its electrons. The charge on a single electron is 1.60×10^{-19} coulomb.

The energy which binds an electron to its nucleus varies from atom to atom and also from electron to electron in a given atom. It is customary to speak of an electron as being loosely or tightly bound to its nucleus. If energy of the proper amount is supplied to an electron it may be detached from the atom. Such a process is called *ionization*. The nucleus with its remaining associated electrons is now positively charged and is called a *positive ion*. If an electron attaches itself to a neutral atom a *negative ion* is formed.

7.2. The Photoelectric Effect. The requisite energy for ionization may be supplied in various ways. An electron may be separated from its atom by direct bombardment with ions traveling at a high velocity. These particles are able to supply the necessary energy by virtue of their speed, or more precisely their kinetic energy. The requirement may also be met by a packet of electromagnetic energy called a *photon,* this method of ionization being known as the *photoelectric effect.* The energy of a photon is proportional to its frequency. The defining equation is written as

$$E = hf \tag{7.1}$$

where h is Planck's constant which plays an important role in phenomena involving the interaction between radiation and matter and which has a numerical value of 6.62×10^{-34} joule sec. If f is the frequency in cycles per second the energy E is given in joules.

The photoelectric effect can occur only when energy is transferred to an electron by a *single* photon. If its energy is insufficient to detach the electron, there is no ionization, because an electron cannot absorb energy from more than one photon. Equation (7.1) shows that a photon possesses a relatively large amount of energy only if it has a high frequency. In order that the quantity of energy shall be large enough to detach even a rather loosely bound electron from its atom, the frequency must be in that part of the electromagnetic spectrum known as visible light. (There are some exceptions to this statement.) Practically, visible light photons are effective for only a rather limited class of metals called the alkalis, of which sodium, rubidium, and cesium are examples. These elements, or their compounds, are used as light-sensitive materials in vacuum or gas-filled phototubes.

The photoelectric ionization of most chemical elements may be accomplished only with the aid of photons with a higher energy content than those associated with visible light. This is especially true of the gaseous elements in which we are immediately interested. The energy cannot be obtained from radio waves, all of which have comparatively low frequencies. Therefore the required higher frequencies must be found on the other side of the visible spectrum in the region known as the ultraviolet. The lowest frequency at which the photoelectric effect may take place for a given element is called its *threshold frequency*. If the photon possesses energy over and above that required to detach an electron from the atom, the excess appears in the kinetic energy of the ejected particle.

The radiation from the sun is rich in ultraviolet photons. As is well known, they produce a severe burning of the skin. Were they not mostly absorbed in the upper atmosphere human life on earth could not exist. As a result of this absorption, energy is obtained whereby appreciable numbers of atoms are separated into positive ions and free electrons.

7.3. Factors Affecting the Existence of the Ionosphere. It is well known that the atoms or molecules of a gas are in rapid motion. Under such circumstances collisions are of frequent occurrence. The rapidity with which they occur will evidently be proportional to the density of the gas. Charged particles partake of the same general motion as that of the gas molecules with which they are mingled. An electron may collide with a positive ion and form a neutral atom. Such a process is known as *recombination*. The larger the number of particles and the greater their speed, the greater is the chance of a collision. The average distance a molecule or a charged particle travels between collisions is called its *mean free path*.

Near the surface of the earth the gas density is relatively high; the mean free path is only 10^{-5} cm and electron collisions occur at the rate of 10^{11} per sec. At an elevation of 300 km where the molecular density is one-billionth of its value at the surface, the mean free path has increased to 100 meters and the rate of electron collisions is reduced to less than 1000 per sec. Here relatively long time intervals will elapse before recombination occurs and, as a result, there will exist a cloud of free electrons. In the region, known as the ionosphere, two conditions favorable for the production and maintenance of an ionized layer exist: (1) intense ultraviolet radiation which produces the ionization; (2) low gas density which slows down the rate of recombination.

Although it seems to be well established that ultraviolet radiation from the sun is the principal source of ionization, contributions of other agencies, especially in what is known as the E layer, must be taken into account. The constant bombardment of the atmosphere by meteors may be sufficient to sustain some of the nighttime ionization. Corpuscular radiation, consisting of charged particles from the sun, upon entering the earth's magnetic field is deflected in a spiral path, especially in polar latitudes. This results in a higher density of ionization in the lower regions of the ionosphere.

As previously stated, the ionosphere consists of layers which are not separated by sharp lines of demarcation. The electron density of these layers varies with the time of day. The density may rise to a maximum about noon, fall off as the sunlight diminishes, and reach a low value during the night. The magnitude and rate of change of these fluctuations will not be the same in all layers. Furthermore, the existence of electric and magnetic fields in a layer has an important effect on its behavior. The actual phenomena are extremely complex, as may be surmised from the following list of influential factors: (1) time of day, (2) season of year, (3) latitude, (4) sunspot cycle, (5) magnetic storms.

7.4. Layers in the Ionosphere. The lowest stratum of ionization is called the *D layer* or D region. It is formed at an average height of about 70 km and is present effectively only during the daylight hours. (The heights given in this discussion are merely representative; actual measurements show appreciable variations.) At the altitude of the D layer the density of the air is relatively great and recombination takes place fairly rapidly. The density of ionization is therefore very sensitive to the height of the sun and the layer is largely absent at night.

The *E layer* or Kennelly-Heaviside layer has its maximum density at a height of about 100 km with little seasonal or diurnal variation. The density of the air is such that recombination takes place at a moderate rate. The state of ionization is in close step with the height of the sun, dropping off but not vanishing during the night. There is considerable experimental evidence that meteoric bombardment is an important source of this nocturnal ionization.

The F_1 *layer* is usually found at 200 km, with limits of 140 to 250 km. The height is nearly independent of the time of day and the time of year. During the daylight hours it changes relatively slowly except at sunrise and sunset. At night it merges with the F_2 layer. The F_1 layer has a greater electron density than the E layer because at higher altitudes recombination takes place more slowly. During the 11-year sunspot cycle, to be discussed subsequently, the F_1 density may vary considerably.

The uppermost stratum is the F_2 *layer* or Appleton layer with an electron density which is the highest and most variable of all the layers. Its maximum height may be over 400 km at noon in June or as low as 250 km at midday in December. At these heights the atmosphere is extremely tenuous and the rate of recombination is very small. As a result, a considerable degree of ionization persists in the absence of sunlight. The ionization reaches a maximum shortly after noon, decreases gradually through the night, and rises rapidly after sunrise. There is excellent correlation between the density of ionization and the sunspot cycle.

As stated above, the F_1 and F_2 layers tend to coalesce at night, the merging being produced largely by the lowering of the F_2 component. The combined strata having a maximum density at an average height of approximately 300 km is often called the *F layer*. (There is a growing tendency to designate both the upper daytime component and the single nighttime stratum as the F_2 layer.) Although the ionization of the F layer is considerably less than the F_2 daytime maximum, its value remains appreciable throughout the night.

Above the F_2 layer the existence of a G layer has been reported. So far as is known it has no effect on sky-wave transmission and reception.

At the E level, but not existing as a separate layer, are ionized patches of uncertain origin with relatively high intensities and sharp boundaries. These clouds are irregular in shape, random in distribution, and transient in existence. They may appear at any time of the day or night especially in temperate latitudes during the summer months. This particular state of ionization is the so-called *sporadic E layer*.

The existence of regions of maximum ionization within the ionosphere may be accounted for by the fact that air is a mixture of gases, principally oxygen and nitrogen. Not only do the proportions of the separate gases vary with the altitude, but each gas is susceptible in a different way to the ionizing influence of ultraviolet waves. Each layer may be identified with the free electrons obtained from the ionization of the molecules or atoms of a particular gas. The electrons in the D layer may be associated with ozone, a triatomic molecule of oxygen; the E layer with molecular oxygen; the F_1 layer with molecular nitrogen; and the F_2 layer with atomic oxygen. Evidence for these conclusions has been obtained from the spectra of the aurora borealis (northern lights) and the faint light given off by the night sky.

Seasonal variations are such as might be predicted from the zenith angle of the sun. In temperate latitudes the electron density is greater and the height of the layer is somewhat lower in summer than in winter, because the ultraviolet radiation penetrates farther into the atmosphere. These statements apply to the E and F_1 layers. The F_2 layer is greatly affected by energy from the sun and may actually have a greater electron density at certain times of day during the colder months.

Black spots, usually surrounded by areas of gray, appear temporarily on the sun's disk. They vary considerably in size. Some are large enough to be visible to the naked eye when the sun is observed through smoked glass. Their actual diameters may be as great as 50,000 miles and the gaseous clouds surrounding them may rise to a height of half a million miles. First observed by Galileo early in the seventeenth century, sunspots have been a source of constant interest to astronomers who have made daily recordings of the number of spots for a long time. Since the number varies appreciably from day to day, occasionally none at all being seen, the yearly average is used. At this writing we are approaching a period of sunspot maximum.

The sunspot cycle, while not exact, is approximately an 11-year period. Its effect on the E layer is unimportant but, as mentioned above, it causes considerable variation in the F layers. Since the sunspots appear dark, indicating lower temperatures and thus smaller amounts of ultraviolet radiation, we might be led to believe that the ionosphere would be less strongly ionized during the maximum of the cycle. Apparently the bright gaseous clouds which surround the spots are powerful generators of ultraviolet energy. At any rate there is good correlation between the number of sunspots and the intensity of ultraviolet radiation. The phenomena are complex and predictions are not easily made. Data are published regularly by the Bureau of Standards and should be consulted for details.

Since the behavior of electrons is influenced by a magnetic field, we may expect the properties of the ionosphere to be affected by the presence of the earth's magnetic field and the occurrence of magnetic storms. The former is substantially constant with only minor variations over a rather long period of time at a given location in the neighborhood of the earth. The latter are entirely sporadic and of short duration.

7.5. Effect of Frequency on Reflection and Refraction. The different layers of the ionosphere produce changes in the velocity of electromagnetic waves. The process, in its widest aspect, is similar to refraction in the troposphere. Since the waves may be returned to the earth, it is often convenient to look upon the ionosphere as a series of mirrors which reflect the waves. This device is another example of the common procedure of describing physical phenomena in terms of a theory which may or may not be "true," but which has the merit of convenience.

It may be even more convenient if, using the analogy proposed by Menzel, we compare the ionosphere to a sieve, or net, and assume that radio signals are balls which may be thrown upward toward the net.* The passage of a ball through the net depends on two factors: (1) the relative sizes of the ball and the mesh, (2) the angle at which the ball strikes the net. Balls of small diameter are equivalent to radio waves of high fre-

---

* Adapted by permission from *Elementary Manual of Radio Propagation*, by Donald H. Menzel, pp. 1–2; copyright, 1948, by Prentice-Hall, Inc., Englewood Cliffs, N. J.

quency. Meshes of small dimensions are equivalent to regions with a high density of ionization. The size of the holes will therefore vary with the layer of the ionosphere and in general will be larger at night than during the day.

Suppose that balls of different sizes are shot vertically upwards. The larger in general will be returned; the smaller will pass through the net. If balls of the same diameter are projected at different angles with respect to the earth, those moving nearly vertically may pass through the meshes, while others, incident on the net at larger angles to the vertical, are reflected.

In order to measure the height of an ionospheric layer, we arrange a transmitter to send up *pulses* vertically and a receiver to detect the echoes. If the frequency of the waves modulated by the pulse is low enough the signals will be returned. The time between the transmitted and received signals is measured, and from its value and the velocity of the waves the so-called *virtual height* of the layer may be computed. This experiment was first performed by Breit and Tuve in 1925; it was the precursor of modern radar. The value of this virtual height is somewhat greater than the actual height because the waves are slowed down in "turning around" in the layer which, of course, is not like a flat mirror but is a region of appreciable thickness, ionization being greatest at the center and thinning out at the edges. The virtual height is the distance above the earth that the waves would travel if they proceeded through a homogeneous medium. The extra distance traversed in attaining the virtual height just compensates for the reduction in velocity within the ionizing layer.

FIG. 7.1. Pulses appearing on the screen of a cathode-ray oscilloscope when the height of the ionosphere is measured.

In measuring the height of the ionosphere an ordinary transmitter is used. The high frequency radiation is emitted as a wave train which is chopped up into pulses of about 100 microseconds duration at a typical rate of 60 per sec. Nearby is a receiver which picks up the signal reflected from the ionosphere. A series of pulses appears on the screen of a cathode-ray oscilloscope as shown in Fig. 7.1. *A* is the incident and *B* the weaker reflected signal. In some cases there are additional pulses (*C*) which represent either reflections from higher layers or multiple reflections between the given layer and the earth. The short irregular lines between the pulses are random signals which are called noise (Sec. 9.1).

Some consideration must be given to the antenna system. It must be designed to project as much energy as possible in a vertical direction. A later study of radiation patterns will show that the use of a horizontal antenna cut for a half-wavelength at the maximum frequency to be radiated is one method of satisfying this requirement. But care must be taken not to locate the antenna a half-wavelength above the ground. The solution of Problem 5.5 shows that with the antenna in this position the ground reflection factor at 90° is zero, thus canceling the vertical radiation.

A further requirement demands that the antenna be capable of transmitting and receiving over a wide range of frequencies. In other words, the antenna must have *broadband* characteristics. This topic will be discussed in Sec. 8.7. In anticipation, two methods by which broadbanding is achieved may be mentioned. The antenna may be either a cage of wires having a relatively large diameter or a vertically oriented rhombic arrangement.

As the frequency of the pulse-modulated waves is increased, a limit is reached at which the signals are not returned. This value is called the *critical frequency,* which may be defined as a measure of the ability of the ionosphere to return high frequency waves to the earth. Representative values are: E, 3 Mc; F_1, 4 Mc; F_2, 8 Mc. These figures, of course, are subject to considerable variation. Since the transition point is a function of the electron density, which varies within a given layer, the critical frequency is usually defined as the value corresponding to maximum density of the layer.

The critical frequency, however, is not a value which can be used to predict the range of reception of radio signals, for the vertically projected pulse is returned to the receiver substantially at the location of the transmitter. But if the waves are projected in a nonvertical direction they will be returned to a different point on the earth. Clearly, from the analogy of the balls and the sieve, waves with frequencies greater than the critical frequency can be reflected. If the direction of the transmitted wave makes the proper angle with the surface of the earth, the signal will just graze one of the ionospheric layers and return to the earth at the required distance from the transmitter. The highest frequency which may be used under these circumstances is called the *maximum usable frequency (MUF)*. The ratio of the maximum usable frequency to the critical frequency varies with the state and layer of the ionosphere. Under favorable conditions it may be as great as four to one. For a single reflection from the ionosphere, the maximum usable frequency increases as the transmission distance increases.

The maximum usable frequencies on which sky-wave operation is based are predicted monthly averages, issued three months in advance by the Central Radio Propagation Laboratory, for transmission over a particular path at a given time of day. The maps depicting this information are comparable to the daily meteorological charts published by the Weather Bureau (Sec. 4.9). Since the MUF's are average values, true upper limiting frequencies above or below the predicted mean are equally probable. If the operating frequency is set equal to the MUF, no allowance is made for daily variations in the ionospheric "weather" and the reception is unreliable. On the other hand, if transmission takes place at frequencies much less than the MUF the waves travel a greater distance through the ionosphere and undergo considerable absorption. In practice it has been found that the most satisfactory results are obtained when the *optimum working frequency* (*OWF*), which is 85 per cent of the average MUF, is employed. It has been recommended that the term *optimum traffic frequency* (*FOT*), equal to 85 per cent of the MUF for the F_2 layer, be used in place of OWF.

7.6. Sky-Wave Communication. In the propagation of high frequency waves, except for areas relatively close to the antenna where the ground wave is responsible for reception, there will be a zone of silence. The distance from the transmitter to the point where the sky wave is first received is called the *skip distance*. This distance depends on the frequency of the radiation and the state of the ionosphere. In general, the skip distance increases as the radiated frequency exceeds the critical frequency. Factors which affect the electron density and the height of the ionospheric layers produce variations in the skip distance. As night falls communication with nearer stations may be lost, and yet more distant ones heard, on the same frequency.

The *skip zone* is not the same as the skip distance. Recall that radio wave propogation, in general, may take place over two routes, namely, via the ground wave and via the sky wave. The relative importance of the two paths depends on the frequency to such an extent that the effect resulting from one of them may be negligible. For example, in the standard broadcast band, daytime reception is limited by the ground wave. At night, unless precautions are taken, the sky wave may provide unwanted reception in distant locations. At intermediate distances, night signals received by both routes may be comparable in magnitude. At higher frequencies, up to about 30 Mc, the ground wave is rapidly attenuated and reception is almost wholly by the sky wave. Between the point where the ground wave is substantially dissipated and the point where the sky wave first returns to the earth, no signals, except scattering (which is not to be confused with "forward scatter" as discussed in Sec. 10.7), are heard; the intervening distance is called the *skip zone*.

The problem of determining the transmitting frequency and the angle at which it should be propagated is not a simple one, especially when multiple-hop transmission is involved. What is the state of the ionosphere where reflection is taking place? In east-west transmission, day and night do not occur simultaneously along a parallel of latitude. On the Hawaiian circuit, for example, the sun may be shining where the first reflection takes place; the stars may be out where the second occurs. Communication may also be between the northern and southern hemispheres, as on the New York–Buenos Aires circuit, where change of seasons must be taken into account. The point of reflection in the ionosphere having the lowest maximum usable frequency determines the highest frequency that can be used for the circuit in multiple-hop transmission. Maximum one-hop distances are about 1250 miles for the E layer and 2500 miles for the F layer.

Furthermore, for multiple hops the electrical nature of the reflecting earth as related to the radiation frequency must be considered. In Chapter 3 we learned that the amount of electromagnetic energy reflected at the termination of a transmission line increases with the degree of mismatch between the line and its termination. For example, all the energy is reflected for two extreme cases of mismatch, the open circuit and the short circuit; no energy whatever is reflected when the line is terminated by its characteristic impedance. We may therefore look upon reflection as the amount of mismatch between the air and the earth. Let us assume that the characteristic impedance of the former is that of free space, namely, 377 ohms, and is independent of the frequency. The earth is a reflecting surface having a characteristic impedance with a range of about 1 to 200 ohms which varies with the frequency of the radiation and the nature of the terrain. For all types of water and soil the impedance is smaller at the lower frequencies, the rate of variation differing with the frequency and the kind of surface. Between sea water and air there is the greatest amount of mismatch. Hence, in general, the ocean may be expected to reflect energy in a very efficient manner. Fresh water and wet soil are less effective reflectors, and dry soil, such as rocky terrain or desert country, is the poorest of all. The state of polarization of the radio waves must not be neglected. Maximum absorption will take place if vertically polarized waves are incident at the Brewster angle. Of course, this treatment has been somewhat oversimplified, but it may be considered adequate in providing the reader with an elementary description of an important phenomenon.

7.7. Sky-Wave Diagrams. The following diagrams, Fig. 7.2 to 7.9, are designed to present in pictorial form important information concerning sky-wave propagation. If studied carefully they will enhance considerably the reader's understanding of long-distance radio transmission and reception.

Fig. 7.2 shows the relative positions of the ionospheric layers above the surface of the earth, but the diagram is not drawn to scale. The presence of the E layer with reduced ionization at night is indicated by a broken line.

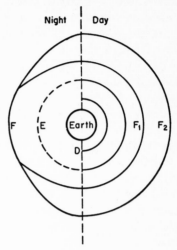

FIG. 7.2. Ionospheric layers above the surface of the earth.

In Table 7.1, the regions most useful for sky-wave communication are denoted by asterisks. The chemical symbols indicate the principal elements ionized. Although a representative height is given for the G layer, the value is tentative and the layer itself is not shown in the diagram.

TABLE 7.1. SKY–WAVE COMMUNICATION

Layer	Representative Height, miles	Chemical Element
D	40	O_3
*E	65	O_2
*F_1	100	N_2
*F_2	250	O
*F	200	—
G	300	—

The two waves A and B in Fig. 7.3 have the same frequency but enter the ionosphere at different angles. During the day the E layer is assumed to be of sufficient density to reflect each wave. Wave B, which makes a larger angle of incidence with the layer, or has a lower angle of propagation, has the longer skip distance. At night both waves pass through the E layer, as a result of its reduced electron density, and are reflected from the F layer. The skip distances are increased with the height of the reflecting layer.

The effect of frequency on refraction is illustrated in Fig. 7.4. The angle α which the propagated wave makes with the earth is constant. A, B, C, and D represent frequencies of *decreasing* magnitude. As the wave penetrates obliquely into the ionosphere, its direction is altered and its group velocity is diminished. The lower the frequency the more easily is

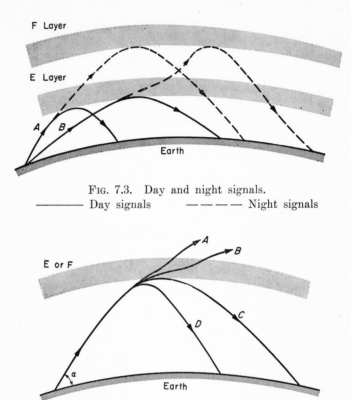

FIG. 7.3. Day and night signals.
————— Day signals   — — — — Night signals

FIG. 7.4. Effect of frequency on refraction.

the signal refracted. If the density of ionization were greater, B, or A and B, might be refracted back to the earth.

A wave is just reflected or just fails to be reflected when the angle of incidence is equal to the critical angle. The latter in Fig. 7.5 is denoted by θ_A and θ_B. A and B represent frequencies of *decreasing* magnitude. Notice that B can attain the critical status when propagated at a steeper angle with respect to the earth. The course of the rays A and B may be equally well represented after contact with the ionosphere by directing them towards the earth at their respective angles θ_A and θ_B.

The effect of sunspot conditions is shown in Fig. 7.6. During the periods of sunspot maxima the F layer attains maximum height and density. Accordingly the maximum usable frequencies during these years are greater. In Fig. 7.6, A is the higher MUF corresponding to sunspot maximum, and B is the lower MUF corresponding to the minimum. The angle of propa-

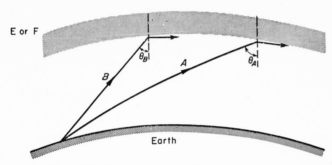

Fig. 7.5. Frequency and the critical angle.

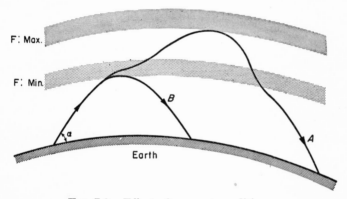

Fig. 7.6. Effect of sunspot conditions.

gation α is constant. Notice that the skip distance may be considerably increased in a period of sunspot maximum.

A typical case of multiple-hop transmission obtained by increasing the angle of propagation is shown in Fig. 7.7. The frequency is constant. Single-hop transmission is usually better because attenuation takes place upon reflection at both the ionosphere and the earth.

Fig. 7.8 shows how fading may be produced by a combination of the ground wave and the sky wave. The height and density of the ionospheric layer vary with the time. If the waves from the two paths are out of phase at a given time, there will be partial or complete cancellation of the signal.

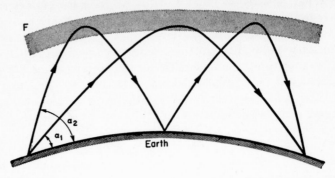

FIG. 7.7.   One- and two-hop transmission.

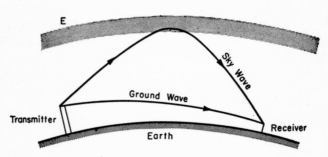

FIG. 7.8.   Fading: ground wave and sky wave.

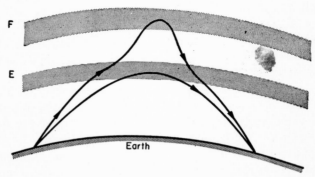

FIG. 7.9.   Fading: two sky waves.

In Fig. 7.9 the fading takes place as a consequence of signals arriving at the receiver from two different layers of the ionosphere which are also varying in height and density.   Since one signal is usually weaker than the other, complete cancellation is rarer than in the instance cited above.

7.8. Fading. *Fading* of radio waves is the term used to describe undesirable changes in the intensity of the signals at the receiver. In general, it is the result of signals from a given transmitter reaching their destination by more than one path with consequent interference effects. If these paths are variable, as they may be especially during the sunset period when the height or density of the ionosphere changes, the shifts in phase may produce large, irregular, and somewhat rapid variations in the received signal.

It has been stated that the character of the reflection from the ionosphere varies with the frequency of the signal. Now, information, i.e., music, speech, or pictures, cannot be transmitted at a single frequency. A range of frequencies, called *sidebands,* is required. In the standard broadcast range these sidebands extend 5 kc on either side of the carrier frequency. For example, the carrier of WGN is 720 kc and the sidebands extend from 715 to 725 kc. In television more information is transmitted and much wider sidebands are required, the range for combined picture and sound being at present 6 Mc. By way of comparison, it is interesting to notice that the frequency range of the entire standard broadcast band is only a little more than 1 Mc. Although a discussion of the theory according to which information is transmitted by means of sidebands is beyond the scope of this book, it should be clear, upon the acceptance of their necessity, that radio communication is a matter of, not single, but multifrequency propagation.

If reception is by the sky wave, all frequencies will not be received with the same relative intensity, for each frequency is reflected from the ionosphere—and partially absorbed in that region—in a somewhat different way. The strength of each frequency signal may vary enough with changing conditions of the ionospheric layers to produce what is known as *selective fading.* This effect can easily be observed on the short-wave broadcasts beamed to this country by European stations; it is especially noticeable in musical programs.

Special receiving systems designed to minimize the effects of fading make use of *diversity reception.* Frequency diversity is based on the observation that signals of different frequencies received at the same location do not fade simultaneously. This system is used in radio telegraphy by modulating the carrier in order to introduce two sideband frequencies. The signals are in effect transmitted over three slightly different frequencies and are accepted by a single antenna connected to a receiver having a bandwidth sufficient to pass them. Although fluctuations in signal strength occur, there is little likelihood that all three frequencies will fade out completely.

Space diversity is based on the observation that signals of the same frequency received at different locations do not fade simultaneously. Usually three antennas, spaced, say six or seven wavelengths apart, are connected to separate receivers which are combined in a common output. The system may also be arranged such that the antenna which is receiving the strongest carrier signal at any instant operates its own particular receiver with little or no contribution to the output from the others. Since the quality distortion is a minimum when the carrier signal is strongest, the latter arrangement is suitable for radio telephony.

It may be well to distinguish between fading and the so-called *radio fade-out* or Dellinger effect, which is the result of unpredictable solar eruptions. It occurs most frequently when the sunspot cycle is at a maximum. The fade-out comes suddenly and without warning, disrupting wholly or partly all sky-wave circuits in the daylight hemisphere, but leaving the darkness zones unaffected. The duration is short, usually less than 15 minutes.

7.9. Electron in an Electric Field. The paths of charged particles in electric and magnetic fields play an important role in electronic physics. Since the trajectories of these particles are similar in some respects to the loci of projectiles in the earth's gravitational field, this subject has appropriately been designated *electron ballistics*. An analysis of an example selected from each of the two types of fields will pave the way for further discussion of ionospheric phenomena.

In Chapter 1 the concept of an electric field was discussed. There it was pointed out that a positively charged particle placed in the field experiences a force in the direction of the latter. Clearly, the force on a substituted electron will be oppositely directed. Suppose, now, the electron is projected horizontally with constant velocity into a uniform electric field directed vertically upward. (These directions are in the plane of the diagram, Fig. 7.10.)

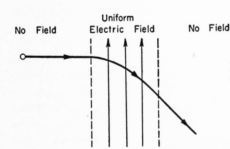

FIG. 7.10. Parabolic path of an electron which is projected perpendicularly into a uniform electric field.

In the horizontal direction the velocity v_x is constant within or without the field. Therefore, in the field the horizontal distance traveled is proportional to the time, or

$$x = v_x t \qquad (7.2)$$

In the presence of the field the charge e experiences a constant downward force F_y which, by Newton's second law, produces a constant downward acceleration a_y. The vertical distance traveled, it will be recalled, is proportional to the square of the time.

$$y = \tfrac{1}{2}a_y t^2 \qquad (7.3)$$

Since $F_y = \mathcal{E}_y e = ma$, where m is the rest mass of the electron,

$$y = \tfrac{1}{2}\frac{\mathcal{E}_y e}{m} t^2 \qquad (7.4)$$

By the principle of superposition (Sec. 5.1) each motion will take place independently of the presence or absence of the other. The relation between x and y may be obtained by eliminating the time from Eq. (7.2) and (7.4),

$$y = \tfrac{1}{2}\frac{\mathcal{E}_y e}{m v_x^2} x^2 \qquad (7.5)$$

Since y is proportional to x^2 in Eq. (7.5) we may choose the constant of proportionality as $2p$ and write

$$y = 2px^2 \qquad (7.6)$$

which is easily recognizable as the equation of a parabola. Hence an electron, or other charged particle, projected with a constant velocity perpendicular to a uniform electric field describes a parabolic path. Notice that the situation is strictly analogous to the case of an object thrown horizontally in the earth's gravitational field.

Within the field-space, the force on the charged particle is always parallel to the field. In the two field-free regions there is no unbalanced force on the electron and, in accordance with Newton's first law of motion, it will travel in a straight line. In the space at the left the motion will be in the direction of the original velocity. At the right the electron will move along a tangent to the parabola at the point of emergence.

7.10. Electron in a Magnetic Field. In Fig. 7.11 an electron is similarly projected into a uniform magnetic field having a direction perpendicular to the plane of the paper and directed downward. By using the thumb and fingers of the *left* hand, the direction of the vertical components of the magnetic field associated with the moving electron can be determined and combined with the uniform field to find the direction of the resultant force on the particle. Since the force exerted by the field is always perpendicular to the direction of motion, the electron will move in a curved path.

The force F producing this curvature is, by Ampere's law, equal to the product of the flux density B and the charge e and speed v of the electron, all of which are constant in *magnitude*.   The radius of curvature is constant and the path is the arc of a circle.

From Ampere's and Newton's laws, $F = Bev = ma$, or $a = Bev/m$.   A body moving in a circular path has a centripetal acceleration $a = v^2/r$. Hence

$$r = mv/Be \tag{7.7}$$

If, however, the electron does not enter the magnetic field perpendicularly, the path becomes a helix.

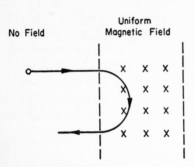

FIG. 7.11.   Circular path of an electron which is projected perpendicularly into a uniform magnetic field.

An essential difference in the effect on a charged particle produced by an electric and a magnetic field should be noticed.   Because the force exerted by the former is always parallel to the field, both the direction of motion and the kinetic energy of the particle may be changed.   Since the force exerted by the magnetic field is not only perpendicular to the field, but also to the direction of motion of the particle, the field can do no work on it. Hence, while a magnetic field can change the direction of motion of a charged particle, it cannot alter its kinetic energy.

7.11. Waves and Electrons in the Ionosphere.   When a radio wave enters the ionosphere the electric field of the wave exerts a force on the electrons.   If the earth's magnetic field has a negligible effect, an electron is under the influence of the electric field alone during the time between collisions with gas molecules, i.e., while traveling, on the average, a distance equal to its mean free path.   Since the field varies sinusoidally, the motion of the electron is simple harmonic and the vibrations are along a line parallel to the field.   According to the principles of simple harmonic motion, the velocity of the electron lags 90° behind the field.   Associated with the moving electron is the kinetic energy which has been obtained from the electromagnetic field.   Since an accelerated charge has the property of radiation, the electron, in a manner similar to a parasitic antenna (Sec. 9.5), now reradiates this energy with the same frequency, but in a different phase.   The effect of this phase difference is the refraction of the wave from a region of high to a region of low electron density.

The greater the frequency of the radiation the smaller are the amplitude and average velocity of the electron.   At high frequencies the elapsed time between reversals of the field is very short.   Therefore the electron does not have sufficient time to attain an appreciable displacement or a high velocity. For a given concentration of molecules the chance of an electron undergoing a collision before reradiating its energy is much reduced at high frequencies.   This fact is of considerable importance.

Provided there is no collision between an electron and a molecule, all the energy which the former has abstracted from the wave is returned.   The total energy of the wave is unchanged.   If, however, a collision takes place before all the energy borrowed from the electric field of the radio wave is returned, the electron changes its direction of motion and transfers part of its kinetic energy to the molecule.   The latter particle is electrically neutral and cannot radiate.   Appearing as heat in the ionosphere, the energy acquired by the molecule is not returned to the wave, which is thereby attenuated.   Hence, the frequency of the waves and the length of the mean free path have an important effect on the absorption of radio waves by the ionosphere.

From a somewhat different point of view we may assume that the ionosphere is a giant capacitor with the space between its plates containing air and free electrons.   The sinusoidal electric field applied across the capacitor produces two components of an alternating current.   Considering the air alone, the fluctuations in the electric field produce a displacement current (Sec. 2.5) which is capacitive, i.e., it leads the voltage by 90°.   The moving electrons are equivalent to a conduction current which, as shown above, is inductive and lags the voltage by 90°.   The presence of the electrons in the space therefore has the effect of decreasing the capacitive current, which is equivalent to reducing the refractive index of the ionosphere below the essentially free-space value of unity.

Using the passage of light from water to air as an illustration, it was shown in Sec. 4.6 that when the angle of incidence in water exceeds a certain angle, called the critical angle, the light is returned to the first medium. In this case there is a sharp boundary between the two mediums.   On the other hand, there is a continuous change in the refractive index over the path of a radio wave entering the ionosphere.   The principle, however, may be extended to curved rays, as was done in the discussion of tropospheric refraction (see Sec. 4.7 and 4.8).

The presence of charged particles in the ionosphere, as stated, lowers its refractive index below unity.   As explained in Sec. 4.6, this means that the wave or phase velocity is greater than that of light in free space.   It is the ratio of these two quantities, i.e., the relative refractive index, that determines the paths of the rays. The energy, however, is propagated with the group velocity which is always less than the free-space velocity.

In addition to the charge and mass of the electron, the ratio of which enters into a great variety of problems, the refractive index of the ionosphere depends on the density of the electrons and the frequency of the waves. Although the mathematical formula will not be stated here, the physical discussion given above should indicate that the index will be diminished by increasing the density or lowering the frequency.

For a given density of ionization a lowering of the frequency reduces the refractive index to zero. As the value of μ decreases, the critical angle diminishes, with the result that a vertically projected wave is reflected from the layer. The highest frequency at which this occurs is the critical frequency. For radiation of lower frequencies the mathematics shows that the refractive index becomes imaginary, i.e., no wave propagation can take place in the ionosphere. (The situation should be compared with the existence of a cut-off frequency in a waveguide in Sec. 11.4.)

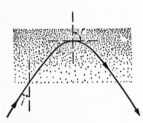

FIG. 7.12. Total reflection of a radio wave in the ionosphere.

In order to obtain a quantitative relation, let us assume that a wave enters the ionosphere at the angle i (Fig. 7.12). The course of the wave carries it into regions of denser ionization and diminishing refractive index. Although refraction takes place at a continuously varying angle, as indicated by the curved path of the ray, we are interested only in the points where it enters the ionosphere and where its direction is horizontal ($r = 90°$). If we write Snell's law in the form of Eq. (4.4), remembering that the refractive index of the unionized air is approximately unity and that $\sin 90° = 1$, we obtain

$$\sin i = \mu \tag{7.8}$$

where μ is the refractive index of the ionosphere for which this particular wave is totally reflected. Thus i is the critical angle. At vertical incidence $i = 0$ and therefore $\mu = 0$.

Returning to the capacitor analog of the ionosphere, we recall that in the absence of collisions the conduction current is inductive and the displacement current is capacitive. In an electrical circuit where this relation between components of the current exists there is an interchange of energy but no dissipation. When there is a collision between an electron and a gas molecule the conduction current lags the electric field (voltage) by less than 90°. The result is the existence of a voltage component in phase with the current. Instead of purely reactive components, there is now a resistance in series with the inductance. The presence of the resistance implies a dissipation of energy to which may be attributed the attenuation of the wave.

In keeping with the principle of diverse viewpoints in physics, the discussion of the preceding paragraph suggests the possibility of representing the ionosphere as a transmission line. Since the analogy will not be pursued further, only a bare outline, in which the earth's magnetic field is neglected, will be presented. Conditions corresponding to the displacement current are delineated by a series inductance and a shunt capacitance per unit length of line as shown in Fig. 3.16. The effect of the conduction current, which in the absence of collisions lags the voltage by 90°, is represented by adding a shunt inductance. When the number of collisions becomes appreciable a resistance is placed in series with this inductance to account for the dissipation of energy.

In general, the earth's magnetic field, which up to this point has been neglected, exerts a force on an electron in the ionosphere. As we have seen, this force, acting always at right angles to the direction of motion, cannot alter the kinetic energy of the particle, but only its direction of motion. Since the latter is also the direction of the electric field radiated by the electron, the direction of polarization will vary. At the higher frequencies the period is so short that there is insufficient time for the electron in the path of the wave to attain a high velocity. The field-deflecting force Bev, which is proportional to the velocity, is small, and the path described is a narrow ellipse. As the frequency decreases the electron has time to acquire a higher velocity and the ellipse becomes wider, thus increasing the fraction of the energy which is reradiated in a different plane of polarization.

This tendency increases until the so-called *gyro-frequency,* which varies from about 0.75 Mc near the geomagnetic equator to 1.5 Mc in the vicinity of the magnetic poles, is reached. At this frequency there is a resonant effect. That is, the period of an electron vibrating in the electric field of the wave is the same as the period of a free electron describing a circular path in the earth's magnetic field. As in all resonant phenomena, the particle attains very high velocities. The motion of the electron is similar to the behavior of a positive ion in the magnetic field of a cyclotron. The particle moves in a spiral-like path of ever widening radius while maintaining the same period of revolution.

An expression for the constancy of the period and its independence of the radius is easily obtained. From Eq. (7.7) the latter is $r = mv/Be$.

For constant speed in a circle we may write $v = 2\pi r/T$. Substituting the value of v in the first equation, we have

$$T = \frac{2\pi m}{Be}$$

Since the frequency is the reciprocal of the period, the gyro-frequency is given by

$$f_g = \frac{Be}{2\pi m} \tag{7.9}$$

As a consequence of the high speeds attained in the neighborhood of this frequency the wave is considerably attenuated. The position of the gyro-frequency in the upper portion of the standard broadcast band therefore imposes severe limitations upon sky-wave reception at these frequencies.

Below the gyro-frequency the path of an electron is relatively complicated, but the details are not of major importance. Its longer period and the presence of the earth's magnetic field combine to reduce the amount of energy reradiated to the wave. The attenuation of the wave, however, is less than at the gyro-frequency.

At high latitudes, say above 60°, disturbances produced by the earth's magnetic field and related auroral phenomena often cause high frequency sky-wave transmission, which is horizontally polarized, to be subject to blackouts. In these regions the low frequency band is used successfully for surface-wave transmission over long distances. This is an especially good method because, in many cases, the path of the vertically polarized radiation lies over salt water for which the attenuation is the least among all varieties of terrain.

7.12. The Huancayo Experiments. A horizontally polarized radio wave will, in general, have components of its electric vector both parallel and perpendicular to the earth's magnetic field. If the two fields were parallel, there would be no effect on the electrons in the ionosphere, because an electron moving parallel to a magnetic field behaves as if there were no field. On the other hand, the effect on an electron will be most pronounced when the electric field in which it is oscillating is at right angles to the earth's magnetic field. If the waves are projected vertically, the field must be horizontal, which is the case only at points on the geomagnetic equator.

The field station established by the Carnegie Institution of Washington at Huancayo in the Andes of Peru is thus conveniently located. Part of the equipment consists of three horizontal antennas—one running north and south; another, east and west; and a third, northeast and southwest. The radiated electromagnetic fields are, of course, horizontally polarized with their electric vibrations parallel to the directions of their respective antennas.

When the north-south antenna is used, electrons travel parallel to the earth's magnetic field. Therefore the electrons in the ionosphere which interchange energy with the wave behave as if the earth's magnetic field were absent. Borrowing an expression from optics, the radio wave returning from the ionosphere under this condition is called the *ordinary* or *o-wave*.

When the east-west antenna is used, electrons in the ionosphere move transversely to the earth's magnetic field and experience a maximum force. The wave returned to the earth under this condition is called the *extraordinary* or *x-wave*. Again, notice the connection between this expression and the terminology of polarized light.

The critical value of the electron density for total reflection is smaller for the x-waves than for the o-waves. Thus, the x-waves are reflected at a lower altitude and returned to earth in a shorter time. As examples, the following cases may be cited: the x-signal may come from the E layer, while the o-signal is reflected from the F layer; or the x-wave may be returned from F_1 and the o-wave from F_2; or the x-signal may be reflected from the F_2 layer, while the o-wave goes off into space.

When the NE-SW antenna is used, the ionosphere separates the signals into o- and x-components, as a crystal of calcite divides a beam of unpolarized light into two waves polarized at right angles to each other. The x-signal is reflected at a lower altitude and returns to the earth first. Thus, there are two echoes: the earlier is plane polarized east-west; the later, north-south. If a rotating horizontal antenna designed to respond to the radiation propagated by the NE-SW structure is used, the intensities of the signals will vary similarly to the ordinary and extraordinary beams of light when a calcite crystal is rotated. Complete experimental proof of the above phenomena was obtained by Berkner and Wells at Huancayo.

PROBLEMS

7.1. The longest wavelength of ultraviolet light which will ionize the air is approximately 1350 A. What is the frequency? What is the energy of the photons?

7.2. With what speed must an electron be moving in order to have the same ionizing energy as the photon in Problem 7.1?

7.3. If the threshold frequency for an element has a value corresponding to 1350 A, with what speed will an electron be ejected if the incident radiation has a wavelength of 1000 A?

7.4. What is the virtual height of the ionosphere if a vertically projected signal is returned to the earth 2000 microseconds after sending? Give the answer in kilometers and in miles.

7.5. The signal in Problem 7.4 is transmitted at the rate of 100 per sec. Its return is observed on the screen of a cathode-ray oscilloscope which traces a horizontal time axis, 5 in. long, from left to right, at the same rate. Where will the "pip," indicating the returned signal, appear on the trace? If the position of the pip can be located to 1/20th in., what is the error in reading the height?

7.6. A radio transmitter used in measuring the virtual height of the ionosphere is adjusted to a frequency of 4 Mc. The pulse width is 100 microseconds and the pulse repetition frequency, 100 per sec. (a) How many radio waves are there in a single pulse? (b) What is the silent time between pulses? (c) If the pulse is rectangular and the power radiated during the pulse is 1 kw, what is the average power over a cycle?

7.7. A signal is projected upward at an angle of 20° with the surface of the earth. After reflection from the ionosphere, it is received at a station 2000 km away. Assuming a flat earth, what is the virtual height of the ionosphere? What is the time of transmission?

7.8. A signal is projected at an angle of 20° with the surface of the earth and undergoes two reflections at the ionosphere. The virtual height is 50 miles at the first reflection and 60 miles at the second. At what distance from the transmitter is the signal received? Assume a flat earth.

7.9. An electron moving with a constant velocity of 4.0×10^7 meters per sec is projected perpendicularly into a uniform electric field of 1000 volts per meter. If the length of the field-space across which the electron travels is 0.8 meter, how far in a direction parallel to the field will the particle be deflected? Use the rest mass of the electron. Diagram.

7.10. An electron moving with a constant velocity of 4.0×10^7 meters per sec is projected perpendicularly into a uniform magnetic field of 1000 amp per meter. If the permeability of the medium is the same as that of free space, $4\pi \times 10^{-7}$ henry per meter, what is the radius of the circular path traveled by the electron in the field-space? Use the rest mass of the electron. Diagram.

7.11. Positive ions as well as electrons in the ionosphere are influenced by the earth's magnetic field. What is the gyro-frequency for a singly ionized nitrogen atom (atomic weight, 14) where the magnetic flux density is 5×10^{-5} weber per meter^2?

7.12. Draw a section of a transmission line representing the ionosphere in a region where the number of collisions between electrons and gas molecules is appreciable. Neglect the effect of the earth's magnetic field.

Chapter 8

FUNDAMENTALS OF ANTENNAS

8.1. Transmission Lines and Antennas. In the discussion of transmission lines the energy generated by the transmitter was assumed to be contained in the space surrounding the wires which serve as guides, a point of view which has received constant reiteration. Magnetic and electric fields may, however, be disengaged from their conductors and set free in space. Thus, wireless communication is carried on through the agency of fields set up by variable currents in a device called an *antenna* which, for the present, it may be assumed, transfers energy to space in all directions. At a distant point there is another antenna across which the magnetic field acts and upon which the electric field impinges, thereby inducing a voltage which reproduces the variations of the original currents in the attached receiver.

At large distances this is really a very good way to accomplish the purpose. On an economic basis the voltage which can be induced in an antenna exceeds the voltage which can be transmitted over wires. The attenuation on the latter is exponential (see Problem 3.7). The variation in the electric field in free space is less rapid, falling off as the first power of the distance, a relation, it is true, that may be appreciably modified by the nature of the terrain over which the radiation passes and the frequency of the signal. As evidence of the effectiveness of the two methods, it may be pointed out that transoceanic telephone communication was first carried on by radio rather than by cable. Considerable progress in engineering was necessary before a transatlantic telephone cable became feasible.

We shall now proceed, in a rather crude way, to convert a transmission line (a nonradiating device) into an antenna (a radiating device). While the discussion may prove to be helpful in establishing the physical picture, it should be remembered that transmission line theory cannot be applied rigorously to antenna radiation.

Fig. 8.1(*a*) shows a circuit where the electric field is for the most part confined between the wires. The oscillator develops a sinusoidal voltage

129

which will be measured with respect to an assumed reference plane halfway between the conductors. At any given distance from the generator the currents in the separate wires are equal in magnitude and opposite in direction; their magnetic fields therefore tend to cancel each other. Since radiation takes place only when varying electric and magnetic fields exist simultaneously, a transmission line radiates very little energy into space. If the line is lossless and open-circuited all the energy must be returned to the source.

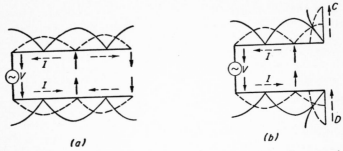

(a)   *(b)*

FIG. 8.1. Transmission line (a) before opening out, (b) after opening out.

Suppose the line is now opened out as shown in Fig. 8.1(b). The end parts C and D form an antenna. The voltages between the wires and the reference plane are the same as in Fig. 8.1(a). The electric fields contributed by C and D extend into space. The magnetic fields of these sections of the wires, now associated with currents in the same direction, *will not cancel* each other. Each field may now expand freely and the condition for the existence of an electromagnetic field in space is fulfilled. A distant receiving antenna will abstract a small portion of this radiated energy, transmit part of it to the receiver, and reradiate the remainder into space.

8.2. Resonance and Q of a Circuit. Since an antenna is an oscillating system, it may be represented by a circuit consisting of inductance, capacitance, and resistance. The last includes not only the ordinary ohmic resistance, but also the radiation resistance, which will be discussed in Sec. 8.6. When the capacitor is fully charged the energy of the circuit appears in the electric field. As the capacitor discharges, this energy is transferred to the magnetic field of the inductor. Although the energy in each field is classified as potential, the case may be considered as analogous to a vibrating spring where there is an interchange of potential and kinetic energy as the system passes through its cycle (Sec. 1.2).

The vibrations of a spring can be maintained at constant amplitude only in the absence of friction. Similarly in an electrical circuit a complete interchange of energy between the electric and magnetic fields is possible only when there is neither resistance nor radiation. In order to maintain the oscillations of an antenna, the generator must supply sufficient energy to compensate both for heat losses and for radiation into space. The ratio of the volt-amperes stored to the watts dissipated is called the Q (quality) of the circuit.

Considering radio circuits in general, the losses in the capacitive element are usually negligible and therefore all the resistance may be associated with the inductor. Calculations may be made on the basis that the generator needs to supply energy to compensate for losses in the "coil" only. If the impedance of the coil consists of a resistance R in series with an inductance L, the voltage across the former is RI and across the latter, $2\pi fLI$. From the definition given above

$$Q = \frac{2\pi fLI^2}{RI^2} = \frac{2\pi fL}{R} \tag{8.1}$$

The ohmic resistance, as a consequence of the skin effect, varies with the frequency used (Sec. 3.3).

The current in an a-c *series* circuit consisting of resistance, inductance, and capacitance is given by

$$I = \frac{V}{\sqrt{R^2 + \left(2\pi fL - \dfrac{1}{2\pi fC}\right)^2}}$$

where V is the constant rms voltage and f is the frequency. At low frequencies the capacitive reactance is large and the inductive reactance is small; at high frequencies the reverse is true. For some intermediate

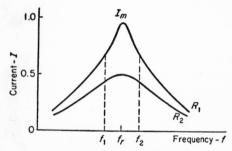

FIG. 8.2. Resonance curves for a series circuit. $R_2 > R_1$. Bandwidth is shown for R_1 only.

value, called the resonant frequency f_r, $2\pi f_r L = 1/2\pi f_r C$. The inductive and capacitive reactances cancel each other and the current is limited solely by the resistance of the circuit. As shown in Fig. 8.2, where current is plotted against frequency and $R_2 > R_1$, the current is a maximum at the resonant frequency, the curve being flatter when the resistance is larger.

The curves show that the variation in the current of an antenna as the frequency changes is more pronounced when its resistance is low. Whether or not this is desirable depends on the use to which the antenna is to be put. For example, if reception corresponding to a carrier wave and its sidebands very close to the resonant frequency is required, the response is excellent within the range, but rather poor outside it. On the other hand, an antenna with a flatter resonance curve may not respond as strongly at the resonant frequency, but it will have more uniformity of response over a wider bandwidth. The ability of a resonant circuit to select a small range of frequencies and to discriminate against all others is called its *selectivity*.

Since the characteristics of a series resonant circuit depend primarily on the ratio of the inductive reactance to the circuit resistance, the sharpness of the resonant curve and the selectivity depend on the value of Q. A high Q means a good selectivity.

In order to compare the selectivity of different circuits it is customary to use the term *bandwidth*, which is the range of frequencies lying between the points where the current is 0.707 of its maximum value. Since the power for a given voltage is I^2R, these limiting frequencies correspond to points at which the power is half of its maximum value. A circuit with a high selectivity has a high Q and a narrow bandwidth.

This discussion shows that the Q of an antenna has an important bearing on its ability to respond to a range of frequencies. For example, a high Q circuit should be employed when reception from only one station is desired. A low Q antenna should be used when reception over a relatively wide range of frequencies is required. In transmission the selectivity of the antenna is likewise governed by its bandwidth requirements.

8.3. Induction and Radiation Fields. If the fundamental equations of electromagnetic theory are applied to an antenna of small dimensions, it is found that the field consists of two parts. In the *near zone*, close to the antenna, the *induction field* predominates. For all practical purposes the strength of this field follows the *inverse square law*. An interchange of energy between electric and magnetic fields takes place as described in the preceding section.

As a consequence of this interchange there is no radiation. Furthermore, since one of the fields is a maximum when the other is zero, they are 90° out of phase in time. The effects of the induction field are important in cases dealing with antennas closely spaced in terms of wavelengths.

In the *far zone* at a distance of, say at least a few wavelengths from the antenna, the *radiation field* predominates. This field contains the energy radiated by the antenna and is inversely proportional to the *first power* of the distance. The radiation field owes its existence to the fact that time is required for its propagation in space. Let the antenna be charged and the field established in its neighborhood. If the charge on the wire is reversed slowly there will be a sufficient interval during which substantially all the energy in the field will be restored to the circuit and there will be very little radiation. If, on the other hand, the charge be reversed quickly, a field of the opposite sign forms near the wire before an appreciable part of the energy in the field can return. Part of the original field becomes detached and is propagated as an electromagnetic wave in space. Frequency is thus seen to be an important factor in determining the relative magnitude of the radiated energy.

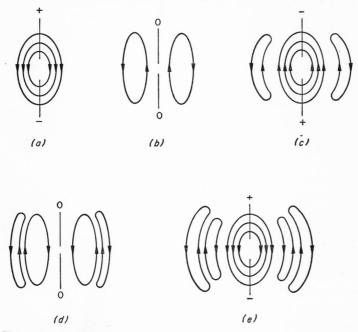

FIG. 8.3. Radiation of electromagnetic waves from an antenna.

Fig. 8.3(a) shows the status of the electric field when the voltage between the two halves of the antenna is a maximum. As the voltage diminishes the charges on the antenna move toward the center and the field lines collapse. If the disturbance in the field moved with infinite velocity all the lines would contract and return to the antenna within the quarter period required for the voltage to reach zero. As a consequence of their finite velocity, however, there is insufficient time for the outermost line, let us say, to complete its return. When the ends of this line meet at the wire a ring-shaped section is cut off, which continues to exist as a closed loop (b). The antenna changes polarity and the field lines, now oppositely directed as in (c), expand outwardly, pushing away the previously detached loop. A second loop, shown in (d), separates itself from the antenna and the process continues (e). Thus an electric field is propagated outward with the speed of light.

Although only the electric field is pictured in the diagrams, there is, of course, an associated magnetic field. It consists of circles concentric with the antenna and increasing in radius as the disturbance moves outward.

The account given in the preceding paragraphs is intended to suggest rather than to describe the detailed process of radiation. The reader who wishes to obtain a clearer picture should view an animated film in which the successive steps are presented in close time sequence.

That part of the field which returns its energy to the circuit is the induction field where, as already stated, the electric and magnetic components are 90° out of phase in time (Fig. 8.4a). The detached portion is the radia-

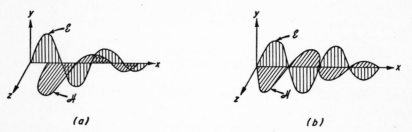

(a)   (b)

Fig. 8.4. Electric and magnetic fields of an antenna. Attenuation is indicated. (a) Induction field (inverse square). (b) Radiation field (inverse first power).

tion field where the two components are in time phase (Fig. 8.4b). The reason for the displacement of one of the components by 90° in order to put them in step is based on Kirchhoff's solution of the wave equation, which may be found in works on optics. The magnitude of the energy in the electric and magnetic components of the radiation field is exactly the same. The variation of one component results in the formation of the other and thus the field is self-perpetuating.

Another reason besides that given in Sec. 5.8 to avoid field and intensity measurements in the immediate vicinity of the source is now apparent. Unless observations are made at points removed from the radiator by at least several wavelengths, the results may be influenced by the induction field.

8.4. Electric Field Strength. We now ask the question: How are we to measure the strength of the electromagnetic field? Evidently, if both components have the same energy, a determination of one component will give the value of the other. Besides, both have the same effect on the receiving antenna, namely, that of inducing a voltage along the wire. If a magnetic field fluctuates in a plane perpendicular to the wire, there will be induced in it a fluctuating voltage which will appear across the grid terminals of a vacuum tube in the receiver. Likewise, a fluctuating electric field in a plane parallel to the wire, in the same neighborhood, will produce a voltage along the antenna.

It is customary to express the strength of the field in terms of its electric component. In MKS units this field is measured in *volts per meter*. To make this clear, let us suppose that two *large* parallel plates A and B are placed 1 meter apart (Fig. 8.5). Since the plates are large, the field

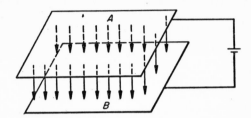

Fig. 8.5. Uniform electric field between two large parallel plates.

between them as represented by lines of force will be uniform, except for a negligibly slight curvature near the edges. If the battery charges the plates to a potential difference of 8 volts, the strength of the field will be 8 volts per meter. Since a volt is a joule per coulomb and a joule is a newton meter, the force which would act on a coulomb of negative electricity, i.e., 6.7×10^{18} electrons, would be 8 newtons. Furthermore, this force would be independent of the position of the charge between the plates.

The magnitudes of electric fields encountered in radio communication are too small to make this unit, volts per meter, a convenient one. Instead, the units *millivolts per meter* (mv/m) and *microvolts per meter* (μv/m) are usually employed.

Many radiations, including those in the standard broadcast band, are vertically polarized. If the earth were an ideally conducting surface the electric vector would always remain perpendicular to it, the value diminishing with an inverse function of the distance. For the *space* component of the ground wave the radiation from a grounded vertical antenna passes through *hemispherical* surfaces, ε varying as $1/r$. For the *surface* component the energy flows through *cylindrical* surfaces of equal height, ε varying as $1/\sqrt{r}$.

The earth, however, has an appreciable resistance: the electric field takes on a horizontal forward component and thus the vertical component diminishes more rapidly than in the idealized case. The two components get out of phase and the electric vector becomes elliptically polarized. The magnitudes of the tilt and the phase difference depend on the conductivity and dielectric constant of the terrain and the frequency of the signal. Although the theory is somewhat complex, it may be stated that for vertically polarized ground waves the angle of tilt increases with the frequency. For ocean communication the electric vector deviates from perpendicularity by only a little more than a degree. Over dry ground, however, the inclination is appreciable, varying from about 4° at 20 kc to 35° at 20 Mc.

In New England and along much of the Pacific coast a representative value of ground conductivity is 2×10^{-5} mho per cm, i.e., a cube 1 cm on a side has a resistance of 50,000 ohms. (Notice that this statement is not equivalent to saying that the resistance of a cubic centimeter is 50,000 ohms.) This value, obtained from a Federal Communications Commission map, indicates rather low conducting earth. In the United States the lowest ground conductivity (1×10^{-5} mho per cm) is found in a relatively small area of central Colorado; the highest (20 to 30×10^{-5} mho per cm) along a corridor running through the plain states from North Dakota to Texas. Fresh water is not a particularly good conductor, as may be seen from the representative value of 10×10^{-5} mho per cm for the Great Lakes.

Examples of magnitudes that may be expected for field strength over terrain where the conductivity is 2×10^{-5} mho per cm are given in Table 8.1.

TABLE 8.1. MAGNITUDES FOR FIELD STRENGTH

f kc	1 kw, 10 mi mv/m	50 kw, 10 mi mv/m	50 kw, 100 mi mv/m
550	10	70	1.4
1000	4	28	0.7
1500	0.7	5	0.3

Over *sea* water, the best conducting terrain, the conductivity is 5×10^{-2} mho per cm, i.e., a cube 1 cm on a side has a resistance of only 20 ohms. Over the ocean all three stations would have a field strength of 140 mv per meter at 10 miles; at 100 miles there would be little difference among them, the value being about 10 mv per meter.

Sometimes it is pointed out that reception in the standard broadcast band, where vertical polarization is used, can be obtained with the aid of a horizontally strung wire. Often as a result of the proximity of the station and its high power, the signal strength at the receiver is relatively great. Thus, even the weaker horizontal component acquired by the ground wave is sufficient to induce in the wire a voltage adequate for reception.

The field intensity required for good reception in the standard broadcast, frequency modulation, and television bands is dependent on the usual noise levels encountered in the area where the receiver is located. Representative values will be quoted merely to give the reader an idea of the orders of magnitude involved. In large cities with business and industrial areas, the signal strength must be high in order to rise above man-made noises and to overcome the shadow effects of large buildings. Signal strengths in these areas may need to be from 10,000 to 25,000 microvolts per meter for standard broadcasting, 1000 for FM, and 5000 to 10,000 for television, depending on whether VHF or UHF channels are used. Residential and suburban communities may obtain satisfactory reception with field strengths of about 20 per cent of these values. In rural areas typical magnitudes are much less, say 300 microvolts per meter for standard broadcasting and 500 for television. Inasmuch as the ignition in internal combustion engines constitutes a major source of noise in the case of vertically polarized radiation, the presence of a large number of automobiles in rural areas may necessitate higher requirements for standard broadcasting. Objectionable tropospheric interference between two television stations on the same channel is determined by field intensity measurements. For example, if the tropospheric signal from a co-channel produces an interference field of at least 5 microvolts per meter for 10 per cent of the time in a 500 microvolts per meter area, the reception is considered unsatisfactory. All of these values, of course, may be modified in accordance with the criterion as to what constitutes good reception.

8.5. Free-Space Radiation Patterns. In deriving the equations of *free-space* radiation patterns for antennas of finite length, the technique of the integral calculus is required. However, an outline of the physical principles involved should make the result reasonably plausible. The method of attack, at least, is straightforward and should be understood by the reader who has mastered the previous discussions in this work.

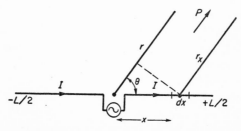

FIG. 8.6. Diagram for finding the radiation pattern of a center-fed antenna.

Let the point P (Fig. 8.6) be a *distant* point, such that the distance from P to any point on the antenna is substantially the same as the distance from P to the center of the antenna; i.e., for the purposes of calculation at the antenna, r and r_x may be considered equal and parallel. It is assumed that the length of the antenna is an integral number of half-wavelengths, that it is fed at its center, and that the leads from the source of power are negligible in length. If the wire is very thin, it may be further assumed that the current distribution is sinusoidal.

The strength of the electric field at P will be the phasor sum of the contributions from each elementary length dx making up the antenna. At any instant, of course, the phase and magnitude of the contribution from each element of length will, in general, be different. Let a mathematical expression for these contributions be found and their summation from $x = -L/2$ to $x = +L/2$ be determined. Evidently the answer will be the resultant field at P. The mathematical process by which this summation is carried out is called integration. The integral calculus may be said to have been invented for the purpose of solving problems of this type.

When the integration is carried out, the answer consists of two parts— one for the induction field, the other for the radiation field. It is only with the latter that we are concerned here.

The general expression for the strength of the electric component of the radiation field for a center-fed antenna, an integral number of half-wavelengths long, and having a sinusoidal distribution of current, is

$$\mathcal{E} = \frac{60I_m}{r} \left[\frac{\cos\left(\frac{\pi L}{\lambda} \cdot \cos\theta\right) - \cos\frac{\pi L}{\lambda}}{\sin\theta} \right] \tag{8.2}$$

where $\mathcal{E}$ is the field strength in volts per meter, I_m is the amplitude of the current, r is the distance between P and the antenna in meters, λ is the wavelength in meters, and θ is the angle measured with respect to the antenna wire.

Now the factor $60\,I_m/r$ consists of quantities of constant values for a given arrangement. If they are omitted and the other factors evaluated, the *shape* of the free-space radiation pattern may be obtained.

For an *odd* number of half-wavelengths the term $\cos \pi L/\lambda$ becomes the cosine of an odd integral multiple of $\pi/2$ ($90°$, $270°$, etc.) for which the value is zero. Under this condition, omitting the constant factor, Eq. (8.2) becomes

$$\mathcal{E} = \frac{\cos\left(\frac{\pi L}{\lambda} \cdot \cos\theta\right)}{\sin\theta} \tag{8.3}$$

For an *even* number of half-wavelengths the term $\cos \pi L/\lambda$ becomes the cosine of an integral multiple of π ($180°$, $360°$, etc.) for which the value is alternately minus one and plus one. For this type of antenna, Eq. (8.2) becomes

$$\varepsilon = \frac{\cos\left(\dfrac{\pi L}{\lambda} \cdot \cos\theta\right) \pm 1}{\sin\theta} \tag{8.4}$$

The physical reason for this difference is that for an odd number of half-wavelengths the maximum current will be at the center of the antenna, while for an even number of half-waves the current will be zero at this point.

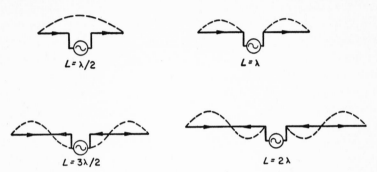

Fig. 8.7. Current distribution for center-fed antennas of different lengths. (Not drawn to scale.)

The point at which the antenna is fed, however, makes a difference in the distribution of current along the wire. If the current is fed at the center the direction of flow will be the same in the two halves of the antenna up to the point where a current node exists (see Fig. 8.7).

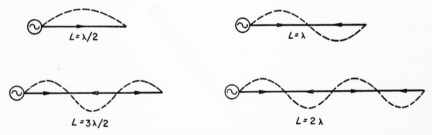

Fig. 8.8. Current distribution for end-fed antennas of different lengths. (Not drawn to scale.)

If, for example, the antenna is end-fed, the situation may be different. The current distribution for end-fed antennas of the same wavelengths as those in Fig. 8.7 is shown in Fig. 8.8.

A comparison of the two figures will show that in the cases where the antenna is an odd number of half-wavelengths the current distribution is the same. When the antenna is an even number of half-wavelengths, the current distribution depends on the feed point. When the antenna is fed so that the direction of the current is reversed in alternate half-wave sections, it is said to be in harmonic operation.

Since we have found that the current distribution in antennas of an odd number of half-wavelengths is the same for center- or end-feeding, Eq. (8.3) may be used for both cases. For antennas with an even number of half-wavelengths, Eq. (8.4) may not be used if the radiator is end-fed. Instead the results of integration show that the electric field strength is given by

$$\varepsilon = \frac{\sin \left(\dfrac{\pi L}{\lambda} \cdot \cos \theta \right)}{\sin \theta} \qquad (8.5)$$

The case of the half-wave antenna is especially interesting in view of the large number of applications. Since we are dealing with an *odd* number of half-wavelengths, Eq. (8.3) may be used. For half-wavelength, $L/\lambda = 1/2$.

$$\varepsilon = \frac{\cos (\pi/2 \cdot \cos \theta)}{\sin \theta} = \frac{\cos (90° \cdot \cos \theta)}{\sin \theta}$$

In general, three-place accuracy, i.e., results obtained with a slide rule, will serve every purpose. When tables are used, round off the values to three decimal places. If a log-log duplex slide rule is available, an appreciable amount of labor can be eliminated by using it. Plotting on polar coordinate paper and tabulation of data should follow the suggestions in Sec. 5.5.

The tabulation of computations and the radiation patterns for a half-wave antenna are given below. Values to 90° only are computed and the pattern is completed from considerations of symmetry.

The radiation pattern in a plane parallel to the antenna and in which the antenna lies has been calculated in the accompanying table and is shown in Fig. 8.9 (a). Notice that the maximum radiation occurs in two directions, extending out at right angles from the center of the antenna. The pattern shown is in one plane but there is an infinite number of planes. The complete figure is one which would be generated if the pattern were revolved about the antenna as an axis, i.e., a solid figure like a doughnut with a small hole.

Although all antenna patterns are three-dimensional, it will be the procedure in these pages to represent only a single cross section in a diagram, usually a plane containing the antenna or a plane perpendicular to its axis. For a horizontal antenna the former may be used to indicate the radiation by a purely horizontal wave. As Fig. 8.9(a) shows, at this angle of elevation there is no radiation along the axis of the antenna. At higher angles, however, this is not true: the field strength along the axis of this radiator becomes increasingly greater. Therefore, in plotting radiation patterns the angle of elevation should be taken into account.

If the radiation is viewed from the *end* of the antenna, a different pattern is obtained as in Fig. 8.9 (*b*). The radiation is equal in all directions in a plane at right angles to the antenna. If the plane passes through the

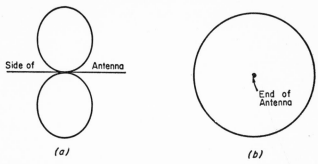

(a)   *(b)*

FIG. 8.9. Half-wave antenna. (*a*) Radiation in a plane parallel to the direction of the antenna and in which the antenna lies. (*b*) Radiation in a plane at right angles to the direction of the antenna and passing through the center of the antenna.

center, the circular pattern will have its greatest radius which is equal to the maximum value of the broadside pattern. For some other plane at right angles to the antenna, but *not* at the center, the pattern will also be a circle but with a smaller radius.

For longer straight antennas the patterns differ markedly. In general, as the wire is lengthened more lobes appear. (This is not the case for the

TABLE 8.2. RADIATION PATTERN

θ	$\cos \theta$	$90° \cdot \cos \theta$	$\cos (90° \cdot \cos \theta)$	$\sin \theta$	ε
0°	1.000	90.0°	0.000	0.000	0.000
10	0.985	88.6	0.0244	0.174	0.141
20	0.940	84.6	0.0940	0.342	0.275
30	0.866	77.9	0.209	0.500	0.418
40	0.766	69.0	0.359	0.643	0.559
50	0.643	57.9	0.532	0.766	0.695
60	0.500	45.0	0.707	0.866	0.815
70	0.342	30.8	0.860	0.940	0.914
80	0.174	15.6	0.963	0.985	0.978
90	0.000	0.0	1.000	1.000	1.000

center-fed antenna of one wavelength.) When a vertical antenna is grounded, as is common practice in AM radio, the radiation may be considered as emanating from the image as well as from the antenna itself. Hence, a grounded quarter-wave vertical antenna has the same idealized radiation pattern as a free-space half-wave antenna with, of course, only the top half of the pattern contributing to actual radiation.

Illustrations of free-space patterns may be obtained from the solutions of problems appended to this chapter. The polar diagram in each case is actually a section of a figure of revolution about the antenna as an axis. The reader should therefore attempt to visualize a radiation pattern as a solid figure in space.

8.6. Radiation Resistance. As previously shown, the velocity of propagation of an electromagnetic wave is less in a material medium than in free space. Although the velocity in air may be considered as practically the same as in free space, the presence of a physical antenna (end effects) in the neighborhood of the earth and other conductors, in addition to the insulating supports, introduces capacitances which effectively diminish the velocity. Since wavelength is proportional to velocity, at a given frequency, the *electrical length* of an antenna is somewhat greater than its physical length. Only in the ideal case of a wire with negligible cross section, isolated in free space, could the two lengths be considered equal. The amount of correction to be applied varies, of course, with the installation. As a working rule, for half-wave antennas only, the physical length is taken to be about 5 per cent less than the corresponding half-wavelength in free space. For best results in practice it is necessary to make the final adjustment by trial and error.

It has been pointed out that an antenna may be considered as a radiating device. Power, energy per unit time, is radiated into space in the form of electromagnetic waves. Hence, there must be a power dissipation which may be expressed in the usual way, $P = I^2R$. If we assume that all of this power appears as electromagnetic radiation, we may divide the power by the square of the current, at the point where it is fed to the antenna, and obtain a fictitious resistance called the *radiation resistance*. That is, because of its radiating properties, the antenna behaves as if it had a resistance of R ohms. Of course, no antenna is without ohmic resistance. Hence the power dissipated is always larger than that accounted for by the radiation resistance. The relative magnitude of the ohmic losses in a given antenna is determined to a great extent by the frequency. At the higher frequencies the resistance losses associated with the antenna are usually negligible in comparison with the radiation resistance and the device is an extremely efficient radiator of electromagnetic energy. At the lower frequencies, where the antenna is electrically short and the ground is an essential component of the radiating system, the ohmic resistance may easily be comparable with the radiation resistance.

A half-wave antenna—sometimes called a half-wave dipole—has a radiation resistance of approximately 73 ohms, if it is located in free space and the measurement is made at the current loop which is at the center of the antenna. Radiation resistances for antennas of various lengths may be found by consulting charts in the handbooks. Since no actual antenna is located in free space, its radiation resistance is affected by the presence of nearby objects, the most important of which is the earth itself.

The reason for the change in radiation resistance with height above ground is as follows: some of the waves radiated by the antenna are reflected from the ground. These reflected waves, in passing the antenna, induce in

Fig. 8.10. Variation in radiation resistance of a half-wave antenna above a perfectly conducting earth.
——————— Horizontal antenna
— — — — Vertical antenna

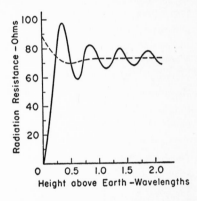

it a current the magnitude and phase of which depend on the distance between antenna and ground. At certain heights, for example, the induced and antenna currents will be in phase, making the total current larger. The result is a series of variations about the free-space value of the radiation resistance. Since the reflected component is the weaker one, the range of the fluctuations decreases as the antenna is elevated above ground. The changes in the radiation resistance of horizontal and vertical half-wave antennas with height above a perfectly conducting ground are shown in Fig. 8.10.

The input impedance of an antenna is an important factor, for maximum power is supplied to the antenna when its impedance is matched to the impedance of the feeder line. Recalling the meaning of impedance, $Z = V/I$, and the standing wave distributions on a half-wave open line, it will be seen that the impedance varies from point to point, being a maximum at the ends and a minimum at the center. In the case of a half-wave antenna, the input impedance when fed at the center is equal to its radiation resistance, that is, about 73 ohms. If the element is fed at the end, where there is a high voltage and a low current, the input impedance is high (about 2500 ohms). Only when a half-wave antenna is fed at its current loop is the input impedance equal to the radiation resistance.

A *folded dipole* is a center-fed half-wave antenna joined to a similar element as shown in Fig. 8.11. The folded dipole behaves as two parallel dipoles, carrying currents in the same phase and in the same direction at a given time. Since the dipoles are in parallel, the voltage distribution is the same in each member. If the two parts are rods or wires of the same diameter, the currents are equal. Now, if each member contributes an electric field $\mathcal{E}$ at a given point in space their resultant must be $2\mathcal{E}$. Since the power is proportional to the *square* of the field strength, this power is *four* times that radiated by an ordinary dipole. For the same current I, the radiation resistance of the folded dipole is $R = 4P/I^2$ or about 300 ohms.

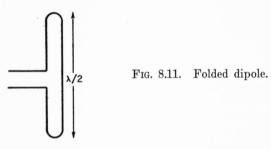

FIG. 8.11.   Folded dipole.

The result may also be obtained through a somewhat different line of reasoning. For a given power the current at the center of a single dipole is I. In the folded dipole the current delivered by the transmission line is the same, but it is equally divided between the two conductors in parallel. Since the resistance is the ratio of the power to the square of the current, the radiation resistance of the folded dipole becomes four times that of the simple half-wave antenna.

If more rods of the same cross section are added in parallel the current divides equally among them. For n components the radiation resistance is increased by a factor of n^2 over the original value of the single dipole. There are also antennas in which the rods are of different diameters. In these instances the current division is of course unequal.

Folded dipoles of the two-rod variety are commonly used as television receiving antennas. They are usually made of $\frac{3}{8}$-in. tubing with a separation of several inches. This type of antenna has several advantages. Its input impedance can be matched to commercial 300-ohm transmission line. Because the center of the closed rod is a voltage node, the supporting mast may be attached to this point without impairing the receptive characteristics of the antenna, thus providing rigidity and lightning protection for the system. In addition, the folded dipole increases the bandwidth of reception, which is of especial importance in television. The underlying principles will be set forth in the next section.

8.7. Bandwidth: The Folded Dipole. As we have seen, an antenna, which for the purpose of discussion we shall assume to be a center-fed dipole, is electrically equivalent to a series circuit (Sec. 8.2). The latter consists of a resistance, an inductance, and a capacitance in series. At the resonant frequency the reactive components cancel each other, the impedance is a minimum, and the current is a maximum. Therefore the antenna operates best at its resonant frequency.

How good the performance will be at other frequencies depends on the Q of the antenna. Since our dipole may be assumed to have a moderate Q, its operation will be satisfactory if the departures from resonance are not too great. However, when the bandwidth requirements become larger, provision must be made whereby the reactance introduced by changing the frequency is compensated by a reactance of opposite sign. In this way the impedance may be kept substantially resistive over a wide band. At the lower frequencies this is accomplished by the addition of coupling circuits with inductors and capacitors of the conventional type. At the higher frequencies the reactive elements may be provided by the antenna itself. An understanding of the fundamental principles involved may be obtained from a study of the folded dipole as a special case.

Now, consider what happens to the current in the case of the resonant dipole, single or folded. At the feed point in the center, current and voltage are in phase. The former travels out to the end over an equivalent path of 90°, is reflected with a phase change of 180°, and returns to the center over an additional distance of 90°—a total phase shift of 360°. The reflected current is thus in phase with the incident current at the feed point, and their resultant is in phase with the voltage. As a consequence, the antenna appears as a resistive load and absorbs all the energy. Equivalent reasoning may be given for either a transmitting or a receiving antenna.

Next, consider the case where the frequency impressed on the antenna is greater than the resonant value. The half-wavelength to which the antenna is cut is greater than a half-wavelength of the new radiation. The reflected current, having traveled over a longer path, in terms of its own wavelength, returns to the feed point with a total phase shift of more than 360°. The resultant current therefore lags the voltage; the antenna appears as a load with resistive and inductive components. Only part of the energy is absorbed.

The same reasoning applied to frequencies below resonance will show that the phase shift is less than 360°, that the current leads the voltage, and that the antenna simulates a load with a capacitive component.

In the case of the folded dipole the departure from pure resistance at off-resonant frequencies is opposed by a compensating factor. From the construction of this antenna it is not difficult to picture it as the equivalent of two shorted stubs attached to the transmission line. At the resonant frequency their length is that of a quarter-wave stub and as such they appear as pure resistances. At a higher frequency (shorter wavelength) the stubs are somewhat longer than a quarter-wavelength. In Fig. 3.11 it is shown that a shorted stub with a length between a quarter- and a half-wave has a capacitive reactance.

Thus when a higher than resonant frequency is impressed on the antenna, its reactive component tends to become inductive, but the effect is reduced by the capacitive reactance of the stub. A similar line of reasoning may be applied when the frequency is below resonance. Although these changes are not entirely compensatory, they have the effect of increasing the bandwidth over which the folded dipole operates satisfactorily.

8.8. Impedance Matching. In communications circuits the power involved is usually relatively small. It is therefore desirable to transfer as much power as possible from the generator to the load, or between different sections of the circuit, for unless a signal of sufficient strength appears at

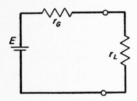

Fig. 8.12. Circuit for maximum power transfer, $r_G = r_L$.

the receiver no information can be communicated. At the outset it should be realized that the problem is one of maximum power transfer, not of efficiency.

The fundamental principle involved can be shown in an elementary way by considering the simple circuit shown in Fig. 8.12. The generator has a constant emf E and a constant internal resistance r_G. The load resistance r_L is variable. The power dissipated will be entirely in the form of heat. The rate at which heat is developed in the load resistor is $P = I^2 r_L$. Since $I = E/(r_G + r_L)$,

$$P = (E^2 r_L)/(r_G + r_L)^2 \qquad (8.6)$$

To find the condition for a maximum it is necessary to differentiate P with respect to r_L and set the derivative equal to zero.

$$\frac{dP}{dr_L} = E^2 \left[\frac{(r_G + r_L)^2 - r_L \cdot 2(r_G + r_L)}{(r_G + r_L)^4} \right] = 0$$

If the numerator in the brackets is equal to zero the equation is satisfied. Expanding and solving

$$r_G{}^2 + 2r_G r_L + r_L{}^2 - 2r_G r_L - 2r_L{}^2 = 0$$

$$r_G = r_L \tag{8.7}$$

Thus for maximum power transfer, the resistance of the generator must be equal to the resistance of the load. We say that the load is *matched* to the generator. Under this condition the efficiency is only 50 per cent: Since the current is the same in all parts of the circuit and since $r_G = r_L$, half of the heat is dissipated in the generator and half in the load.

If the generator and the load have reactive components it can be shown that matching occurs when the two have equal resistances, and reactances which are equal in magnitude and opposite in sign, one being inductive and the other capacitive.

Transmission lines of different characteristic impedances are generally available. Suppose, however, a 600-ohm line is the only one at hand for connection to an end-fed half-wave antenna for which the impedance is about 2500 ohms. As shown immediately above, maximum power is transferred from one section of a circuit to another only if the impedances are matched. Let us recall the properties of a shorted quarter-wave stub (Sec. 3.7). At the open end the impedance is high; at the shorted end, low.

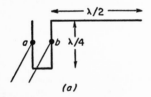 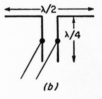

FIG. 8.13. Impedance matching with a quarter-wave stub. (a) Shorted stub. (b) Open stub.

Somewhere between the open and closed ends there will be two points, say a and b, across which the impedance of the stub will be 600 ohms as in Fig. 8.13(a). If, by trial and error or otherwise, this location is found and the transmission line connected there, an impedance match between the line and the antenna will be effected. If the antenna were fed at the center, which is a low impedance point of 73 ohms, a quarter-wave open stub would be used with the 600-ohm line as in Fig. 8.13(b).

Another method by which an impedance match may be made between a transmission line and an antenna also makes use of the properties of a quarter-wave line. Let it be recalled that, for this type of line, a high impedance looks like a low impedance and a low impedance looks like a high impedance. In this problem we shall match a 70-ohm line to a center-fed 300-ohm folded dipole. Let LL' in Fig. 8.14 be a quarter-wave line.

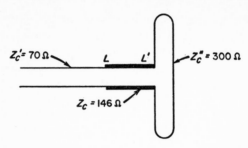

Fig. 8.14. Impedance matching with a quarter-wave section.

It is terminated on the left by a relatively low impedance, 70 ohms; on the right by a relatively high impedance, 300 ohms. Since a quarter-wave line inverts the load, LL' should have a characteristic impedance somewhere between 70 and 300 ohms such that it will be possible to "look right" and "see" 300 or to "look left" and "see" 70 ohms. Under these conditions the antenna and the line will be effectively matched. In Sec. 3.13 this intermediate value is given as the geometric mean of the impedances of the antenna and the line. In the problem under consideration $Z_c = \sqrt{(70 \text{ ohms})(300 \text{ ohms})} = 146$ ohms. For all practical purposes, a quarter-wave section of 150-ohm polyethylene cable, which is available, could be used to effect the match.

In Sec. 3.3 it was explained that transmission lines, since they absorb energy from and later return energy to a circuit, behave analogously to inductors and capacitors and at appropriately high frequencies, where the dimensions are practicable, may be used as such. Furthermore, it may be recalled that a properly designed transformer may be used to transform voltages, currents, or impedances—although the last is not usually discussed in elementary treatments of the subject. In the problem just considered we have an illustration of a *quarter-wave transmission line* used as an *impedance matching transformer*.

The theory of the transformer as an impedance matching device is given as follows. As is well known, the relation between the voltages and the number of turns in the primary and secondary of an ideal transformer is

$$V_s/V_p = n_s/n_p$$

Since there are no power losses the current ratio is the inverse of the turns ratio

$$I_s/I_p = n_p/n_s$$

Using the relation $Z = V/I$ and performing the necessary algebra,

$$Z_s/Z_p = (n_s/n_p)^2 \text{ or } n_s/n_p = \sqrt{Z_s/Z_p} \tag{8.8}$$

As an example, let the output impedance of the final stage in a radio receiver be 12,000 ohms and that of the coil in the loudspeaker be 10 ohms. The amplifier may be matched to the speaker by a transformer having a turns *ratio* of

$$n_s/n_p = \sqrt{10 \text{ ohms}/12{,}000 \text{ ohms}} = 1/38$$

The concept of the geometrical mean has many applications in physics, all of which do not properly come within the province of our subject. One further example, however, will be given. Suppose we wish to install a single antenna which will serve as a compromise for reception from all 12 television channels in the VHF band. Its length should be chosen to be one half-wavelength at the geometrical mean of the limiting frequencies. Substituting values, the mean frequency is

$$f_m = \sqrt{(54 \text{ Mc})\ (216 \text{ Mc})} = 108 \text{ Mc}$$

for which the corresponding length is approximately 4.5 ft. This procedure, however, would be placing a considerable bandwidth demand on a single antenna. Since channels No. 6 and 7 are separated by a gap from 88 to 174 Mc, a better solution of the problem would be the use of two antennas, one cut for the geometric mean of each section of the band. In this case manual or electrical switching would have to be provided.

8.9. Power Density Patterns. It is customary to represent antenna patterns by plotting either the *electric field strength* or the *power density,* at a fixed distance from the antenna, against the angle measured in a specified plane. Although magnetic field strength is seldom used, the resultant pattern has the same configuration as that for the electric field.

The power density pattern may be obtained by squaring the values read from the electric field pattern (Sec. 8.5). If the latter is normalized so that its maximum value is unity, the relation between the two patterns becomes apparent. The power density reaches half of its maximum value at the angles for which the normalized electric field is 0.707, i.e., $1/\sqrt{2}$. The two points on the power density pattern which satisfy this condition are known as the *half-power points.* The *beam angle* is defined as the angle between the half-power points. For a half-wave antenna the beam angle is approximately 78° (Problem 8.13). For specialized antennas used in radar and in radio astronomy the beam angle may be less than one degree. A small beam angle indicates a high concentration of energy in space.

8.10. The Reciprocity Theorem. Certain theorems or principles of a rather general nature have been found very useful in dealing with some of the problems encountered in this book. The superposition principle and the maximum power theorem have already been dealt with in Sec. 5.1 and Sec. 8.8. Another theorem, involving the reciprocal relations between the transmitting and receiving properties of an antenna, is of equal importance. It is called the *reciprocal* or *reciprocity* theorem.

In its general form this theorem is rather abstract and is not confined to the subject of antennas. Fruitful results have been obtained in electrical circuit theory and in acoustics. For illustrative purposes only, let us consider a simple four terminal network with which we are familiar, the T section of Fig. 3.12. A voltage may be applied by connecting a generator to the terminals at the left while a load impedance may be inserted between the terminals at the right. The network itself contains no source of energy and dissipates none, except that absorbed in the resistors. It is therefore a device whereby energy may be converted from one form to another and, as such, it is known as a *transducer*. The reciprocity theorem states that the generator and the load may be interchanged without altering the current in the latter. Loudspeakers and microphones are likewise types of transducers to which the reciprocity principle may be applied. The same device may be used either as a source or as a receiver of sound.

As applied to antennas, the reciprocity theorem may be stated as follows: If an emf is inserted at A in one antenna, thus producing a current at B in a second antenna, the same emf inserted at B in the second antenna will produce the same current at A in the first. When a receiving antenna abstracts energy from a passing wave, its characteristics are the same as when it is used as a transmitter. Under proper matching the input impedance of the transmitter is equal to the internal impedance of the receiver. The radiation pattern is also the same in each case for similarly polarized plane waves. The theorem, therefore, does not hold if the wave is propagated in an ionized medium where a magnetic field exists.

Although identical field patterns are associated with an antenna without regard to its use as a transmitter or a receiver, it must not be assumed that a given antenna is always equally desirable for both purposes. For example, in television a transmitting antenna should radiate omnidirectionally in a horizontal plane; an antenna designed to receive these radiations should be highly directive.

The radiation field is explored with the aid of field-strength measuring apparatus, a description of which may be found in books on electronic measurements. When an antenna is of large dimensions it may be used as a transmitter. The receiving equipment is then carried around the antenna at a fixed distance which, of course, must be large enough to exclude the near zone. Alternatively a portable transmitting device may be employed to direct its radiation toward the fixed structure, which in this case acts as a receiving antenna. For smaller arrays the antenna may be mounted on a rotating table and used either as a transmitter or a receiver. In the latter instance radiation is received from a fixed transmitter called a target antenna which is usually made directive in order to avoid spurious effects produced by reflections from surrounding objects. The method is dictated solely by convenience, for the same pattern is obtained whether the antenna under test is used as a receiver or as a transmitter.

8.11. Effective Length and Aperture of an Antenna. A receiving antenna located in the field of a traveling electromagnetic wave is a collector of energy. The field induces a voltage in the antenna and sets up a current in the circuit. Part of the energy thus abstracted from the wave is absorbed by the antenna and part is reradiated.

An expression for the energy removed from the wave may be derived by employing an artifice similar to the one used in defining the radiation resistance of an antenna. Accordingly, we assign to the antenna a *fictitious* aperture or cross-sectional area over which it can abstract energy from the wave. If we assume that the antenna can absorb all the energy from a plane wave over this area, the power W in watts is expressed by

$$W = PA \qquad (8.9)$$

where P is the Poynting vector, or radiation intensity, in watts per meter^2, and A is the aperture in square meters. Since the ideal case is not realized, we define the ratio of the power W absorbed in the terminating impedance of the antenna to the intensity P of the incident wave as the *effective aperture* A_e, which is often conveniently measured in square wavelengths.

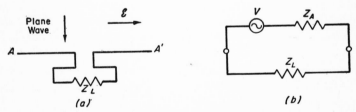

FIG. 8.15. (*a*) Receiving antenna with incident plane wave and terminating impedance. (*b*) The equivalent series circuit.

First consider an antenna AA', having the same polarization as the incident wave and oriented for maximum response, connected to a load impedance Z_L, as indicated in Fig. 8.15(*a*). The system may be represented by the equivalent series circuit of Fig. 8.15(b) in which the antenna is replaced by a generator having an open-circuited voltage V and an internal impedance Z_A. If I is the current in the circuit, the voltage induced by the passing wave is

$$V = I(Z_A + Z_L) \tag{8.10}$$

If we consider the special case where the antenna is matched to the load the analysis will be simplified. The reactive components cancel each other and $R_A = R_L$ (Sec. 8.8). The antenna resistance may be divided into two parts, the ohmic resistance R_0 and the radiation resistance R_R. If the former is negligible, $R_A = R_R$. Thus,

$$V = 2IR_L \tag{8.11}$$

Under these conditions the power delivered to the termination of the antenna is a maximum.

$$W_m = I^2R_L = V^2/4R_L = V^2/4R_R \tag{8.12}$$

This is also the value of the power reradiated by the antenna.

The *maximum* effective aperture, or collecting aperture, may be defined as

$$(A_e)_m = \frac{W_m}{P} = V^2/4PR_R \tag{8.13}$$

The problem now arises as to the magnitude of the voltage V. We cannot compute it by multiplying the electric field strength by the length of the antenna because the voltage is nonuniformly distributed. The result must be obtained by integration after the general method outlined in Sec. 5 of this chapter. Accordingly we define the *effective length* L_e of a receiving antenna such that the product $\mathcal{E}L_e$ is the equivalent open-circuited voltage V across the terminals of the antenna in Fig. 8.15(b). The value of L_e depends on the geometry of the antenna and its current distribution. By the reciprocity theorem the effective length is the same when the antenna is used for transmitting.

As an illustration the maximum effective aperture of a center-fed half-wave antenna will be calculated. When the integration is performed, the effective length turns out to be λ/π. Recalling that $P = \mathcal{E} \times \mathcal{K} = \mathcal{E}^2/Z_c$, where $Z_c = 120\pi = 377$ ohms is the characteristic impedance of free space, and using 73 ohms as the radiation resistance of the dipole, substitution of the appropriate quantities in Eq. (8.13) leads to the result that $(A_e)_m$ for a half-wave antenna is equal to $(30/73\pi)\lambda^2$, or $0.13\lambda^2$.

The physical interpretation of this result is as follows. Since 0.13 is about 1/8, the maximum effective aperture of a half-wave antenna may be approximated by a rectangular area of dimensions $\lambda/2$ by $\lambda/4$. The power absorbed by the terminating resistance is equal to the power abstracted from this area of the incident wavefront.

A similar line of reasoning, often with attendant mathematical difficulties, may be employed to determine the apertures of antennas having various sizes and shapes. If the above restrictions as to orientation, polarization, impedance matching, and negligible ohmic resistance are not satisfied, they must be accounted for in the analysis. The effective aperture, in general, is less than $(A_e)_m$ and is often expressed as a fraction of that quantity. Since the capture area varies as the square of the wavelength, it is clear that the area from which a half-wave antenna can abstract energy diminishes rapidly as the frequency is increased.

8.12. Model Measurements. As we have seen, the free-space radiation pattern of an antenna depends only on the ratio of its physical dimensions to the wavelength (Sec. 8.5). The characteristics of low-frequency systems, such as broadcast tower radiators, may therefore be determined with high-frequency models of smaller dimensions at a considerable saving of time and money. Model measurements in the case of an antenna mounted on an airplane are also useful, not primarily because of size, for the antenna itself may be relatively small. The currents induced in the surface of the plane actually make it a part of the antenna system. To determine empirically the best location for the antenna proper in a series of test flights is inconvenient and expensive. The required data are obtained more easily by mounting the complete model on a tower which is rotated to simulate flight.

The quantities to be scaled are the linear dimensions of the antenna, the frequency, and the conductivity of the antenna metal. If the model is 1/100 of full scale, the frequency must be increased by a factor of 100. For accuracy the conductivity of the metal should also be increased in the same ratio. But if the larger antenna is made of copper, the conductivity of the model can be increased only a small fraction by using silver which is the best of conductors. By assuming that the metal employed is a perfect conductor, reasonably satisfactory measurements have been made on pattern, gain, and impedance.

The principle also applies in the opposite direction. At microwave frequencies it may be more convenient to carry out the preliminary work with antennas of larger dimensions. In this case, scaling of the antenna's conductivity is possible.

PROBLEMS

8.1. A series circuit has a capacitance of 300 micro-microfarads. What inductance will make the circuit resonant at a frequency of 1 Mc?

8.2. Knowing the emf E of the source, the Q of a series resonant circuit may be determined by measuring the voltage V_c across the capacitor at resonance with a voltmeter of negligible power consumption. Show that $V_c/E = Q$. This is the principle of the Q meter.

8.3. Compute the voltage induced in a half-wave antenna by radiation with a frequency of 12 Mc where the electric field strength is 5 mv per meter. The effective length of the antenna is λ/π.

8.4. A thin sheet of conducting material has uniform thickness. Show that the resistance of any *square* area has a constant value.

In the next three problems draw the free-space field strength patterns in a plane parallel to the antenna and in which the antenna lies. Values need be computed for angles 0° to 90° only. The *complete* pattern may then be drawn from symmetry. Show the orientation of the antenna on the graph.

8.5. A full-wave antenna. Show patterns for both center- and end-feeding.

8.6. A one and one-half wave antenna.

8.7. A two full-wave antenna. Show patterns for both center- and end-feeding.

8.8. In Fig. 8.12, $E = 6$ volts and $r_G = 30$ ohms. Plot power developed in the load resistor against the resistance of the load using values of 0, 10, 20, 30, 40, 50, and 60 ohms for the latter. Discuss the results.

8.9. Find the conditions under which the *efficiency* of the circuit in Fig. 8.12 approaches 100 per cent.

8.10. Two antennas matched to their respective transmission lines are operated simultaneously from the same transmitter which is equally distant from the antennas. What will be the effect of introducing a *half-wave* section into one of the lines? Diagram.

8.11. A three-quarter-wave section is used for impedance matching in Fig. 8.14. What is its characteristic impedance? What will be the effect at the receiver?

8.12. A film of transparent material a quarter-wavelength thick is often deposited on the surfaces of lenses and prisms in order to minimize the reflection of light. In principle the problem is equivalent to matching the impedances of the air and the glass with a quarter-wave section of film. Assuming that the refractive indices of the mediums are proportional to their characteristic impedances, find the refractive index and the thickness of a film which eliminates reflection when the wavelength of the light is 6000 A and the index of refraction of the glass is 1.56.

8.13. Plot one lobe of the power density pattern for a half-wave antenna, using data from Sec. 8.5, and *measure* the beam angle *on the graph*.

8.14. Use the T section of Fig. 3.12. Let a generator of emf E be connected to the left-hand terminals and an ammeter of negligible resistance to the right-hand terminals. Show that the current in the meter is given by

$$\frac{4ER_2}{R_1{}^2 + 4R_1R_2}$$

8.15. If the antenna wire does not lie in the direction of the electric field, only the component parallel to the antenna induces a voltage in the dipole. What is the effective length of the antenna in Problem 8.3 when the angle between the field and the antenna is (a) 60°, (b) 90°?

8.16. A center-fed half-wave antenna is cut to cover the complete FM band from 88 to 108 Mc. What is its length? The antenna is matched to a 150-ohm transmission line by inserting a section of another line between the antenna and the 150-ohm line. What is the length and the characteristic impedance of this section?

Chapter 9

DIRECTIONAL ANTENNAS

9.1. Advantages of Directional Antennas. The radiation pattern for a half-wave antenna has been shown to resemble a doughnut with the antenna wire passing through its center. If the dipole is set up *vertically* it will radiate at a given vertical angle equally in all compass directions. In other words, this type of antenna is *omnidirectional* in azimuth. If the dipole is rotated 90° such that it lies in a *horizontal* direction, the maximum radiation takes place in a line perpendicular to the center of the antenna. The pattern clearly has a bidirectional characteristic in the horizontal plane.

In some cases it may be desirable to send out signals of equal strength to all points of the compass. Such a procedure is typical in the upper frequencies of the standard broadcast band and in television. In many cases, however, some sort of *directive* system will be better, for the following reasons.

1. *Population density.* In broadcasting the aim is to reach as many listeners as possible and in an economical manner. Radiations projected into sparsely inhabited regions or over the ocean should be eliminated. It may even be desirable *not* to have some groups as listeners!

2. *Protection of other stations.* The broadcast band for North America, which at present extends from 540 to 1600 kc, is not wide enough to accommodate all stations with separate frequencies of their own. It is necessary therefore to require by law that the radiation from a given station shall not interfere with the radiations of other stations assigned to the same carrier frequency. In technical language these stations must be *protected*. This can be accomplished in most cases only by using some sort of directive antenna system.

3. *Point-to-point operation.* Many radio stations are not designed for broadcasting at all. Their function is the transmission and reception of signals to and from other stations. The requirement of a directional system for such stations is clearly evident. As a consequence of the reciprocal theorem their antennas are equally directive for transmission and reception (Sec. 8.10).

Furthermore, although the subject will not be treated in detail here, it should be pointed out that the *signal-to-noise* ratio tends to improve in a directional system. This ratio is an important factor in all electronic communications systems. The random motions of electrons in the wires and tubes of the receiver constitute a source of noise within the instrument itself. Noise entering the antenna with the signal may be classified as man-made static which occurs in various types of electrical equipment, especially in the ignition systems of automobiles, and as atmospheric disturbances, particularly thunderstorms. The level of these disturbances must be surpassed if the signals are to be recognized. Amplification is not a remedy, for the intensity of the disturbances will, in general, be multiplied by the same factor as the signals themselves. If the noise external to the receiver may be assumed to have an entirely random distribution in space, a minimum amount will be picked up by a highly directive antenna. *Noise* may be used as a general term applied to these disturbances, whatever the type of information conveyed. Specifically, in sound the disturbance is often designated as *noise;* in television, as *snow;* in radar, as *grass.*

4. *Reduction in power needed.* Energy is as much a commodity as any tangible article which is bought and sold. Capital and labor are required for its production. Economic factors operate to keep the cost of these two items as low as possible. Let us suppose that a certain expenditure is required to produce a field adequate for reception at a radius of, say 100 miles from the transmitter. If there are few or no listeners in half of the circle, a system which will direct the energy into the other half of the circle will cut the power requirements by 50 per cent. From another standpoint, the expenditure of the same amount of energy would give the station additional coverage, if this were desirable.

9.2. Basic Field Patterns for Two Antennas. Let us now proceed to examine some of the fundamental procedures by which directivity can be accomplished. We are familiar with the general method of attack, having studied it in connection with ground reflection patterns, which we obtained by using the concept of electrical images (Sec. 4.4 and 5.5). Let us recall that in this procedure the resultant field in a given direction was obtained by computing the phase difference between the antenna and its image. This phase difference was made up of two terms, one determined by the relative phase between the antenna and its image, the other by converting the additional distance traversed by the reflected wave into a phase angle. In what follows immediately we shall be dealing with actual antennas, not with their images, and we shall be able to assign at will the relative phasing between the antennas and their distribution in space. The fundamental principles of interference, however, will be unchanged.

Consider two antennas No. 1 and No. 2 set vertically, as shown in Fig.

9.1, and separated by a distance d. No. 2 lags No. 1 by a phase angle ϕ, the value of which may, of course, include zero. What is the value of the electric field strength at a *distant* point P, which is at a distance r from the midpoint of the line joining the two antennas? Let θ be the angle between this line and r. If the distance r is large compared with d, the *angles* which lines drawn from either of the antennas to the point P make with the line joining the antennas will be substantially θ.

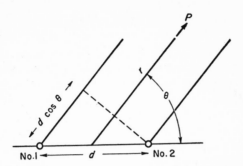

FIG. 9.1. Radiation from two point sources.

The *difference in paths* traversed by the radiations in traveling from the two antennas to the point P, however, is not small compared to the wavelength of the signals. This path difference, as shown in Fig. 9.1, is equal to $d \cdot \cos \theta$. In order to convert this distance into a *phase angle*, we must multiply by $360°$ and divide by the wavelength λ. Thus,

Phase angle resulting from antenna separation $= 360° \, (d/\lambda) \cdot \cos \theta$

From the diagram we see that, so far as this phase angle is concerned, No. 1 lags No. 2. But from the statement originally given, the antennas are fed so that No. 2 lags No. 1 by the angle ϕ. Hence the *net* difference in phase between the radiations from the two antennas is

$$\Delta = \phi - 360° \, (d/\lambda) \cdot \cos \theta \tag{9.1}$$

Let us make the additional assumption that the currents in the two antennas are equal in magnitude. Then the resultant, as was worked out in the case of ground reflection (Sec. 5.5), will be

$$R = 2 \cos (\Delta/2) \tag{9.2}$$

We now proceed to consider some basic types of antenna arrays. Let No. 1 and No. 2 be in phase ($\phi = 0°$) and separated by a half-wavelength. Δ will therefore be $360° \, (1/2) \cdot \cos \theta$ and $R = 2 \cdot \cos (90° \cdot \cos \theta)$. When the curve is plotted the pattern, called a *broadside* array, is obtained (Fig. 9.2).

Like the half-wave dipole it is bidirectional but the lobes are narrower and longer.

The general outline of the pattern may be seen, however, from purely physical considerations. Since both antennas are in phase and their radiations travel equal distances to any point on the perpendicular bisector to the line joining the antennas, the waves will always be in phase on this line and there will be maxima at 90° and 270°. Along the line joining the antennas it will be found that when the wave from No. 1 reaches No. 2 after having traveled a distance of $\lambda/2$ in the time $T/2$ the phase of the latter will have changed by 180° and the two waves, being of equal magnitude, will cancel each other. Similar reasoning may be applied to the wave going from No. 2 to No. 1. Hence there will be nulls at 0° and 180°.

Another basic arrangement is the *end-fire* array (Fig. 9.3). The two antennas are separated by a half-wavelength and fed 180° out of phase, $\Delta = 180° - 360° \ (1/2) \cdot \cos \theta = 180° \ (1 - \cos \theta)$. $R = 2 \cdot \cos [90° \ (1 - \cos \theta)]$.

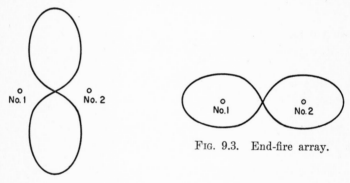

FIG. 9.2. Broadside array.

FIG. 9.3. End-fire array.

Recalling that the two antennas are fed 180° out of phase and using reasoning similar to that employed in the discussion of the broadside array, it may be seen that there is complete annulment along the perpendicular bisector of the line joining the antennas. Along the connecting axis it will be seen that when a wave from No. 1 reaches No. 2 the latter has changed its polarity by 180° such that reinforcement takes place.

A third type is the unidirectional couplet called the *cardioid* (Fig. 9.4). The antennas are separated by a quarter-wavelength and fed such that No. 2 lags No. 1 by 90°. $\Delta = 90° - 360° \ (1/4) \cdot \cos \theta = 90° \ (1 - \cos \theta)$. $R = 2 \cdot \cos [45° \ (1 - \cos \theta)]$. Notice that values of θ between 0° and 180° must be calculated for the cardioid.

The maximum and the null opposite to it along the line connecting the antennas may be accounted for as follows. At a given time let the respective phases of No. 1 and No. 2 be 90° and 0°. When the wave from the former reaches No. 2 the phase of the latter will be 90° and the radiations will be reinforced. For a wave traveling in the opposite direction, the phase of No. 1 will be 180° when the wave from No. 2 reaches its companion and the resultant will be zero.

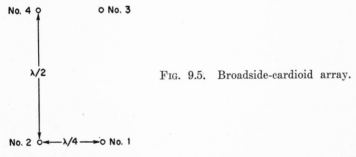

Fig. 9.4. The cardioid.

As a note of caution it should be mentioned that the above patterns are plotted on the assumption that the currents in the elements of an array are mutually independent. But when the antennas are relatively close together they behave like coupled circuits. Each antenna induces a voltage in its neighbor, thereby changing the input impedance and altering the over-all pattern. The deviations are corrected by appropriate modifications in the design of the electrical system.

9.3. Multiplication of Patterns. In order to study methods of handling more complex arrays, let us set up an arrangement of four vertical antennas as shown in Fig. 9.5. Antennas No. 1 and No. 3 are spaced a half-wavelength and are fed in phase. The azimuthal pattern for these two

No. 4 ○   ○ No. 3

λ/2   Fig. 9.5. Broadside-cardioid array.

No. 2 ○←—λ/4—→○ No. 1

elements has a bidirectional broadside characteristic (Fig. 9.2). Antennas No. 2 and No. 4, also spaced a half-wavelength and fed in phase, produce the same pattern as the combination No. 1 and No. 3. If the currents in No. 1 and No. 3 lag the currents in No. 2 and No. 4 by 90° and the spacing between these two *pairs* is a quarter-wavelength, their effective pattern is a cardioid (Fig. 9.4).

For the broadside combination we write $R_1 = 2 \cdot \cos\ (90° \sin\ \theta)$. Here we replace the cosine by the sine for we wish to measure the azimuthal angle with respect to the line joining the antennas and at the same time retain the coordinate system of Sec. 9.2.　For the cardioid array the resultant is the same as given above.

$$R_2 = 2 \cdot \cos \left[45° \left(1 - \cos \theta \right) \right]$$

The equation for the four-element array will be given by the *product* of R_1 and R_2

$$R = 4 \cdot \cos \left(90° \sin \theta \right) \cdot \cos \left[45° \left(1 - \cos \theta \right) \right]$$

from which the complete polar diagram may be plotted.

If, however, the separate patterns for the two combinations are known, there is available another method, known as the *multiplication of patterns*, which has the advantage of enabling one to sketch rapidly, almost by inspection, the patterns of complicated arrays.　The method is illustrated in Fig. 9.6 which, like the other patterns, is not drawn to scale.

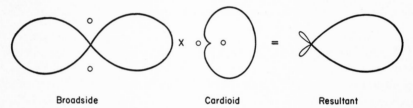

Broadside　　　　　　Cardioid　　　　　　Resultant

Fig. 9.6.　Multiplication of broadside and cardioid patterns.

Notice that the resultant always shows a null in the direction wherever a null appears in one of the factors.　This is a consequence of the fact that if any number is multiplied by zero the product is zero.　In the example the broadside has nulls at 90° and 270°; the cardioid has a single null at 180°.　The relative magnitude of the resultant at 0° is 4, i.e., double the broadside or double the cardioid in that direction.　Minor lobes appear at approximately 135° and 225°.

Logically the resultant should be obtained by including as a factor the horizontal pattern for a single vertical antenna which is the unit composing the array.　Since this pattern is a circle its effect on the magnitude and shape of the array would be equivalent to multiplication by unity and therefore it is not expressed explicitly.

Of course, the pattern for a unit antenna, in general, is not circular. If, for example, the horizontal pattern of two horizontal antennas separated by a half-wavelength and fed in phase is desired, the pattern of the unit must be drawn, as shown in Fig. 9.7.

Although the graphical device is used chiefly for the rapidity by which an approximate pattern may be drawn for a complicated array, the method itself is exact, for a point-by-point multiplication of the separate factors will reproduce the resultant in all its details.

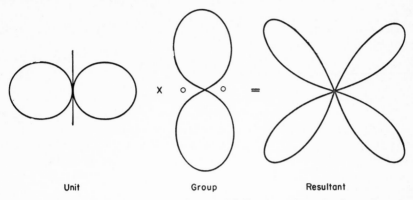

Unit   Group   Resultant

FIG. 9.7. Horizontal pattern obtained by multiplication of two horizontal antennas spaced one half-wavelength and fed in phase.

As another illustration consider a four-element co-linear array of antennas nondirectional in azimuth (Fig. 9.8). All radiate in phase and are separated by a half-wavelength. Since the broadside pattern for two inphase antennas $\lambda/2$ apart is known, it is replaced by a black circle in the diagram, thus forming two groups separated by a wavelength. The pattern for the latter having been obtained from the solution of Problem 9.2, the multiplication may be performed at once.

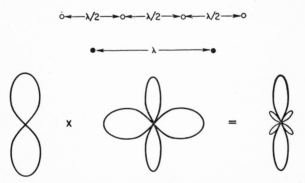

FIG. 9.8. Multiplication of patterns in four-element co-linear array.

If an eight-element uniform co-linear array is set up it may be grouped into two units, each having the resultant pattern of Fig. 9.8 and separated by two wavelengths. The pattern for the latter group being known, the final resultant may be quickly determined. This resultant has a narrower pair of major lobes but it is complicated by the presence of a dozen minor lobes. In uniform co-linear arrays secondary lobes always appear in the patterns.

To obtain a resultant pattern that has only primary lobes a so-called *binomial array* is used. Let the four antennas used in Fig. 9.8 be arranged as in Fig. 9.9. Since the two middle antennas coincide, they are replaced in practice by a single antenna carrying double the current. Clearly the

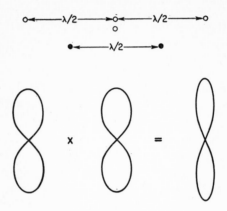

FIG. 9.9.   Binomial array. "Figure eight squared" pattern.

resultant is the product of two figure-eight patterns. Since the factors are identical and with no minor lobes, they do not appear in the resultant. The arrangement derives its name from the current ratios $1:2:1$ which are the same as the binomial coefficients. An extension to higher powers than the square follows from a knowledge of the binomial theorem (see Problem 9.8).

The binomial array is a special case of a large class of linear arrays by means of which patterns can be made to have almost any desired shape. It should be noticed that, in eliminating the minor lobes, the binomial array has increased the beam widths and extended the radiation of the major lobe to all directions except along the line of the array. This is not always satisfactory because the magnitude of the radiation from the binomial array in an unwanted direction may be excessive. The problem is solved by effecting a compromise between the beam width and the magnitude of the minor lobes. By means of a suitable distribution of current supplied to the separate antennas, the beam width is made intermediate between those of the uniform and the binomial arrays, and the magnitude of the minor lobes is reduced to a specified fraction of the principal lobe. The resultant field distribution is called the *optimum* pattern.

Attention should now be called to the statement in Sec. 5.5 regarding the meaning of ground-reflection patterns. They are factors by which the free-space patterns must be multiplied in order to take into account reflection by the earth. As an illustration consider the vertical-plane pattern for a horizontal half-wave antenna at a height of $\lambda/2$ above an ideal ground.

The free-space pattern in this plane is a circle shown above the earth as a broken line in Fig. 9.10; the ground-reflection pattern (Problem 5.5) is drawn as a solid line. Clearly the resultant is identical with the latter. For other planes the resultant may be obtained by multiplication of the appropriate patterns.

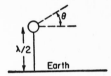

FIG. 9.10. Vertical-plane pattern for the electric field of a half-wave horizontal antenna $\lambda/2$ above an ideal earth.

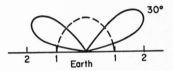

9.4. Gain. The scheme of amplification measurement now in use in acoustics and electrical communications is based upon a logarithmic concept. The fundamental unit is the *bel*, named in honor of the inventor of the telephone and defined as

$$\text{Bels} = \log_{10} P_2/P_1$$

where P_1 is the input and P_2 the output power. If P_2 is greater than P_1 there may be a local energy supply, say a battery, whose output is controlled by a triode to which the input is connected. If P_2 is greater than P_1 the value of the logarithm will be positive. On the other hand, if P_2 is less than P_1, as is the case when energy is dissipated in traversing an actual transmission line, the value of the logarithm will be negative. Thus we may speak of positive and negative gain.

It so happens that the bel, like certain other units which have been derived on a strictly logical basis, e.g., the farad, is inconveniently large. Another unit, one-tenth of the bel, called a *decibel* (*db*), is now in general use. Conveniently the decibel measures the response of the human ear to sounds which have a just perceptible difference in intensity. We may write

$$\text{db} = 10 \log_{10} P_2/P_1 \tag{9.3}$$

The power may be expressed in any suitable unit, provided it is the same for P_1 and P_2.

Let us suppose that the ratio P_2/P_1 is 2. Since $\log_{10} 2 = 0.301$, the gain is approximately $+ 3.0$ db. If the ratio P_2/P_1 is 1/2, $\log_{10} 1/2 = \log_{10} 1 - \log_{10} 2 = 0.0 - 0.301$ and the gain is $- 3.0$ db, i.e., loss or attenuation.

Notice that the decibel relation rates the power output in terms of the power input, but tells nothing about the magnitudes of power involved. That is, for the ratios 1000 watts : 500 watts and 20 milliwatts : 10 milliwatts, the gain is the same, $+ 3.0$ db. This point should be kept clearly in mind, for it is often misunderstood.

The decibel scale of amplification is based upon power ratio but it is often used for voltage or current ratios, with the restriction that the voltages are always measured across and the currents through the same impedance. Since power is proportional to the *square* of either the voltage or the current, we may write

$$\left. \begin{array}{l} db = 20 \log_{10} V_2/V_1 \\ db = 20 \log_{10} I_2/I_1 \end{array} \right\} \tag{9.4}$$

The decibel is sometimes used for measuring *power levels*. Since the unit was established as a *ratio* concept, it will now be necessary to choose an arbitrary reference, or *zero level*, just as in measuring the heights of mountains, sea level is used as a reference plane. No level has been universally accepted as a standard. In communications a power level of 1 milliwatt is widely used; the abbreviation is dbm, meaning decibels above or below 1 milliwatt. In acoustics, where the power involved is very small, the arbitrary zero level of intensity is 10^{-12} watt per meter^2. The base for field strength measurements is often 1 microvolt per meter.

Among the advantages of a directional antenna enumerated in Sec. 9.1 is the reduction in power needed to produce a field adequate for reception at a given distance in a specified direction; or, looking at the advantage from another viewpoint, the expenditure of the same power to produce additional range. The term used to measure this advantage is called *power gain*. It is defined as the ratio of the power that must be radiated by a standard comparison antenna to produce a given signal strength to the power that must be radiated by a directional antenna to produce the same signal strength in the direction of maximum radiation at the same distance from the antenna. The standard is usually an *isotropic* radiator which produces waves of equal intensity in all directions. Although having only a theoretical existence, this concept is a useful one because of its mathematical simplicity. The sharper the principal lobes of a directive antenna, the greater is the gain, for the energy is radiated through the smaller surface area of its solid radiation pattern instead of being dispersed over a sphere. Comparisons may also be made with a half-wave antenna mounted under the same conditions as the directive array, reference being made to the long axis of the dipole's lobe. Using a rather crude analogy, a directive antenna may be compared to an amplifier, although there is no amplifying action in the usual sense of the word.

The pattern of a half-wave antenna, as depicted in Fig. 8.9, shows that the field is a maximum in a plane perpendicular to the axis of the antenna. In comparison with an isotropic radiator, the half-wave antenna may be said to possess a certain *directivity*. The directive properties of an antenna, or an array, may be expressed as a power ratio which we shall call the *directive gain g*. An expression for this quantity, as a function of the wavelength of the radiation and the effective aperture of the antenna, may be derived as follows.

From Eq. (8.2) the field strength for a half-wave antenna is given by

$$\mathcal{E} = \frac{60I_m}{r} \left[\frac{\cos \left(\frac{\pi}{2} \cdot \cos \theta \right)}{\sin \theta} \right] \tag{9.5}$$

The intensity, in watts per square meter, is accordingly

$$\mathbf{P} = \frac{\mathcal{E}^2}{Z_c} = \frac{(60)^2 I_m{}^2}{120\pi r^2} \left[\frac{\cos \left(\frac{\pi}{2} \cdot \cos \theta \right)}{\sin \theta} \right]^2 \tag{9.6}$$

where $Z_c = 120\pi$ ohms, the characteristic impedance of free space.

The rms value of I_m is $I = I_m/\sqrt{2}$, as obtained in Problem 1.10. Hence, the rms current squared is $I_m{}^2/2$. Since the maximum radiation for the half-wave antenna is in the direction for which $\theta = 90°$, the quantity in the brackets becomes unity.

The intensity in the specified direction is therefore

$$\mathbf{P} = 15I_m{}^2/\pi r^2 \tag{9.7}$$

If an isotropic radiator were to produce this value over a spherical surface of radius r, the total power W_0 in watts would be

$$W_0 = \frac{15I_m{}^2}{\pi r^2} \cdot 4\pi r^2 = 60I_m{}^2 \tag{9.8}$$

For the half-wave dipole the power radiated is

$$W = I^2 R_R \tag{9.9}$$

where R_R is the radiation resistance of 73 ohms.

$$W = I_m{}^2 R_R/2 = I_m{}^2 \cdot 73/2 = 36.5I_m{}^2 \tag{9.10}$$

The directive gain for a lossless antenna is defined as

$$g = W_0/W \qquad (9.11)$$

For the half-wave antenna in the direction of maximum radiation, this expression becomes

$$g = 60I_m{}^2/36.5I_m{}^2 = 1.64 \qquad (9.12)$$

The directivity of an antenna is based on the shape of its pattern. If the directivity is increased, the maximum effective aperture is increased proportionately. For antennas which may be assumed to be lossless and matched for maximum power transfer, the directive gain is numerically equal to the directivity.

$$g/g_o = (A_e)_m/(A_e)_{mo} \qquad (9.13)$$

where $(A_e)_m$ is the maximum effective aperture, as defined in Sec. 8.11, and the subscript o refers to an isotropic radiator.

In Sec. 8.11 it was stated that the maximum effective aperture of a half-wave antenna is $(30/73\pi)\lambda^2$. By definition, the directive gain of an isotropic radiator is unity. By substitution in Eq. (9.13),

$$(A_e)_{mo} = \frac{(30/73\pi)\lambda^2}{(60/36.5)} = \frac{\lambda^2}{4\pi} \qquad (9.14)$$

which is the maximum effective aperture of an isotropic source.

If g is the gain for any antenna system, with reference to an isotropic radiator, we may write

$$g = 4\pi(A_e)_m/\lambda^2 \qquad (9.15)$$

The directive gain is expressed in decibels by using the relation

$$G = 10 \log_{10} g \qquad (9.16)$$

We are now in a position to calculate the effectiveness of a transmitting-receiving system separated by a distance r. In the following analysis, the subscripts R and T refer to the receiving and transmitting antennas, respectively.

The total power W_T radiated by the transmitter is equal to that of an isotropic radiator divided by the gain g_T.

$$W_T = 4\pi r^2 \mathbf{P}/g_T \qquad (9.17)$$

where $\mathbf{P}$ is the average intensity of the radiation at the receiver. Substituting the value of g_T in Eq. (9.15), we obtain

$$W_T = \mathbf{P}r^2\lambda^2/(A_e)_{mT} \qquad (9.18)$$

The total power W_R abstracted from the wave by the receiving antenna is

$$W_R = \mathbf{P} \cdot (A_e)_{mR} \qquad (9.19)$$

The ratio of the received to the transmitted power is

$$W_R/W_T = (A_e)_{mT} \cdot (A_e)_{mR}/r^2\lambda^2 \qquad (9.20)$$

Since the effective aperture of each antenna may be expressed in terms of λ^2, it may be seen that for a given distance between transmitter and receiver, the effectiveness of the system varies directly as the square of the wavelength or inversely as the square of the frequency.

9.5. Parasitic Arrays. We have seen how essentially nondirective antennas may be combined to produce a directive array (Sec. 9.2). The fundamental principle involved is that of interference. When the radiations combine in phase, the electric field is strengthened; where the components are out of phase, the field is weakened or becomes zero. But it is unnecessary to excite all the elements. Only one needs to be energized. Its field will excite the other conductors and thereby cause them to radiate. The unenergized antennas are called *parasitics* and the combination, a *parasitic array*. If the proper phase relations exist, the separate fields of the driven and parasitic elements will combine in one direction and tend to cancel each other in the opposite direction, thus producing a directive pattern.

The relative positions and lengths of the parasitics determine the interference effects between their reradiations and the radiation of the driven element. If the parasitic is placed in front of the driven radiator, i.e., the main lobe is on the same side of the driven element as the parasitic, the latter is called a *director;* if the principal lobe and the parasitic are on opposite sides, i.e., behind the driven element, it is called a *reflector* (Fig. 9.11).

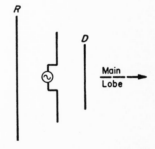

FIG. 9.11.   Parasitic array.   D: director.
R: reflector.

With reference to an optical system, a director may be compared to a lens; a reflector, to a mirror. Strictly speaking, a reflector may be a system of wires, screens, or conducting sheets. In this section the term will be used in its narrow sense as applying only to a single wire.

The physics involved in the operation of a parasitic array with one reflector may be clarified if we first consider the phenomenon as being produced by the radiation field only. When energy is supplied to the dipole, radiation occurs. The parasitic reflector, which for the moment we assume has the same dimensions as the dipole, receives some of this radiation and immediately reradiates part of it with a phase change of 180°. If the elements are separated by a quarter-wavelength, the time required for a wave to travel the distance over and back is one-half period. Meanwhile the polarity of the dipole has reversed and the wave arriving from the reflector is reinforced in the forward direction.

In the rear of the reflector the field consists of two components, one from the dipole and the other from the parasitic. These components are of opposite polarity and in time phase, although not equal in magnitude. Consequently the field is diminished in the backward direction. The system would be roughly equivalent to two half-wave antennas spaced a quarter-wavelength apart and fed with currents 90° out of phase. The space pattern would have a qualitative resemblance to that of the cardioid (Fig. 9.4).

Now, it must be pointed out that the field distribution cannot be considered from the viewpoint of the radiation field alone. In fact, the elements are separated by a distance at which the induction and radiation fields are of the same order of magnitude. The alternating current in the dipole is accompanied by a fluctuating magnetic field which induces a voltage in a conductor—the parasitic—located in the immediate neighborhood. In other words, we have the equivalent of a primary and a secondary circuit. The magnitude of the induced voltage is equal to the rate at which the lines of magnetic induction are cut. So far as the near field is concerned, it is assumed that no time is required for the spreading of the magnetic lines to the space occupied by the reflector. But the density of these lines will clearly diminish as the distance increases and the magnitude of the induced voltage will be lower.

As a consequence the elements function as if they were two coupled circuits, the behavior of which can be described in terms of a *mutual impedance*. This is defined as the ratio of the voltage induced in the reflector to the current in the dipole. (By the reciprocity theorem the same value is obtained if an equal voltage is induced in the dipole by a current in the reflector.) The magnitude and phase angle of the mutual impedance between two antennas depend on their geometry and their separation in space. The impedance of an antenna is therefore not determined solely by its self-impedance but also by the mutual impedance between it and any neighboring antenna.

As a result of combining the contributions of the induction and radiation fields it is found that a spacing of less than a quarter-wavelength is desirable. The distances are greater for a reflector than for a director and usually vary from 0.1 to 0.2λ. The computations involved being rather complex, it is generally recommended that in most cases the adjustments be made by cut-and-try methods.

Often satisfactory results can be obtained by using only a reflector. If it has a low resistance and is properly designed and spaced, the reflector field will be approximately 85 per cent of the driven element field. Hence there will be almost complete cancellation behind the reflector. In the opposite direction, however, the two fields will be in phase. A typical pattern is shown in Fig. 9.12.

When there is a lack of signal response behind the antenna the reception ahead is better and a good *front-to-back ratio* exists. An antenna having a good front-to-back ratio can be used to advantage in television recep-

Fig. 9.12.   A typical radiation pattern from a parasitic array.

tion where a reflection from some object behind the antenna produces a ghost image on the screen. When an antenna with a reflector is used, the ghost signal is reduced to negligible magnitude, because the array will respond only weakly to signals arriving from behind it.

A variety of patterns may be obtained from an array which includes a director and a reflector. The phase relations among the radiations depend on two factors: the electrical length of the parasitics and the spacing of the elements. If the latter is fixed, control of the phase of the parasitics may be accomplished by changing their physical length or inserting tuning circuits between them and the ground. At higher frequencies these tuning reactances may consist of short elements of transmission line which may be varied in length (Sec. 3.3).

The adjustment of phase relations by altering the length of the parasitic is an application of the principle that the current lags in a circuit which is essentially inductive and leads in a circuit which is essentially capacitive. Since, for optimum conditions, the reflector is placed at a distance nearer the driven element than that which would insure correct phasing by spacing alone, the parasitic must be made sufficiently inductive to produce the required lag. This is accomplished by making the reflector *longer* than the driven element. Stated in another way, the resonant frequency of the reflector must be made lower than that of the driven element.

In the case of the director, provision must be made for the necessary lead. The parasitic, in order to be capacitive, is made *shorter* than the driven element. From a different point of view, we may say that the resonant frequency of the director must be higher than that of the energized unit.

Charts are generally available in the literature which show the relative power gain of parasitic arrays for different reflector and director spacings. Generally the spacing of the latter is more critical. The question may now arise as to which would be the more desirable for a two-element array, a reflector or a director. Results from numerous experiments show that the reflector is to be preferred. In view of the necessity for cut-and-try methods in adjusting parasitic arrays, this should be an acceptable answer.

Unfortunately the practical condition for the greatest attenuation of the backward signal is not exactly the same as for maximum gain in the forward direction. However, for certain television or frequency modulation antennas a clear signal is more desirable than extra gain, for amplification can be added in the receiver to produce the requisite intensity. Directivity may also be more important than gain when the array is used for transmitting purposes.

To increase directivity and gain, several parasitic elements may be used. Usually only one reflector is employed because the field behind it is so small that additional reflectors have a negligible effect. A Japanese named Yagi was the first to experiment with an array consisting of a reflector, a driven element, and a number of directors which, in one of his investigations, was as high as twenty. However, the increase in directivity, i.e., the de-

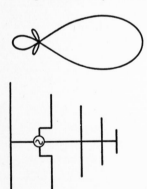

Fig. 9.13. Yagi antenna and representative field pattern. The spacing between the elements is not uniform.

crease of the beam angle, does not change enough after four or five directors have been added to compensate for the awkwardness incident to handling such a large array. An early type of air-borne radar carried a *Yagi antenna* of four parasitic elements, a reflector and three directors, with a beam angle of about 40° (Fig. 9.13). With the increasing use of higher frequencies the cumbersomeness of a Yagi having many directors is no longer a handicap and its employment to obtain all possible gain in critical reception areas may be recommended, provided the range of frequencies to which the antenna will respond satisfactorily is not exceeded.

One great advantage in the use of a parasitic array at shorter wavelengths lies in its flexibility. It may be mounted on a rotatable frame, thus enabling the operator to sit at his transmitter or receiver and by remote control orient the system at will. This arrangement is called a *rotary-beam* antenna.

Usually when specific apparatus is designed to provide certain advantages, other desirable qualities must be compromised. A multiple parasitic array will provide, as we have seen, greater directivity and power gain. Such an array, however, will operate satisfactorily over a smaller range of frequencies. A compromise may be effected by adjusting the director for resonance at the highest frequency and the reflector for resonance at the lowest frequency. Some gain is sacrificed at all frequencies but the gain over the whole band is more nearly uniform.

9.6. Loop Antennas. Another type of directional antenna more frequently used for reception than for transmission is the loop antenna. Consider a loop of wire placed in the path of a vertically polarized radio wave (Fig. 9.14). The dimensions of the loop are small with respect to a

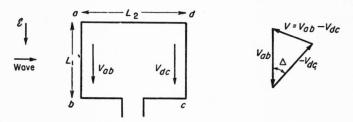

FIG. 9.14. Principle of the loop antenna.

quarter-wavelength such that standing waves are not set up on the wires. A wave of field strength ε induces a voltage $V_{ab} = \varepsilon L_1$ in ab. Somewhat later the wave reaches dc and induces there a voltage of the same magnitude. V_{dc}, however, lags V_{ab} by an angle Δ which is proportional to L_2 in terms of wavelengths.

$$\Delta = 2\pi L_2/\lambda$$

The net voltage induced in the loop is therefore the phasor difference between V_{ab} and V_{dc} which is equal to V. If L_2 is a small fraction of a wavelength Δ will be small, such that its arc may be assumed equal to its chord. We may write

$$V = V_{ab} \cdot \Delta = \varepsilon L_1 \cdot 2\pi L_2/\lambda = 2\pi \varepsilon A/\lambda \qquad (9.21)$$

where $A = L_1L_2$, the area of the loop.   If the loop is wound with n turns of wire, the voltage will be n times as great.

Equation (9.21) was derived on the assumption that the loop is pointed in the same direction in which the wave is traveling.   Let us now turn the loop so that it makes an azimuthal angle θ with the direction of the wave. The distance the wave travels in passing from a to b now becomes $L_2 \cos \theta$ (Fig. 9.15).   The general expression for the induced voltage is

$$V = (2\pi n \mathcal{E} A / \lambda) \cos \theta \qquad (9.22)$$

As may be proved by the methods of the integral calculus, this equation is valid for any shape of plane loop.   In fact, the result is analogous to

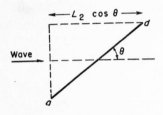

FIG. 9.15.   Loop antenna at azimuthal angle.

that obtained for the emf of a generator when a coil of any shape moves in a magnetic field.

Since the induced voltage is proportional to the cosine of the azimuthal angle the loop antenna has a figure-eight directional pattern (Fig. 9.16).

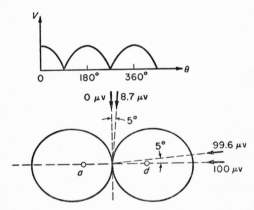

FIG. 9.16.   More accurate bearings may be obtained by using the minimum response of a loop antenna.

It may be seen from physical principles or from mathematics that when the plane of the loop is at right angles to the direction of wave propagation, the received signal is zero.   It is this characteristic which gives the loop its directional properties. From the null point the direction of the transmitted signal may be determined. In practice the null rather than the maximum is used because the former is much more sensitive to changes in voltage (Fig. 9.16).

Notice that at right angles to the plane of the loop the pattern is similar to that of a dipole. Therefore in the plane of the loop the pattern must be a circle. But there is an important difference between the two antennas: the electric and magnetic fields are interchanged. For this reason the loop is sometimes called a *magnetic dipole*.

In addition to serving as an antenna in portable broadcast receivers, the loop is used extensively in navigation. Employing the loop as a radio compass, the navigator of a ship or plane may determine his position from the directions of the signals received from two fixed stations separated by a known distance. This method of navigation should be compared with loran which is described in Sec. 5.3. The loop antenna may also be used as a transmitter of radiation, thus serving as a *radio beacon* to guide aircraft to their destination.

Radio beacons usually operate on frequencies for which there will be a sky wave at night. It will be recalled from Sec. 7.11 that, when vertically polarized waves are propagated to the ionosphere, the plane of polarization may be rotated and the reflected signal may contain a horizontal component. Thus voltages are induced in the horizontal as well as the vertical arms of the loop. The null position is affected and incorrect bearings are obtained.

Fig. 9.17.   Principle of the Adcock antenna.   The terminals TT′ are connected to the receiver.

This so-called *night error* is eliminated by using an *Adcock antenna* which, in its simplest form, consists of two short vertical antennas crossed over at their centers to form the letter *H* (Fig. 9.17). So far as the vertically polarized waves are concerned, the response of this antenna is similar to that of an ordinary loop. The horizontally polarized components, however, induce opposing voltages in the horizontal wires such that they cancel each other and do not produce any signal.

The essentials of a typical radio beacon for the guidance of aircraft are shown in Fig. 9.18. Two loop antennas are set up at right angles to each other. By an appropriate switching arrangement, energy is fed successively to the two antennas causing one loop to transmit the letter A ($\cdot -$) and the other the letter N ($- \cdot$). These signals are interlocked so that the dot of the A completely fills the space between the dot and dash of the N.

The field strength around the two loops, each a figure-eight pattern, is shown in Fig. 9.18. Depending on its direction of flight, a plane will, in general, receive stronger signals from one loop than from the other. When the plane is on-course, along a bisector of an angle between the planes of the loops, the strength of the signals from both antennas is the same. Hence

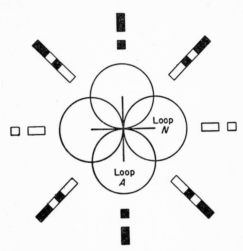

FIG. 9.18.　Principle of the A and N radio beacon.

the two signals merge into a continuous tone. A deviation to the left or right will cause A or N to predominate, for the width of the equisignal zone is only a degree or two.

9.7. Traveling Wave Antennas. The distinction between traveling waves and standing waves has been discussed in Sec. 3.1. Most antennas operate with standing waves of voltage and current; they constitute what are known as resonant antennas. If, like a transmission line, an antenna is terminated by its characteristic impedance there exists only a traveling wave; the antenna is of the nonresonant type.

Perhaps the simplest of the traveling wave antennas is the *Beverage* or *wave* antenna. An explanation can best be given by considering the device as a receiver. By use of the reciprocity theorem (Sec. 8.10) its characteristics as a transmitter may be determined, although as a radiator the losses are generally too great to permit extensive use. In a typical arrangement a straight wire is strung horizontally above the surface of the earth and terminated by its characteristic impedance and the receiver shown in Fig. 9.19.

Whereas the functioning of most antennas is impaired by the finite conductivity of the earth, over an ideal ground the wave antenna would not operate at all. As explained in Sec. 8.4, a vertically polarized ground wave always has a horizontal component, shown as $\mathcal{E}_x$ in Fig. 9.19. The emf's induced by this component produce signals in the receiver. When the

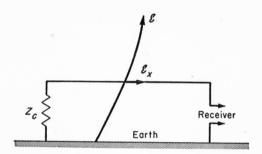

FIG. 9.19. Principle of the Beverage or wave antenna.

wave is traveling toward the receiver all the currents add in phase there because they travel at the same rate as the wave. Waves traveling in the opposite direction are absorbed in the characteristic impedance. Hence the antenna has high directivity which may be further increased by combining two or more wires in an array. If the receiver is replaced by a transmitter radiating vertically polarized waves it is easy to see from the magnitude of $\mathcal{E}_x$ and the dissipation of half the energy in Z_c that the efficiency is very low.

The Beverage antenna is used extensively for long wave reception. A four-element array has been built at Houlton, Maine, for the reception of transatlantic telephone signals at 60 kc. Each antenna, constructed of high-grade telephone wire, is 3.5 miles long with a maximum separation of about 2 miles. Because of poorer conductivity soil in the United States, the wave antenna has been used more successfully here than in England.

Typical of areas in which the use of low frequencies is desirable are: mountainous country where the longer waves bend more readily in passing over the earth's contours and the higher latitudes where the sky wave is unreliable because of magnetic storms. The Beverage antenna which is well adapted for use at the lower frequencies is employed in these areas for both reception and transmission. The problem of transmission is solved by increasing the radiated power and using a highly directive array.

A form of traveling wave antenna used widely for transmission and reception is the *rhombic*. If a rather long parallel-wire transmission line is pulled apart at the center to form a rhombus, one of the fundamental properties of the line, that of equal and opposite magnetic fields at a given point in the neighborhood of the wires, ceases to exist. The transmission line becomes an antenna (Sec. 8.1). A typical rhombic arrangement is shown in Fig. 9.20. The length of the legs and the magnitude of the tilt angle ψ are adjusted for optimum working conditions. To insure the existence of traveling waves the end opposite the input is terminated by the characteristic impedance.

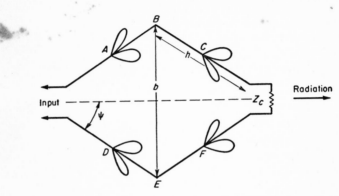

FIG. 9.20. Rhombic antenna. Patterns show directional characteristics of individual wires. For clearness, smaller secondary lobes are omitted.

The correct phasing for maximum radiation in the direction of the long diagonal is obtained as follows: Let A, C, D, and F be the midpoints of the legs. The radiation at C is 180° out of phase with the radiation at A, as may be seen by imagining one-half of the rhombus straightened out. Therefore the direct path from A to C must be a half-wavelength less than the distance ABC in order that the current from A may arrive in correct time phase to produce reinforcement of the radiation. Similar reasoning may be applied at the points D and F. Radiation from the secondary lobes —the smaller are omitted in the figure—is annulled in the direction of the shorter diagonal.

Since the antenna is terminated by its characteristic impedance its operation should be independent of frequency. This is not quite true, for optimum performance is possible at one frequency only. But excellent results may be obtained over a range of, say 4 to 20 Mc. Wideband operation is especially advantageous in point-to-point continuous communication for the antenna can be accommodated to the diurnal changes in frequency required by ionospheric conditions. With proper design the directivity is high with a representative gain of 16 db compared to a half-wave dipole. A single disadvantage, the 50 per cent power loss in the terminating characteristic impedance, is more than compensated for by the advantages. Rhombics may be constructed horizontally or vertically, although the former is more usual. Ground reflection is an important factor, for it determines the angle of tilt of the maximum lobe (Fig. 9.21).

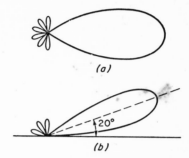

FIG. 9.21. Rhombic antenna. (*a*) Horizontal directive pattern. (*b*) Vertical directive pattern (adapted to reception of descending sky wave).

9.8. The Turnstile Antenna. In compliance with a directive of the Federal Communications Commission, the transmitting antenna of a television station must be horizontally polarized with an approximately circular radiation pattern in the horizontal plane. Were vertical polarization permitted, the vertical half-wave antenna would seem to be an ideal radiating element (Sec. 10.5).

The *turnstile* antenna is illustrative of an array which satisfies the legal requirements. Consider two horizontal half-wave antennas No. 1 and No. 2 placed perpendicular to each other and energized with equal currents 90° out of phase (Fig. 9.22). The patterns for the separate dipoles

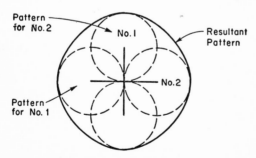

FIG. 9.22. Field pattern of simple turnstile antenna.

are drawn with broken lines and are identical with Fig. 8.9. Since the two antennas are in *time* quadrature the resultant field is given by $\varepsilon = \sqrt{\varepsilon_1^2 + \varepsilon_2^2}$. From calculations or an inspection of the diagram it is seen that the azimuthal field pattern is approximately a circle—the departure is about 5 per cent—which is satisfactory so far as horizontal directivity is concerned.

When the dipole array described above is used, the energy radiated above its horizontal plane is wasted because it will not be picked up by receivers. In the interests of economy the pattern must be modified in order to direct more energy toward the horizon. One method consists in *stacking* additional pairs of dipoles one above the other and feeding the elements of a given column in phase. The resulting vertical broadside directivity is increased but the horizontal pattern is unchanged.

The diagram (Fig. 9.23) shows the stacking of two crossed pairs. The two dipoles No. 1a and No. 1b in a vertical column must be fed in phase; likewise, No. 2a and No. 2b. But the two elements at a given level must be in

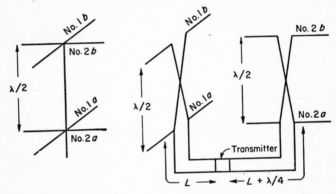

FIG. 9.23. Stacked turnstile antenna, showing the arrangement of the elements and the feeding system.

quadrature. This phase difference is accomplished by making the transmission line to one set of antennas a quarter-wavelength longer than the other. However, since each bay is separated by a half-wavelength, No. 1a and No. 1b, for example, would normally be 180° out of phase. This situation is corrected by transposing the feeders between the bays, the extra 180° shift maintaining the inphase relationship. The vertical directivity may be further improved by increasing the number of bays.

PROBLEMS

9.1. Using the arrangement in Fig. 9.4, plot the azimuthal field pattern for the cardioid. What will be the result if No. 2 *leads* No. 1 by 90°?

9.2. Two antennas are fed in phase and spaced one wavelength apart. Plot the azimuthal field pattern.

9.3. Two antennas are fed in phase and spaced one and one-half wavelengths apart. Plot the azimuthal field pattern.

9.4. Two antennas are spaced $\lambda/3$ apart and have a phase difference of 120°. Plot the azimuthal field pattern.

9.5. Two antennas are spaced $7/8\lambda$ apart and have a phase difference of 90°. Plot the azimuthal field pattern.

9.6. Two antennas are spaced $\lambda/4$ apart and have a phase difference of 90°. The current in one is 0.8 of that in the other. Plot the azimuthal field pattern. NOTE: Since the currents are unequal, Eq. (9.2) cannot be used. A more general expression for the resultant must be obtained.

9.7. Four identical vertical antennas are erected at the corners of a square one-half wavelength long. The two at the left are in phase. The two at the right are also in phase, which differs by 180° from the phase of the left pair. By inspection, sketch the unit and group azimuthal patterns and obtain the resultant by the principle of multiplication of patterns.

9.8. Arrange eight uniform antennas or their equivalent in a binomial array and find their resultant by the principle of multiplication of patterns. Indicate all the steps in the solution.

9.9. Two vertical antennas fed 180° out of phase and spaced one wavelength apart are located on an east-west line. Using physical reasoning, if possible, show that stations directly north, south, east, and west will be protected, and that the maximum field strength is in directions making an angle of 60° with the east-west line. Diagram and explanation.

9.10. Two sounds have intensity levels of 50 and 60 db above the reference level of 10^{-12} watt per meter². If these sounds are produced together, what is (a) the intensity, (b) the intensity level of the resultant sound?

9.11. Find the gain in decibels of: (a) an isotropic radiator, (b) a half-wave antenna.

9.12. What is the effective area of an antenna array operating on a frequency of 300 Mc with a gain of 20 db? Give the result in square wavelengths and square meters.

9.13. Show that the ratio W_R/W_T in Eq. (9.20) may be expressed as $g_T g_R c^2/(4\pi rf)^2$.

9.14. The transmitted power is 1000 watts and the distance between transmitter and receiver is 10,000 meters (about 6 miles). Each antenna is a lossless half-wave dipole at the frequency used and is matched for maximum power. Find the received power when the frequency is (a) 100 Mc, (b) 10,000 Mc.

9.15. Find the radius of a circular loop antenna for which the induced voltage will be the same as for a square loop antenna.

9.16. A square loop antenna of 10 turns and 0.2 meter on a side is oriented for maximum voltage in a 30 Mc field of 4 mv per meter. The characteristic impedance of the antenna is 1000 ohms. (a) What is the voltage developed at the terminals? (b) How much power is generated by the antenna? (c) If the antenna is connected to an amplifier which amplifies the signal to 10 volts across a 1000-ohm coil, what is the gain in decibels?

9.17. What are the dimensions in feet of the stacked turnstile antenna, shown in Fig. 9.23, for television Channel 9?

Chapter 10

WAVE PROPAGATION AND ANTENNAS

10.1. Wave Propagation at Low Frequencies. In the beginning all radio communication was carried on at low frequencies. Long ranges, it was generally believed, could be obtained only by using long wavelengths. Later, as the result of the discovery of ionospheric propagation, the development of radar, and the establishment of television, there was a shift to higher frequencies. Increasing demands by all types of services for available channels could be satisfied only by going into the higher frequency spectrum. As shown by Table 4.1, the number of channels of equal frequency width increases by a factor of ten as we pass from one band to the next higher. From this viewpoint we may say that there is ten million times as much "room" in the EHF spectrum as there is in the VLF band.

Depending principally on the relatively stable surface waves, in contrast with the sky waves, which may be relatively unstable, the lowest frequencies have the advantage of reliability. Furthermore, as indicated by the examples given in Sec. 8.4, the attenuation of the ground wave is much less at lower frequencies. The background noise level, however, is high and varies considerably. At the lower frequencies this factor limits communication more than fading. Thunderstorms are a principal source of static or atmospheric noise. In the tropics where these storms are most prevalent communication at the lower frequencies is extremely unreliable and sky-wave propagation with short wavelengths must be employed. On the other hand, in the polar regions, where magnetic disturbances, which interfere seriously with ionospheric transmission, are the worst, thunderstorms are rare. Hence lower frequencies have been used extensively and successfully in the higher latitudes. Experiments with forward scatter, however, indicate that some of these advantages may not be maintained (Sec. 10.7).

Typical uses of the lower frequencies, which may be said to comprise the VLF, LF, and the lower part of the MF bands, include long-distance point-to-point service, marine communication, and navigational aids. The megawatt transmitter of the United States Navy, located at Jim Creek

Valley in the Cascade Mountains of Washington, operates on very low frequency in order to insure reliable transmission to naval units throughout the world. As a consequence of the diminished skin effect at low frequencies (Sec. 3.3), the signals will penetrate to submarines cruising below the surface of the ocean.

Although every a-c circuit radiates electromagnetic energy, the efficiency is high only when the dimensions of the circuit are comparable to the wavelength of the radiation. A half-wavelength antenna, desirable in view of its resonant properties, involves constructional difficulties at the lower frequencies. A grounded quarter-wave vertical antenna, on account of its image, is effectively a half-wave radiator, as shown in Fig. 10.1, but the

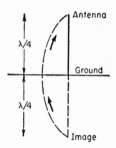

Fig. 10.1.   A grounded quarter-wave vertical antenna is effectively a half-wave radiator.

structure may still be of considerable height. Further difficulty is encountered if more than one antenna is needed for a directive system. Despite the fact that at 300 kc, for example, a quarter-wave antenna is more than 800 ft high, towers with heights of this order of magnitude have been employed where they are technically and economically feasible.

Partial compensation for low efficiency may be obtained by using a transmitter of higher power, but the problem of increasing the effective height remains. If a grounded vertical antenna is less than a quarter-wavelength, the current at the feed point, located at the base of the structure, is diminished. The field strength, which is proportional to the antenna current, is thereby reduced. A longer antenna may be realized by first making the physical height as large as practicable, and then adding some form of top-loading. The latter is exemplified by a horizontal section which is attached to the vertical structure to form an L- or a T-type of antenna (Fig. 10.2). Note that only the radiation from the vertical part of the antenna is effective. The horizontal component is canceled by its image as shown in the diagram.

The current distribution of a vertical grounded antenna, fed at the base, is assumed to be sinusoidal for the purpose of this discussion. (The requisite modification will be introduced in the next section.) The current is therefore zero at the top and a maximum at the base. When the height is a quarter-wavelength, the distribution is along the sine curve AE as shown in Fig. 10.3. If the height is less than $\lambda/4$, say h_1, the current distribution corresponds to that section of the sine curve designated as AD. For example, if h_1 is equivalent to 30 electrical degrees, the current at D is one-half the value at E. If the height of the vertical element is reduced to

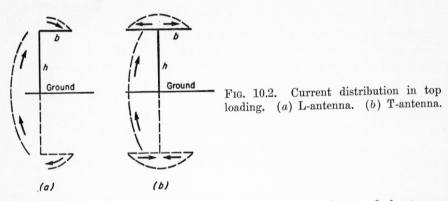

FIG. 10.2.   Current distribution in top loading. (a) L-antenna. (b) T-antenna.

h_2, e.g., 20°, the current curve becomes AC, with a maximum of about one-third the value at E. If, however, top-loading is added to h_2 to make the over-all electrical length equal to h_1, the current distribution along the horizontal component is AB and that along the vertical radiator is BD. Thus a feed-point current equivalent to that of a 30° antenna has been

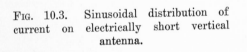

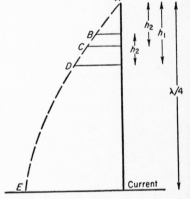

FIG. 10.3.   Sinusoidal distribution of current on electrically short vertical antenna.

obtained without increasing the physical height of the tower. However, it should be noted that, because the charges are differently oriented in the upper section of the antenna when top-loading is substituted for additional vertical height, the current distribution is not exactly the same in both arrangements.

Besides increasing the effective length, top-loading performs an additional function: it decreases the capacitive reactance which is characteristic of an antenna shorter than its resonant length. Thus the ohmic losses in the tuning coil, which is required to furnish a compensating inductive reactance, are reduced. The net effect is an increase in the efficiency of the system.

An electrically short antenna is characterized by low efficiency. The radiating system may conveniently be represented by a series circuit comprising the radiation resistance of the antenna, its ohmic resistance, the equivalent resistance of the insulation losses at the high voltages employed, the resistance of the ground, the capacitive reactance characteristic of a short antenna, and the resistance and inductive reactance of the loading coil. If we assume that the circuit is resonant, the net reactance is zero. When the antenna is very short electrically, the radiation resistance may have the smallest value of all the resistive components in the system. The current being the same in all parts of a series circuit, the radiation efficiency is equivalent to the ratio of the radiation resistance to the total resistance. Accordingly, only a small fraction of the energy fed to the antenna is available for radiation.

Higher efficiencies are obtained by using longer antennas with their correspondingly larger radiation resistances and by minimizing the ohmic losses in the components of the circuit. If mechanical requirements preclude the use of copper throughout, these losses are increased. Systems of buried wires extending radially from the antenna, which are used successfully in the broadcast band to reduce the ground resistance and which will be described in Sec. 10.2, are not always satisfactory at the lower frequencies. The problem may be one of considerable technical difficulty. Sometimes the solution is effected by employing a combination of over-ground and buried wires near the antenna base. A ground system mounted on insulated supports a short distance above the earth is called a *counterpoise.*

In the broadcast range it is standard practice to use steel towers or masts as vertical radiators and, while this technique may be applied in special cases at the lower frequencies, most antennas in this range consist of systems of aerial wires. An installation tends to become an individual problem, for no optimum design, as in the broadcast band, has been found. The use of scale models has proved advantageous from an economic standpoint (Sec. 8.12).

Although vertical polarization is the rule at the lower frequencies, wave antennas which respond to the horizontal component of an originally vertically polarized ground wave are used for directive service within these frequency ranges (Sec. 9.7).

At the lowest frequencies, say below 100 kc, reliable transmission may be obtained by the use of either surface or sky waves. Ground-wave propagation is characterized by relatively low attenuation, especially over sea water, and may be used at all times. The sky wave undergoes very little absorption in the lower layers of the ionosphere at these frequencies, although the signal strength is affected by diurnal and seasonal variations. Best reception is usually obtained at night and in the winter. When the frequency is increased the attenuation of the ground wave and the daytime absorption of the sky wave tend to increase. As the broadcast band is approached the latter is completely absorbed during the day and is useful only at night.

10.2. The Standard Broadcast Band. The frequency range between 540 and 1600 kc is reserved for broadcasting. In this type of service the signal must be relatively free from distortion and fading. These requirements are not necessary in all forms of communication. In many instances the only condition imposed is that the information be received correctly. Ordinary telephone conversation, for example, falls within this category. Continuously reliable transmission at adequate field strength within the broadcast band is achieved by using vertically polarized ground or surface waves. Well designed systems employ one or more steel towers of uniform cross section as the radiating antennas. As a result of Balantine's investigations (1924), methods have been developed whereby field patterns characteristic of a maximum ground wave and a minimum sky wave may be obtained.

We shall first consider a single vertical grounded tower. Its azimuthal field pattern is of course a circle, but as a result of interference between the directly radiated and the ground reflected waves the vertical field distribution undergoes appreciable changes as the height of the antenna is increased. Illustrative patterns, obtained by passing a vertical plane through the axis of the antenna, are shown in Fig. 10.4. A sinusoidal distribution of current in the antenna and a perfectly conducting earth are assumed.

When the height h is very small, the vertical pattern consists of two semicircles (a) which become only slightly flattened as h is increased to $\lambda/4$ (b). Between $h = \lambda/4$ and $h = \lambda/2$, the field strength at low angles is considerably enhanced as indicated by the increased flattening of the lobes in (c).

But an optimum value is soon reached. When $h = 5\lambda/8$, the ground lobe attains its maximum strength, but unfortunately it is accompanied by an appreciable high-angle secondary lobe (d). The presence of the latter is undesirable. Although its daytime energy is absorbed by the ionosphere, its nighttime sky wave may interfere with the local coverage of other stations on the same frequency or with the ground wave from the same station in those regions where both waves are of comparable strength. Above the optimum height an increasing amount of the total energy goes into a high-angle lobe, as illustrated in (e). In practice an antenna height of 0.6λ is a satisfactory compromise for low-angle radiation. The variation in field strength on the horizon for a given power input is shown in Fig. 10.5.

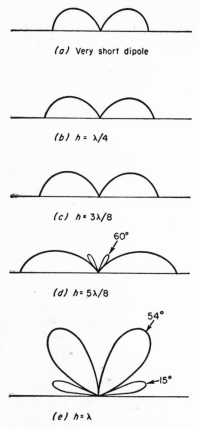

(a) Very short dipole

(b) h = λ/4

(c) h = 3λ/8

(d) h = 5λ/8

(e) h = λ

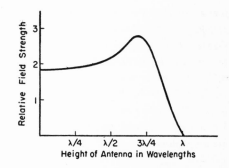

Fig. 10.5. Vertical grounded antenna: Variation in field strength on the horizon for a given power input.

Fig. 10.4. Vertical field intensity patterns for grounded vertical antennas of different heights.

The theoretical optimum height of 5λ/8 for a vertical antenna, by means of which maximum ground-wave field strength is obtained, results from a combination of the free-space and the ground reflection patterns. As in the discussion of low-frequency radiators, a sinusoidal distribution of current, with a value of zero at the top of the antenna, has been assumed (Fig. 10.3).

This is not strictly true. The distribution depends on the change in the cross section of the radiator with its height. A uniform steel tower, used as the antenna directly, substantially fulfills the sinusoidal requirement and it has therefore become the prevalent type in medium-frequency broadcasting. The currents in the guy wires, necessary for the support of the structure, are made small by the insertion of insulators at short distances along the wires.

It will be recalled that when the earth forms a part of the antenna circuit the current is diminished by the resistance of the ground. In order to reduce this loss a *ground system* is employed. At medium frequencies the best arrangement consists of copper wires extending radially from the antenna and buried a short distance below the surface of the earth. If the wires are made a half-wavelength long with an angular separation of 3°, the ground losses are almost entirely eliminated.

A single tower has a uniform field strength in azimuth for the ground wave. The circular pattern is modified however if the electrical characteristics of the soil vary with the direction. At broadcast and lower frequencies the earth is primarily resistive. The conductivity of the soil is a function of the frequency of radiation. As a consequence of the skin effect, currents penetrate deeper into the earth at low frequencies. Variations in the properties of the soil at different depths must be taken into account. The obvious method of analyzing selected samples in the laboratory may not be satisfactory. For dependable results actual field measurements are necessary.

The conductivity of the ground may be determined by measuring the electric field strength at varying distances from the transmitter. If the earth were a perfect conductor, ε would vary inversely as the first power of the distance. The measured values, however, are always less than the theoretical values. The ratio of the actual field strength to that for an ideal ground is calculated and the values are compared with a set of theoretical curves, from which the conductivity may be obtained. The method is especially reliable in the broadcast range where an accurate knowledge of the dielectric properties of the soil and the use of distances involving the curvature of the earth are not required. At higher frequencies the ground must be considered as highly capacitive; at lower frequencies, for which the attenuation of the ground wave is small, measurements must be made at greater distances from the antenna.

The electric field strength of the ground wave, for which typical numerical examples are given in Sec. 8.4, must be sufficiently high to override the background noise. This condition is typical of what is known as the *primary service* area, which may include regions where there is some sky-wave reception at night. In order to eliminate interference, the weaker signals from the latter should be definitely overridden. *Secondary* coverage may be obtained through the sky wave at night. It is of poorer quality, being characterized by variations in intensity and by selective fading.

Since the impedance of an antenna varies with the frequency, the design of a radiator should insure that the departure from resonance is small for the bandwidth employed. For example, a maximum attenuation of 1 db in the side frequencies is usually permitted in broadcasting. At medium frequencies the bandwidth required to transmit the necessary information does not exceed 10 kc, a value which is of the order of 1 per cent of the carrier frequency. The standard method of using radiators of large cross section ordinarily provides an adequate solution to the problem.

The reasons for modifying the horizontal field pattern of a broadcast transmitter and the methods by which it may be accomplished through the employment of an array of antennas have been discussed in Chapter 9. A given pattern is obtained by the straightforward application of the principles of interference. Of course, in the design of a practical antenna array, additional problems of circuitry must be considered.

Since the broadcast spectrum is limited, the need for additional protection has increased as more stations have been put into service. The number of radiators required to provide more complex radiation patterns has therefore increased. To alleviate the situation, certain frequencies are designated as local channels over which the assigned stations are permitted to broadcast only between local sunrise and sunset. In these cases only a single vertical mast is required. Many stations have two radiation patterns: one, a circle, covers the primary service area during the day; the other, a directive configuration, insures protection to other stations on the same frequency at night. A typical illustration is shown in Fig. 10.6.

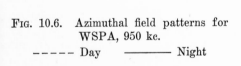

Fig. 10.6. Azimuthal field patterns for WSPA, 950 kc.

– – – – – Day   ———— Night

No particular problems, however, are associated with broadcast receiving antennas. Because of the high sensitivity of most receivers, a single wire a few feet long is usually adequate. Almost any conducting object, such as a metal plate, which has capacitance to ground, may be used. Since reception from all directions is usually desired, an antenna with strongly directive properties should be avoided. Many radio sets, especially those of the battery-operated portable type, have built-in loop antennas. Poor reception from a given direction, in this case, may be easily improved by changing the orientation of the set.

10.3. Propagation at FM and TV Frequencies. At the relatively low frequencies treated in the two preceding sections, both transmitting and receiving antennas were located at the surface of the earth. If, for simplification, we assume there is no sky wave or *refracted* tropospheric wave, propagation may take place by means of surface, direct, or ground-reflected waves (Sec. 4.8). For ground-based antennas the last two components cancel each other and only the surface wave need be considered.

At much higher frequencies, e.g., in frequency modulation and television, neither sky-wave nor surface-wave propagation can be employed, for these radiations are refracted upward by the ionosphere and are rapidly attenuated along the ground. The antennas are usually located an ap-

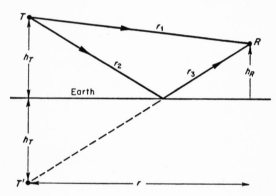

FIG. 10.7. Paths of the direct and ground-reflected waves between transmitting and receiving antennas.

preciable distance, in terms of wavelengths, above the surface of the earth. When the radiators are so elevated, the direct and the ground-reflected waves no longer cancel each other and the resultant field at the receiver is the phasor sum of the two components.

In discussing this type of wave propagation, a number of simplifying assumptions, substantially in agreement with many practical cases, will be made. These assumptions are: (1) Each wave, the direct or the ground reflected, has a field strength that is inversely proportional to its distance from the transmitter. (2) The earth is a flat and perfectly conducting surface. (3) The heights of the antennas are small compared with the distance between them, such that the angle intercepted by the incident ray and the earth will also be small. (On the basis of this assumption, reflection with a phase change of 180° will take place for vertical as well as horizontal polarization.)

The signal propagated from the antenna T is received at the antenna R as the resultant of two waves, the direct wave over the path r_1 and the ground-reflected wave over the path $r_2 + r_3$ (Fig. 10.7). But, at grazing incidence these two paths are practically equal to each other and to the distance r between the antennas. Since there is no loss on reflection, the *magnitudes* of the components of the electric field at R are equal and have a value of ε_1/r, where ε_1 is the strength of the field at unit distance from the transmitter. Although the magnitudes of these fields are the same, they differ in phase. There are two causes. One is a phase change of 180° introduced at the point of reflection. The other is the difference in path, $r_2 + r_3 - r_1$, which is not negligible because in this instance it is compared with the wavelength λ.

From the geometry of the figure,

$$r_1 = \sqrt{r^2 + (h_T - h_R)^2} = r\left[1 + \left(\frac{h_T - h_R}{r}\right)^2\right]^{\frac{1}{2}} \tag{10.1}$$

Since $(h_T - h_R)/r$ is small compared with unity, Eq. (10.1) may be expanded by the binomial theorem and higher order terms neglected. The approximate expression is

$$r_1 \doteq r + \tfrac{1}{2}\left(\frac{h_T - h_R}{r}\right) \tag{10.2}$$

By making use of the image antenna T', the path of the reflected wave is

$$r_2 + r_3 = \sqrt{r^2 + (h_T + h_R)^2} = r\left[1 + \left(\frac{h_T + h_R}{r}\right)^2\right]^{\frac{1}{2}} \tag{10.3}$$

which, using the above approximation, becomes

$$r_2 + r_3 = r + \tfrac{1}{2}\left(\frac{h_T + h_R}{r}\right) \tag{10.4}$$

The path difference is obtained by subtracting Eq. (10.2) from Eq. (10.4)

$$r_2 + r_3 - r_1 = 2h_T h_R/r \tag{10.5}$$

The phase difference is $2\pi/\lambda$ times the path difference which, added to the phase shift of π introduced by reflection, gives for the total phase difference

$$\Delta = \pi + 4\pi h_T h_R/\lambda r \tag{10.6}$$

Since ε_1/r is the strength of the electric field for either wave at a distance r from the transmitter, the resultant field strength ε, by a modification of Eq. (5.2), becomes

$$\varepsilon = 2\varepsilon_1/r \cdot \cos\ (\pi/2 + 2\pi h_T h_R/\lambda r) \tag{10.7}$$

Recalling that $\cos\ (\pi/2 + x) = \sin\ x$, we may write Eq. (10.7) in the form

$$\varepsilon = 2\varepsilon_1/r \cdot \sin\ (2\pi h_T h_R/\lambda r) \tag{10.8}$$

On the basis of our assumption that the distance between the antennas is large compared with their heights, the angle $2\pi h_T h_R/\lambda r$ is small, such that the sine may be expressed by the angle.

$$\varepsilon = \varepsilon_1 \cdot 4\pi h_T h_R/\lambda r^2 \tag{10.9}$$

Subject to the basic assumptions enumerated above, this equation enables us to determine certain important characteristics of wave propagation at television frequencies. In the first place, it turns out that, although the field strengths of the individual waves vary inversely as the distance in free space, the resultant field obtained from their combination varies *inversely as the square* of the distance from the transmitter. A second important characteristic is that the field strength is directly proportional to the height of either the transmitting or the receiving antenna. Finally, the presence of λ in the denominator shows that the field strength is also directly proportional to the frequency.

Other factors being equal, it is seen that the field strength falls off much more rapidly at FM and TV frequencies than it does in the standard broadcast band. Transmitters of high power, directing their energy as much as possible in a horizontal direction, as exemplified in the stacked turnstile array of Sec. 9.8, are employed as compensating factors.

The reason for locating transmitting antennas at a high elevation and for mounting receiving antennas on the roofs of buildings also becomes apparent from the equation. However, when conditions are such that the approximation involving the equality of sine and angle is not valid, raising the height of one of the antennas will cause the resultant field strength to pass through a series of maximum and minimum values. If the distances involved require that the sphericity of the earth be taken into account, the actual heights of the antennas may be transformed into effective heights analogous to the effective radius of the earth in Sec. 4.8.

The increase in field strength which results from an increase in frequency is not so promising a characteristic as it appears to be upon casual examination. In Sec. 8.11, the effective area from which a receiving antenna abstracts energy from a radio wave is shown to be proportional to the square of the wavelength. Hence, the effective field strength is inversely proportional to the frequency. Therefore, the advantage gained by increasing the frequency at the transmitter is counterbalanced by the decrease in voltage at the receiver. A further disadvantage at ultra-high frequencies is the magnitude of diffraction effects: as a consequence of the shorter wavelengths, shadow zones formed by buildings or other obstacles become more prevalent.

10.4. Broadbanding in Television. The necessity for sidebands in the transmission of all forms of information by radio was discussed in Sec. 7.8. The extent of the bandwidth is not a fixed quantity; it depends upon the character of the information to be conveyed. A few examples will be cited. The dot-and-dash signals of the Morse code may be transmitted within a bandwidth of only 100 cycles per sec, using a typically low carrier frequency of 100 kc. In standard broadcasting where a bandwidth of 10 kc is employed and where the range of the entire service is only a little more than a megacycle, a receiving antenna is for all practical purposes matched throughout the band. In television a different situation prevails. The transmission of the radiated signals in a given channel covers a range of 6 Mc. For reception, where more than one channel is included, a wider band is required, although compromises may be made in the quality of the signal.

In Sec. 8.7 the subject of broadbanding was discussed briefly in relation to the folded dipole, with particular reference to its use as a receiving antenna. The topic will be treated here in more detail, special consideration being given to the fundamental principles involved in the design of a transmitting element.

An important factor in the operation of a transmitting antenna is the variation of its impedance with the frequency. In Sec. 3.13 it was shown that the energy supplied to a transmission line, not terminated by its characteristic impedance, is, in general, partly absorbed and partly reflected at the load. If the source is not matched to the line, some of the energy is reflected again. In television both the original and the doubly reflected signals, separated by a short time interval, are radiated from the transmitting antenna. The latter appears on the receiving screen as a ghost. The unwanted image may be eliminated by keeping the SWR on the line as close to unity as is practicable. This can be done by using an antenna the impedance of which is relatively insensitive to changes in frequency.

The desired characteristic may be realized in various ways. Two methods, which fall within the subject matter of this book, will be outlined. The first involves the use of antennas terminated by their characteristic impedance, such that the current distribution is nonresonant. In this category are rhombic antennas, the operation of which is substantially independent of frequency (Sec. 9.7). Such antennas, on account of their directivity, are suitable for reception or point-to-point relay service rather than for omnidirectional broadcasting.

The second method involves the design of a radiator with a low Q. By viewing the folded dipole as two shorted stubs in parallel, it was shown in Sec. 8.7 that the stubs tend to compensate for any reactive component acquired by the dipole when its electrical length changes with the frequency. In that discussion nothing was said about the diameter of the wires which were implicitly assumed to be very thin.

If the diameter of the wire is increased, the Q of the antenna is reduced. When the diameter is large, the length of the lines of flux in the neighborhood of the conductor is greater. A larger wire is accordingly encircled by less flux and thus has a smaller inductance L. For a given current, the energy stored in the magnetic field, $1/2 LI^2$, is directly proportional to the inductance. Since a wire with a large diameter provides more area over which the charge may be distributed, the larger wire has a greater capacitance. For a given charge, the energy stored in the electric field, $1/2 Q^2/C$, is inversely proportional to the capacitance. An increase in the diameter of the wire thus has the effect of reducing both the electric and magnetic fields in the neighborhood of the antenna. Since the ratio of the energy stored to the energy dissipated—in this case, radiated—determines the Q of a circuit, it is clear that making the diameter of the wires larger lowers the Q and consequently increases the bandwidth.

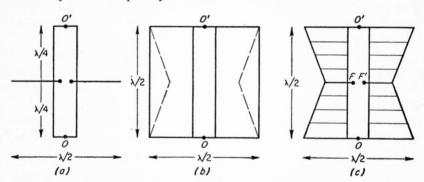

FIG. 10.8. Evolution of the batwing antenna from the basic dipole.

We shall now proceed to apply these principles, showing how the *batwing* antenna, used on a superturnstile radiator, may be evolved from the basic dipole. The latter is adjusted to a length which makes the antenna equivalent to a series circuit resonant at the average frequency of the bandwidth. Two shorted quarter-wave stubs are connected in parallel across the dipole in the manner shown in Fig. 10.8(a). When the applied frequency differs from the resonant frequency of the antenna, the reactance of the stubs tends to balance out the reactive component of the dipole, as previously explained. Electrically only one stub is needed, but the second provides a symmetrical arrangement by means of which the antenna may be supported at two points of zero potential, O and O'.

The rods are now replaced by the conducting sheets shown in Fig. 10.8(b). The dimensions of the antenna become larger, thereby lowering the Q and further increasing the bandwidth. Next, the vertical sheets are shaped as indicated by the broken lines. This change in the geometry alters the current distribution in the sheets, producing a maximum flow at the upper and lower edges. The arrangement may be considered as substantially equivalent to two broadband antennas stacked vertically a half-wavelength apart. These batwing elements are used in stacked crossed pairs to produce the omnidirectional azimuthal pattern and the horizontal directivity of the turnstile array described in Sec. 9.8. The use of metallic sheets is satisfactory from an electrical, but not from a mechanical, standpoint. Since they have considerable wind resistance, they are replaced by a series of horizontal conducting rods as shown in Fig. 10.8(c). The batwing is fed at the points FF' and supported at OO'.

The problem of broadbanding the television receiving antenna has resulted in a large number of apparently quite different arrays. In general they are based on the fundamental principle of increasing the area of the dipole in order to diminish the rate of change of reactance with frequency. The simplest way in which this can be done of course is to take advantage of the wide band characteristics of the folded dipole.

In another arrangement several thin rods are joined together at the terminals of the transmission line. The increased effective area maintains a satisfactory impedance match over a wide range of frequencies. Depending on the number of rods, these modified dipoles are known variously as V, forked, or fan antennas (Fig. 10.9). They may be stacked vertically a half-wavelength apart in order to increase the horizontal gain, or they may be used with reflectors of similar construction to form parasitic arrays.

FIG. 10.9. Forked antenna, side view.

Since the rate of change of reactance is smaller for a conductor of large area, a dipole in which the elements are solid metal sheets should display exceptionally good broadband characteristics. The principle has been applied in the construction of the vane antenna illustrated in Fig. 10.10. The resistance which it offers to the wind is considerable. For this reason it has been used only in the ultra-high frequency band where the dipole has a length of the order of 1 ft.

A television antenna, transmitting or receiving, with the dimensions of a half-wavelength, has the familiar two-lobed horizontal field pattern only at the corresponding channel frequency. At higher frequencies the antenna becomes electrically longer, the pattern in general being characterized by an increase in the number of lobes, as may be verified by the solution of the appropriate problems in Chapter 8.

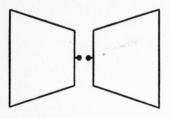

Fɪɢ. 10.10.   Vane antenna, side view.

When an antenna is used for transmitting, its electrical length changes only for frequencies within the operating bandwidth of 6 Mc. In this case, the *relative* change is small and the radiation pattern is not greatly altered. For example, on Channel 2, where the effect is relatively the greatest, the maximum deviation from the average frequency is only about 5 per cent.

The situation as to pattern is different as we pass to receiving antennas. They may be required to respond to more than one station over a wide range of frequencies for which the ratio in the VHF channels alone is four to one. Here a wire cut for a half-wavelength at the lowest frequency (Channel 2) is equivalent to a two-wave antenna at the highest frequency (Channel 13). The shape of the radiation pattern will therefore undergo considerable variation when the receiver is switched from one channel to another. A compromise may be made by employing more than one antenna with the resonant length of each corresponding to the geometric mean of the frequency range for which it is designed (Sec. 8.8). The solution of the problem depends on local conditions. A highly directive pattern is an advantage in that the intensity of unwanted signals, which may be randomly distributed, is minimized. On the other hand, it may be a disadvantage where reception from differently oriented stations is desired.

10.5. The Higher Frequencies. Not far above the standard broadcast band, beginning at, say, 2 Mc, the attenuation of the surface wave is great and reception is limited to short distances. As we have seen, the sky wave may ordinarily be employed for frequencies ranging from about 5 to 30 Mc. In this band lower frequencies and high-angle radiation are used for relatively short distances. For longer ranges the frequency is higher and the propagation angle is lower. Since the fundamental principles of ionospheric propagation have already been discussed, they need not be detailed here.

Typical radiating systems include half-wave dipoles, or directive arrays composed of these elements, and rhombic antennas. The latter are used on many long-distance commercial circuits and their design has therefore received much attention. The V antenna, which may be considered as half of a rhombic, with or without its terminating characteristic impedance, has also been employed in point-to-point service.

In the absence of special transmitting and receiving equipment or of abnormal weather conditions in the troposphere, the range at very high frequencies and upwards is confined substantially to line-of-sight distances. Either vertical or horizontal polarization may be used, but the latter is preferred. In television where an omnidirectional horizontal pattern is required for horizontal polarization, a turnstile arrangement (Sec. 9.8) or a slotted cylinder (Sec. 11.11) may be used.

The decision in favor of horizontal polarization for television in the United States was arbitrary. In some European countries, for example, vertical polarization is used. A single vertical dipole, with its radiation a maximum along the horizontal and none directly upward, appears to be an ideal transmitting antenna for a circular service area. However, in order to obtain high power gain, television radiators are composed of a number of elements. Since an array is required, the elements may be conveniently arranged, by quadrature and by stacking, as in the turnstile radiator, to produce a horizontally polarized field, substantially uniform in azimuth.

Probably the outstanding advantage resulting from horizontal polarization is the freedom from noise in reception. Much of the noise (snow) at television frequencies originates in automobile ignition systems and other electrical equipment. We may assume that these electrical systems generate randomly oriented electromagnetic waves which may be resolved into horizontally and vertically polarized components. The sources being relatively close to the earth, the horizontal components are for all practical purposes shorted out, and only the vertical components have appreciable strength. Since the noise is propagated as a vertically polarized surface wave, it is not detected by a horizontal antenna.

Although special problems arise as the result of significant changes appearing in the behavior of vacuum tubes and transmission lines at the higher frequencies, the shorter wavelengths associated with these frequencies afford substantial advantages in antenna design. Both the antenna and the supporting structure occupy a smaller space. This advantage is particularly desirable where portable or mobile equipment is necessary. Highly directive systems, consisting of arrays of half-wave antennas with the required phasing and spacing, which are impracticable at the lower frequencies, have become standard practice at higher frequencies. The underlying principles of directive arrays have been established in Chapter 9. A further example, called a mattress antenna, which is used extensively in radar, will be described in the next section.

Directivity may also be achieved by using reflectors of various shapes to channel the energy in the required directions. The most widely used reflector is the paraboloid with a half-wave antenna at the focus. As shown in Sec. 4.3, the parallelism of the reflected beam is exact only for a point source. In order to approach this ideal, the aperture of the reflector must be large in terms of wavelengths, a condition which can be realized in practice only at relatively high frequencies. Furthermore, since the energy is propagated through the agency of waves, diffraction, which causes a spreading of the beam, can be minimized, in the case of a reflector of practical dimensions, only by using radiation of relatively short wavelengths.

In the study of transmission lines it was shown that maximum energy is transferred to the load only if it is matched to the line. An antenna may be considered as an intermediary device to provide a better impedance match between the transmission line and free space. In acoustics a horn fulfills a similar function in the transfer of energy between the vibrating source and the region into which the sound is to be propagated.

Likewise an electromagnetic horn is used to ease the transition between the waves on the transmission line (or waveguide) and the waves in space, particularly at the highest frequencies. Typical examples of this class of radiators are the conical and pyramidal horns illustrated in Fig. 10.11.

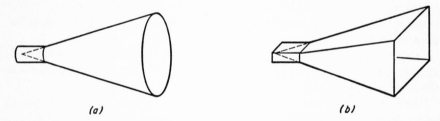

(a)　　　　　　　　　　　　　　　*(b)*

Fig. 10.11. Typical electromagnetic horns. (*a*) Conical horn. (*b*) Pyramidal horn. The radiators are fed by a waveguide.

If the wavelength of the radiation is small in comparison with the aperture of the horn, the energy travels into space as a beam of plane waves. That is, barring absorption, the power per unit area is uniform. When the wave reaches the mouth of the horn all the energy proceeds forward, without reflection, as if no boundary existed or, from another viewpoint, as if it were continuing in a medium of the same characteristic impedance. The fulfillment of this condition depends on the relation between the wavelength of the radiation and the geometry of the horn.

Fig. 10.12 shows a longitudinal section of a horn antenna, having an axial length L, an aperture with a diameter D, and a flare angle ϕ. A wave reaching the aperture along the axis travels a distance L; a wave reaching the aperture by any other path, say along the side, travels a distance L'. The path difference $\Delta = L' - L$. If Δ is small, in terms of wavelengths, the electric field is substantially in phase over the entire aperture and the wavefront may be considered plane. If Δ is not small, the field at the axis will

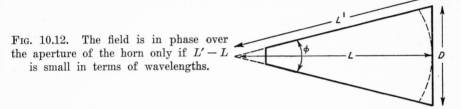

Fig. 10.12. The field is in phase over the aperture of the horn only if $L' - L$ is small in terms of wavelengths.

not be in phase with the field at other points in the plane of the aperture. These variations in the field produce a pattern of less directivity. Uniformity of field at the mouth of the horn can be achieved by making the flare angle small, but the aperture may also be small unless the horn is inconveniently long. A compromise in the form of an optimum pattern, as described in Sec. 9.3, is usually effected. Changes in L, D, or ϕ, for a given free-space wavelength, produce variations in the maxima and minima of the forward signal as a consequence of changing phase relations in the contributions from the individual Huygens' sources on the wavefront in the plane of the aperture (Sec. 5.7).

Other forms of radiators which are used at the higher frequencies include slot antennas, dielectric rods, and lens directors. These will be described in the next chapter.

10.6. Radar. *Radar*, like balun and loran, is a coined word. It means *ra*dio *d*etection *a*nd *r*anging. The principles upon which a radar set operates are essentially the same as those in the apparatus employed by Breit and Tuve to determine the height of the ionosphere (Sec. 7.5). A directive antenna sends out periodically short pulses of radiation, of high frequency and high power. Some of this energy is intercepted by an object, say an airplane or a ship, and is reflected to the source where the received signals are observed on the screen of a cathode-ray oscilloscope. Since the velocity of the radiation is known, the time delay of the returned echo may be used to measure the distance to the target.

Originally designed for military operations, radar also has peacetime uses, principally in navigation. The propagation of radio waves is unaffected by poor visibility or by darkness. Since the reflectivity of different objects varies considerably, the changes in the intensity of the returned signals, as the antenna is swept over a given area, provide information which is equivalent to a map of the region. In meteorology the approach of storms may be determined from the reflection of certain microwave frequencies by clouds.

In accordance with the plan of this book, the discussion on radar will be confined to methods of wave propagation and types of antennas. Information regarding the admittedly important topics of timers, modulators (pulsers), oscillators, receivers, and indicators must therefore be obtained from other sources.

Since highly directive antennas must be used in radar, their dimensions will be practicable only if the frequencies are very high, say from several hundred up to 25,000 Mc. The circuits are designed to transmit and receive energy in the form of short rectangular pulses with relatively long intervals between them. Because of the importance of these pulses in determining the general performance of a radar set, some attention will be given to their characteristics. These are the pulse width or duration, the pulse repetition frequency, i.e., the number of pulses per second, the power level within the pulse (called the peak power), and the average power.

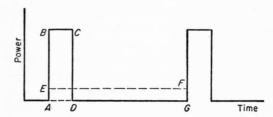

FIG. 10.13. Diagram from which the relationships among the characteristics of radar pulses may be obtained. (Not drawn to scale.)

In Fig. 10.13, the height AB represents the peak power, and the width AD is the duration of the pulse. The interval between the start of successive pulses, i.e., the time of one cycle, is the distance AG. (Since Fig. 10.13 is for illustrative purposes only, it is not drawn to scale.) Now, the energy generated by the transmitter during a single pulse is the product of the peak power and the pulse width, and may be represented by the area of the rectangle $ABCD$. If the transmitter were operating at a constant rate over the entire cycle, the energy equivalent to that contained in the pulse could be represented by the rectangle $AEFG$, where $ABCD = AEFG$. The height AE may then be designated as the average power.

The ratio of the pulse width to the time between the leading edges of successive pulses is called the *duty cycle*. This quantity may be expressed as AD/AG. Since the two rectangles specified above have equal areas, $AD \cdot AB = AG \cdot AE$, and we may write $AD/AG = AE/AB$. Hence, the duty cycle is also the ratio of the average power to the peak power.

In practice the pulse width may vary from 0.1 to 10 microseconds. Although systems have been used in which the pulse repetition frequency was only 60 per sec in order that the timing might be done by the 60-cycle supply, the rate usually extends from several hundred to 10,000 per sec. Peak power is ordinarily measured in hundreds of kilowatts, although values of several megawatts are not unusual.

As a typical example, let the pulse width be 1 microsecond, the pulse repetition frequency, 1000 per sec, and the peak power, 500 kw. From the relations given above, the duty cycle is 0.001 and the average power is only 500 watts. Note that the average power must be relatively small in order to avoid overloading the tubes in the power supply and transmitter. On the other hand, the peak power must be relatively high in order that the signal reflected from the target may be strong enough to be detected by the receiver.

Assuming free-space propagation, the *intensity* of the transmitted signal varies inversely as the square of the distance from the transmitter. The energy intercepted by the target is in turn reflected, part of the radiation returning to the source, where the intensity is again diminished in accordance with the same inverse square relation. Hence, the echo signal has an intensity which varies inversely as the *fourth power* of the range. For example, if the range is to be doubled, the peak power must be increased by a factor of 16.

The maximum range is determined by the pulse repetition rate. If it is too high, there will not be time enough for the echo from the target to return to the receiver before the next pulse is transmitted. In the numerical example given above, the pulses are spaced approximately 1000 microseconds apart. During this time the electromagnetic wave travels, to and from the target, a total distance of 300,000 meters. The maximum range is therefore 150,000 meters or 93 miles.

If the rate is too low, the number of echo pulses received from a given target, as the area is swept over by a rotating antenna, will be too few to produce a signal strong enough to be unambiguously distinguishable from the random noise appearing on the screen of the cathode-ray oscilloscope (see Fig. 7.1). The pulse repetition rate should be adjusted to the rotational speed of the antenna such that a sufficient number of pulses may be returned from a single target in order to build up a readable trace on the indicator. Since the number of reflected pulses required depends on the persistence of the screen, the phosphor chemical used in the cathode-ray tube is also a factor in determining the lowest repetition rate.

The minimum range is determined by the width of the pulse. That is, the pulse must end before the echo is returned to the receiver; otherwise the signal will be masked by the transmitted pulse. For a pulse of 1-microsecond duration, the distance traveled is 300 meters. Therefore the minimum range is 150 meters or about 500 ft. With a 10-microsecond pulse a target could not be detected unless it were nearly a mile away. A radar set with a wide pulse is thus comparable to a farsighted eye.

As previously stated, radar antennas must be highly directive. The array employed in a given radar set is determined by the frequency of the radiation and the type of search for which the system is designed. By taking advantage of the properties of quarter-wavelength transmission lines, the same antenna can be used for both transmission and reception (Sec. 3.7). At the higher frequencies it has become standard practice to use paraboloids or parabolic cylinders, both of which have been described in Sec. 4.3.

Typical of the lower frequencies is an array designated as a billboard or mattress antenna, an example of which is shown in Fig. 10.14. A stacked broadside array, consisting of 16 half-wave antennas spaced a half-wave-

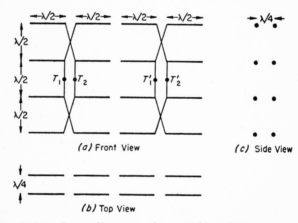

Fig. 10.14. Space diagrams of a curtain or billboard array.

length apart and known as a curtain, is illustrated in the front view section of the diagram. All elements are fed in phase as indicated by the application of inphase voltages at the terminals $T_1 T_2$ and $T_1' T_2'$. Horizontal directivity is obtained from the broadside configuration in the horizontal plane and vertical directivity from the stacking in the vertical plane. The width of the beam can be narrowed, either horizontally or vertically, by increasing the number of individual antennas in the required direction. A similar curtain, as indicated in the top and side views of the diagram, is placed a quarter-wavelength behind the first array. In order to provide a unidirectional pattern, radiation in the backward direction is suppressed by introducing a phase difference of 90° between the currents in the two curtains. The entire array is then located at a designated height above the earth such that the ground reflection factors will concentrate the radiation in the required directions.

The pattern of this array provides a good example of the method of multiplication of patterns. Five factors, all of which have been previously discussed, are required: (1) the free-space pattern of the individual half-wave elements; (2) the directional characteristic of the horizontal broadside array; (3) the directional characteristic corresponding to vertical stacking; (4) the cardioid pattern resulting from the spacing and phasing of the curtains; and (5) the ground reflection factors. The distribution of current in the individual antennas modifies the details of the pattern with respect to the magnitude and angular width of the major and minor lobes. In radar it is important that the latter be eliminated, or at least reduced to insignificant amplitudes.

Instead of a second curtain of antennas, a large reflector, which in practice is a mesh screen or a system of wires parallel to the elements, may be substituted. If the edges of the reflector extend an appreciable distance beyond the array, the screen is essentially an infinite plane and the method of images may be used to determine the pattern. A unidirectional pattern may also be obtained by placing an unenergized curtain less than a quarter-wavelength behind the forward array, after the manner of a parasitic reflector. Mattress antennas used in radar are mounted for rotation in either azimuth or elevation, or both.

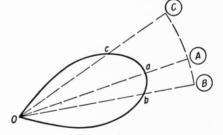

FIG. 10.15. Single-lobe pattern of radar antenna, showing relationship between bearing of target and signal strength.

The simplest form of a rotating antenna for the measurement of azimuth is an array with a single-lobe pattern, which is the same for transmitting and receiving (Fig. 10.15). When the axis of the lobe passes through the target, as at A, the relative signal strength, denoted by the line Oa, is the greatest. If the target were at B or C, and the position of the lobe as shown, the signal strength would be smaller, as indicated by the distances Ob and Oc.

Hence the bearing of the target is determined by observing the angle at which the echo signal is a maximum.

The accuracy with which a target can be located depends on the angular width of the beam. If the signal strength varies slowly, as it does near the axis of the lobe, the echoes received from targets at A or B differ very little in magnitude. By using a narrower beam, the difference in the strength of the signals becomes greater and the direction of the target can be determined more accurately. Furthermore, were there targets at both A and B, their separate existence, which might be masked by a wide-angle lobe, would be revealed by a narrower pattern. The resolving power of an antenna is increased by concentrating the energy in a small beam angle.

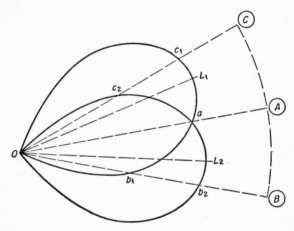

FIG. 10.16. Double-lobe pattern of radar antenna. The bearing of the target is given when the signals received by the two lobes are of equal strength.

The change in signal strength as the antenna is rotated forms the basis of the double-lobe (or lobe-switching) method for improving the accuracy of azimuthal measurements. Two beams are produced by the use of two antennas from which signals are transmitted and received alternately, the oscillation being accomplished by electronic switching. The patterns of the two antennas, with lobe axes in the directions OL_1 and OL_2, are shown in Fig. 10.16. When the target is in the direction indicated by A, echo signals of equal strength, proportional to the line Oa, are produced by each antenna. They are observed on the screen of a cathode-ray oscilloscope as two pips of equal height, say above and below a point corresponding to the range, on a linear time axis. If the target is at B, the strength of the echo signals will be unequal, the larger being proportional to Ob_2, and the smaller to Ob_1. If the target is at C, the signals will also be unequal, but in this instance the larger pip will be on the opposite side of the time axis.

In order to locate completely an object in space, elevation as well as range and azimuth must be known. Since azimuth and elevation involve the measurement of angles only, the same methods in principle should be applicable to both. However, when an antenna is located near the ground, the presence of the earth modifies considerably the directional pattern in a vertical plane. In accordance with the principle of interference, ground reflection factors are introduced whereby the single free-space lobe is broken up into a number of narrower lobes separated by nulls, as explained in Sec. 5.5. Although the concentration of energy in the lobes may produce substantial increases of field strength in certain directions, the presence of the nulls constitutes a series of so-called "blind spots" in which no echoes are received from the target.

From the solutions of ground reflection problems in Chapter 5 we recall that raising the height of the antenna, in terms of wavelengths, increases the number of lobes and decreases the angle between the axis of the lowest lobe and the surface of the earth. This procedure is equivalent to keeping the antenna height constant and increasing the frequency of the radiation. Under these conditions, low flying objects may be more readily detected; and, although the blind spots are more numerous, they are also of shorter duration, thus lessening the interval during which the target is not under surveillance.

10.7. Forward Scatter of Radio Waves. In order to account for unexpected discoveries it has been found necessary throughout the history of radio to modify from time to time the existing theories of electromagnetic wave propagation in the atmosphere. Before 1901, when Marconi first transmitted radio signals across the Atlantic Ocean, it was common scientific opinion that their range would be limited to a distance of a few hundred miles. Later it was believed that the future of radio communication lay in the exploitation of ground-guided waves in the lower frequency bands. Consequently when it became necessary for governments to impose restrictions on the use of the radio spectrum, the higher frequencies fell to the lot of the amateurs who unexpectedly and almost immediately began to establish communication on an intercontinental basis. The investigations which followed led to a useful knowledge of the properties of the ionosphere. For a long time the sky wave has been used extensively for long-distance circuits.

As we have seen, the use of conventional methods of transmission limits communication via the ionosphere to frequencies not much in excess of 30 Mc. Recently, however, there has been discovered a new mode of radio propagation in the ionosphere known as *forward scatter,* or *beyond the horizon,* transmission which is useful in the frequency range from 25 to about 60 Mc and over distances extending from approximately 600 to 1200 miles. The stratum of the ionosphere from which this scattering takes place is the E layer.

Although it is believed that the phenomenon occurs as the result of the existence of small irregularities in the ionization of the E layer, the word *scattering* should be considered in the nature of a technical term. Forward scatter is more closely related to reflection than to the diffusion of radiation in all directions. The energy which reaches the receiver is obtained from a small volume on which the transmitted radiation is incident and at which the receiving antenna is directly pointed.

The geometry of the path in which the scattering occurs is illustrated in Fig. 10.17. Omitting for the present any reference to a mechanism by which the scattering is implemented, we shall assume that a powerful trans-

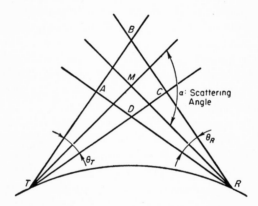

FIG. 10.17.   Diagram showing the geometry of forward scatter.

mitting antenna T is directed towards M, a point in the ionosphere which is midway in the path between T and the receiving antenna R. We shall further assume that all useful energy transmitted and received is confined within the half-power beam width of the antennas as denoted by θ_T and θ_R. The common volume of the two beams $ABCD$ is the region in which the scattering takes place. The *scattering angle* α is defined as the angle between the incident wave and the scattered wave which reaches the receiver.

It is generally supposed that the three ionizing agents, solar radiation, charged particles ejected by the sun, and meteors, which are responsible for the existence of the E layer, are also factors which contribute to ionospheric scattering. Agreement on the specific contribution of each factor has not been reached. The basic point, however, is that scattering occurs as a consequence of fluctuations in refractive index from point to point in the ionized medium. The variation may be compared to the agitation or turbulence which occurs in the air of the troposphere.

Since only a small portion of the transmitted energy reaches the receiver, the signal must be transmitted with very high power and both antennas must have high gain and sharp directivity. In most of the ionospheric experiments rhombic antennas have been employed. Yagis, sometimes in a stacked array, have also been used. Beam angles are less than 10°. Although fading is always present, it is minimized by employing a space diversity system of antennas. Extensive experiments have shown that a usable signal can be received almost continuously.

The limits of long-distance communication should be greatly extended as a result of ionospheric forward scattering, as well as by its tropospheric counterpart which will be described below. New frequency channels in sky-wave communication can be used perhaps up to 100 Mc. However, the signal strength falls off rapidly as the frequency increases. On the other hand, if the frequency is lowered, the scatter reception may be affected by the ordinary reflection or refraction which takes place at the E layer. The maximum range is limited to a single hop from the E layer because not enough energy is available for a second hop. Service of high reliability has been obtained in regions of severe auroral disturbances where conventional ionospheric communication is often badly dissipated.

In Chapter 4 the general features of tropospheric wave propagation were pointed out. Under normal weather conditions the range of VHF and higher frequency signals does not extend much farther than the line-of-sight distance. Ordinary extensions are readily accounted for by diffraction and by the existence of a normal refractive index gradient. Abnormal extensions are shown to be the results of different forms of temperature inversion or the simulated waveguide propagation of the radiation through ducts. As radar sets with higher power and sharper directivity were built, an increasing number of cases, far in excess of those which could be attributed to the meteorological conditions required by the duct theory, were observed. The study of these and other examples of unexpected long ranges eventually led to a theory of tropospheric forward scatter.

Points of similarities as well as points of differences exist between ionospheric and tropospheric scatter. The frequency bands in which they are useful may be considered complementary. The upper limit of the ionospheric scatter may be taken as 60 Mc, while tropospheric scatter appears to be useful from 60 Mc up to more than 10,000 Mc. The lowest range for the ionospheric, about 600 miles, is the highest for the tropospheric propagation. Although both types are attributed to small inhomogeneities in the scattering medium, the tropospheric scattering, in contrast to its ionospheric counterpart, is practically independent of frequency. At wavelengths of the order of a centimeter the tropospheric wave is subject to considerable absorption.

By assuming that the scattering takes place in the troposphere instead of in the ionosphere, Fig. 10.17 also gives a satisfactory idea of the geometry of tropospheric scattering. Although the theory is not complete in all its details, it is generally conceded that this form of scattering has its origin in the turbulence of the troposphere. This turbulence produces small fluctuations in the density of the air which cause its refractive index to vary in the common volume where scattering takes place. As may be recalled from previous discussions, the refractive index of the troposphere depends on its density, temperature, and humidity, whereas that of the ionosphere is a function of the electron density.

At the ultra-high and super-high frequencies involved in tropospheric scatter, the antennas are ordinarily large paraboloids located at a considerable distance above the ground. However, when due allowance is made for variations in the design of transmitters, receivers, and antennas, within the different frequency bands, the general requirements of high transmitting power, sharply directive antennas, and diversity reception apply equally well to ionospheric and tropospheric scatter. The cost of these systems is prohibitive insofar as they may be expected to replace certain line-of-sight systems, but their utilization to increase the path length between radio relay stations is technically feasible.

10.8. Radio Astronomy. Nearly all the evidence regarding the nature of the world external to the earth has been obtained from observations of effects produced by some form of electromagnetic radiation. Clearly, the radiations which supply us with the information must be able to penetrate the atmosphere which, unfortunately, is opaque over most of the spectrum.

There are, however, two important "windows," or regions of transparency. The first is the visible region with a frequency range extending roughly from 400 to 750 mega-megacycles. With this may be included the adjacent and partly transparent ultraviolet and infrared spectra, the three regions being classified together as the optical window. Through this window, with the aid of the telescope, the spectroscope, and the camera, most of our knowledge of the extraterrestrial universe has come. Limitations are imposed by the fact that only matter which is at a relatively high temperature can emit optical radiations.

The second window transmits radiations extending from about 30 to 30,000 Mc, which correspond to radio waves of the highest frequencies. This window is limited on the high-frequency side by absorption in the gases of the atmosphere. The low-frequency limit is determined by the opaqueness of the ionosphere. Since the transparency of the ionized medium is the same whether the radio waves are traveling toward or away from the earth, this lower limit corresponds approximately to the maximum frequency at which conventional sky-wave communication is possible.

Matter at all temperatures emits electromagnetic radiations. Under appropriate conditions of temperature and pressure, certain discrete frequencies which are uniquely characteristic of the atoms composing the substance are observed. For example, the spectroscope shows us the characteristic radiation of sodium in the form of two closely spaced yellow lines which correspond to two nearly equal frequencies of approximately 600 mega-megacycles. There is also a general radiation which is distributed continuously throughout the spectrum as a result of the random motions of the electric charges of which the atoms are composed. Unlike the characteristic spectrum, its general features are common to all radiating matter. If we assume that the substance is a *black body*, i.e., one which is a perfect emitter and a perfect absorber of electromagnetic energy, two important statements may be made with respect to the general radiation. (1) The radiation is proportional to the fourth power of the absolute temperature. (2) The frequency at which the radiation is a maximum is directly proportional to the absolute temperature.

These statements regarding general, or black body, radiation may be applied to the emission of electromagnetic waves by any of the heavenly bodies. For bodies of high temperatures, the magnitude of the radiation is very large and the frequency at which it is a maximum lies within the visible spectrum. The sun, for example, emits both optical and radio waves. In the case of the latter, however, the emission is only a small fraction of the maximum. Nevertheless it can be detected with a very sensitive receiver.

For bodies at low temperature, such as the moon, the maximum corresponds to radio frequencies, and the actual light emitted is negligible. In making observations it has, of course, been necessary to exclude the sunlight reflected from the surface of the moon. This is done, in effect, by making the measurements at microwave frequencies, e.g., in the neighborhood of 24,000 Mc. Thus there are available methods for detecting, by means of radio waves from outer space, the presence of matter at temperatures too low to emit appreciable visible radiation.

Optical astronomers have always been hindered in their observations by clouds of water vapor in the atmosphere and by interstellar dust in outer space. An important difference between light and radio waves is the ability of the latter to penetrate these clouds. When radiation extending over a band of frequencies traverses a cloud of particles, some of the energy is scattered transversely and thus removed from the direct beam. The character of the scattered radiation, i.e., its color in the case of visible light, depends on the relative magnitude of the wavelength and the linear dimensions of the particles. If the size of the particles is not small compared to the wavelength, as may be the case for water droplets and dust in the troposphere, ordinary diffuse reflection takes place and the reflected sunlight appears white. But if the size of the particles is appreciably smaller than the wavelength, the situation is different. Theory and experiment show that, for a given size of the particles, the scattering is inversely proportional to the fourth power of the wavelength.

A simple computation shows that violet light is scattered approximately ten times as much as red light. Accordingly, the shorter wavelengths in sunlight are scattered most by the molecules in the atmosphere, with the result that the color of the sky is predominantly blue. At sunset and sunrise the light traverses a comparatively thick layer of air, which almost completely scatters the shorter waves, and thus the sun appears red.

In the case of radio waves, their wavelength is always much larger than the diameter of the particles which they encounter and, as a consequence of the inverse fourth power relation, they undergo a negligible amount of scattering. Their passage through space being unimpaired either by tropospheric clouds or by interstellar dust, the longer radio waves have the advantage of enabling the radio astronomer to pursue his investigations without regard for the weather and to ''see'' much farther into outer space.

All the advantages, however, do not lie on the side of the radio astronomer. His observations are seriously handicapped by limitations in resolving power. As explained in Sec. 5.10, the resolving power for both optical and radio telescopes is determined by the ratio of the diameter of the objective lens, or the receiving antenna, to the wavelength of the radiation. The largest optical telescope, the Palomar Mountain reflector, has a diameter of 200 in. For an average wavelength of visible light, 5.6×10^{-5} cm, its minimum angle of resolution, on the basis of Rayleigh's criterion, is less than 0.03 sec of arc. As a result of the enormously greater wavelengths used in radio, a parabolic dish of the same diameter, receiving typical 20-cm waves, would have a minimum angle of resolution of approximately 28°. The resolution of a radio antenna is measured in terms of the beam width of a principal lobe at the half-power points (Sec. 8.9).

Although with our present knowledge it is impracticable to build a radio telescope which will match the resolving power of the best optical instruments, there are various ways in which the resolution may be improved. One method which readily suggests itself is the selection of shorter wavelengths for reception because, for a given antenna system, the minimum angle of resolution is proportional to the wavelength of the radiation. The method, however, precludes the possibility of investigating the characteristics of the radiation at lower frequencies where the observed phenomena may not be the same.

A more promising line of endeavor is the construction of larger antennas. By this procedure, as in optics, both the resolution and the energy-gathering power of the instrument are enhanced.

In order to determine accurately the size and position of a relatively small source or the distribution of radio energy over a larger source, that portion of the sky must be scanned with an antenna having a beam width smaller than the angular dimensions of the regions under observation. In other words, the antenna must be highly directive. The fundamental methods by which this directivity may be accomplished are described in Chapter 9. For the most part, there has been little innovation in fundamental design. In addition to parabolic reflectors, broadside arrangements of half-wave dipoles backed by a sheet reflector, end-fire, rhombic, and Yagi arrays have been used.

An interesting form of directional antenna now being used successfully in radio astronomy consists of a wire loosely wound in the form of a helix. The helical antenna is actually a quite general form of antenna with characteristics varying considerably in accordance with its geometry, which includes the diameter and length of the helix, as well as the pitch angle, the number of turns, and their spacing. For example, when the spacing is zero, the pitch angle is also zero, and the helix has the characteristics of a loop; when the diameter is zero, it becomes a linear antenna. But if the circumference is of the order of a wavelength and the spacing is not zero, the field pattern is a narrow lobe directed along the axis of the antenna, similar to an end-fire array. The response is relatively broadband and the radiation is circularly polarized.

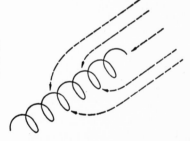

Fig. 10.18.   The helical antenna used in radio astronomy refracts the radiation toward the helix after the manner of a lens.

The effectiveness of this type of helical antenna lies in its focusing action. When a plane radio wave arrives from outer space, that part of the wavefront which is directly incident upon the wire of the helix will proceed with diminished velocity. The other parts, traveling in air at a higher speed, will be refracted toward the helix after the manner of a lens, as shown by the curved rays in Fig. 10.18. In this way the effective area from which the antenna may gather energy is increased. By combining many helices—

approximately a hundred have been used—in the form of a rectangular array, substantial increases in area, as well as in resolving power, have been obtained.

Limitations of size in the construction of radio telescopes of adequate resolving power have led to the use of methods based on the principle of interference. It was pointed out in Sec. 5.2 that the two slits in Young's experiment are analogous to a pair of either transmitting or receiving antennas in radio. With regard to observational technique, however, there is an important difference between the two cases. In optics the interference pattern is determined by observing the variations of intensity in space, that is, locating visually or photographically the positions of maxima and minima. In radio astronomy the direction from which the radiation is proceeding is obtained by observing the variations of intensity with respect to time.

One type of radio interferometer, as the apparatus is called, consists of two identical antennas, spaced a considerable distance apart in terms of wavelength, and connected to a single receiver. The arrangement is thus analogous to Young's experiment, with a large slit separation, in which the fringes are narrow and close together.

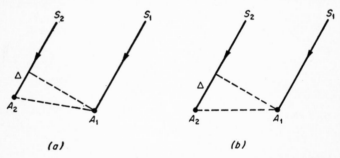

(a)   (b)

Fig. 10.19. Principle of the two-antenna radio interferometer. A_1 and A_2 are the antennas. In (a) the path difference $S_2A_2 - S_1A_1 = n\lambda$. In (b) the rotation of the earth has shifted the positions of the antennas in space such that $S_2A_2 - S_1A_1 = (n + \frac{1}{2})\lambda$.

Plane radio waves from outer space will reach antenna A_1 before they reach A_2, as shown in Fig. 10.19(a), and produce an interference effect, the magnitude of which depends on the phase difference. If the antennas are mounted on an east-west line, the rotation of the earth is continuously changing their position with reference to the stars. Let the second position be indicated by Fig. 10.19(b). The direction of the radio waves is the same but the angle at which they approach the antennas has changed and the phase angle is different. For example, assume that the path difference at

(a) is an integral number of wavelengths, the condition for reinforcement. At (b) let the path difference be increased by a half-wavelength in order to obtain complete annulment. Continued rotation of the earth causes the interferometer to sweep over the sky with a series of fine lobes. A source with an angular diameter which is smaller than the space between the lobes produces in the receiver a signal whose strength varies periodically from zero to twice the value which would be received from a single antenna.

It has been found that some of the radiation appears to be emanating from sources small enough to be called radio stars, none of which, however, seems to coincide with stars observed by optical methods. In practice there is always a background of general noise which remains relatively constant over most observational periods. The radiation from radio stars, as recorded by a moving pen on a rotating drum, therefore appears as a periodically varying trace superimposed on this background.

Although multiple-antenna interferometers with relatively high resolving power have been constructed, the fundamental principles are the same. A coordination of the subject matter may be better achieved by discussing a simple variation of the two-element apparatus. By mounting a single antenna on a cliff overlooking the sea, the principle of electrical images may be used. The arrangement is illustrated in Fig. 10.20, which should be

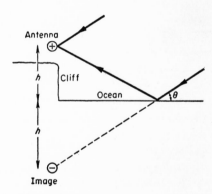

FIG. 10.20. Principle of the cliff interferometer which employs a single antenna and uses the concept of electrical images.

compared with a similar diagram in Fig. 5.6. A parabolic antenna, which is polarized horizontally to take advantage of the nearly ideal reflection coefficient, is directed at a source near the horizon. Interference is produced between the direct waves and those reflected from the ocean. Effectively, the image provides the second antenna, the two being separated by a distance $2h$. The criteria for maxima and minima are, however, different from the two-element interferometer. Since reflection from the water introduces a phase change of 180°, nulls, for example, are observed when the path difference is an integral number of wavelengths.

Radio astronomy may be said to have begun in 1932 when Jansky, while studying atmospheric radio disturbances with a rotating directional antenna, observed signals that seemed to originate in the plane of the Milky Way. Because of the low resolving power of his antenna, he was unable to do more than determine the general direction of the waves. His investigations were extended by other observers, but a general interest in the subject did not develop until after wartime advances in radar had provided the new science with its needed stimulus. During the past decade, research in radio astronomy has been undergoing a tremendous development and radio telescopes have been erected all over the world.

It is possible to enumerate only a few of the results here. With the aid of instruments of ever-increasing resolving power, several thousand "radio stars"—relatively small centers of radio emission—have been catalogued. Radio signals have been received from the sun and moon, and also from the planets Venus and Jupiter. Analysis of radio measurements on the sun has led to information regarding physical conditions in the chromosphere and the corona and may reveal the origin of sunspots. As a result of systematic observations of the reflections of radio waves from meteoric trails, which employ radar and therefore may be carried on independently of the time of day or the condition of the weather, our knowledge of the role which meteors play in the mechanism of the ionosphere will be increased. The discovery of the 21-cm line in the spectrum of hydrogen, to be described in the next section, has opened up the possibility of extending our observable universe beyond the limits imposed by optical methods.

Plans are now in progress for the erection of a national radio observatory near the village of Green Bank in West Virginia. The location, which would never be selected for an optical observatory, is ideal for this purpose. Meteorological surveys show that the region is comparatively free from hurricanes, tornadoes, and excessive snowfall. The flat, shallow valley, surrounded by mountains, insures that the site will be adequately shielded from higher frequency noise created by man-made radio. Although larger instruments have been constructed, it is planned to build first a versatile 140-ft parabolic reflector of high resolving power designed to give results of high precision for wavelengths in the vicinity of 21 cm and to cover the entire celestial hemisphere.

10.9. The 21-cm Hydrogen Line. At this point we must extend our knowledge of the planetary model of the atom which was described in the barest outline in Sec. 7.1. Here we shall be concerned only with the hydrogen atom. Because of the abstractness of the theory of wave mechanics which ultimately replaced the planetary theory, it will be more convenient if we continue to picture this atom as consisting of a positively charged nucleus, called a *proton,* around which a single negative electron can revolve in certain fixed orbits only. In contrast to the so-called classical theory, according to which an accelerated charge has the property of radiation (Sec. 7.11), the electron in the atom does not radiate so long as it remains in one of its allowed stationary orbits. When the electron is found in its most probable, or ground, state, it occupies the orbit nearest the nucleus. In order to shift to an orbit farther removed from the proton, the electron must absorb energy. (In Sec. 7.1 on *Ionization* it was seen that, if the amount of energy absorbed is sufficiently great, the electron may be entirely detached from the atom.) When an electron jumps discontinuously from an outer to an inner orbit, energy in the form of electromagnetic radiation is emitted.

It will be more in keeping with the facts of experiment if we speak of energy levels instead of orbits. When an electron transfers itself from a higher to a lower level, a definite amount of radiant energy is emitted. The magnitude of the energy involved in this transition is $E = hf$ (see Eq. 7.1). Hence the frequency of the radiation is proportional to the difference in the energy levels. Under ordinary experimental conditions, e.g., when hydrogen gas is confined at low pressure in a glass tube and excited by a high voltage, the frequencies involved are within what may broadly be called the optical range, i.e., the visible, ultraviolet, and infrared regions of the spectrum.

In order to understand how the hydrogen atom emits radiation which may be characterized as falling within the radio range, it is necessary to consider an additional property of the constituent charged particles. Both the proton and the electron, like the sun and the earth in an astronomical planetary system, spin on their own axes. Since charged bodies in rotation are accompanied by magnetic fields, the nucleus and the electron may attract or repel each other, depending on the direction of their spins. When the electron is in the ground state a change in the direction of spin of either particle produces an appreciable change in the energy of the system. The internal energy of the atom is higher when both particles rotate in the same sense, i.e., their spin axes are parallel. If the electron reverses its direction of rotation, so that its spin axis is antiparallel to that of the proton, the energy state is lower. Analogous to the jump of an electron from a higher to a lower orbital energy level, a transition from the parallel to the antiparallel state is accompanied by the emission of electromagnetic radiation. From the change in energy, $E = hf$, theory shows that the frequency should be 1420 Mc and the corresponding wavelength, 21 cm.

This radiation was first observed in the laboratory by using the magnetic resonance method. Resonance, as we have learned in the case of antennas, takes place whenever a system having a natural frequency of its own is acted upon by an external agent having the same period of oscillation. The phenomenon may be detected either by an intense response of the system or by a strong reaction on the source producing the vibrations. The experimental method employed with hydrogen is essentially one in which the gas is subjected to a combination of a steady magnetic field and a high-frequency electromagnetic field, the former being applied at right angles to the magnetic component of the latter. At the frequency corresponding to the transition of electrons between their parallel and antiparallel spins the reaction of the microwave circuit is detected by observing the point at which a peak appears within a range of signals swept over by the oscillator.

Prior to the discovery that hydrogen under laboratory conditions emits energy of radio frequency, astronomers had reasoned, as a consequence of their studies of the visible spectrum in regions near very hot stars, that most of the gas particles widely scattered in interstellar space are hydrogen atoms. Because of exceedingly low temperatures these rarefied hydrogen clouds emit no light and therefore cannot be observed with optical telescopes or spectroscopes. The Dutch astronomer van de Hulst, however, made the surprising prediction that, although there is not enough energy in the cold regions of outer space to raise an electron from its ground state to a higher orbital level, sufficient energy does exist to produce radiation with a frequency of 1420 Mc. His predictions were verified when Ewen and Purcell of Harvard in 1951 first detected the radiation in signals originating in a constellation near the center of the Milky Way. Incidentally, it is interesting to note that the discovery came at a time when van de Hulst was visiting Harvard as a guest lecturer.

A parabolic antenna, connected by a waveguide to a sensitive receiver, is used to detect the hydrogen radiation. The rate at which this energy is received by the entire earth does not exceed a few watts. Although the intensity of the radiation is weaker than the circuit noise in the receiver, the apparatus has been made so sensitive that signals of only a small fraction of a per cent of the background value can be distinguished. The intensity of the radiation is recorded on a chart by a moving pen as the frequency to which the receiver is set is slowly varied over the band in the immediate vicinity of 1420 Mc.

Most of the signals received from hydrogen clouds by radio telescopes show peaks on the chart which differ from the value of 1420 Mc as determined by magnetic resonance methods. The discrepancy is to be expected as a consequence of the Doppler effect, whereby the observed frequencies from a radiating source may be displaced a little toward higher or lower values as a result of the motion of the source along the line of observation. The phenomenon is familiar to all in the apparent rise in the pitch of a sound while the source is approaching the observer, and the apparent fall when it is moving away. When the velocity of the hydrogen cloud is small compared to the speed of light, as is the case within our own galaxy, the *change* in frequency $\Delta f = f \cdot v/c$, where v is the velocity of the source. Some astronomers have detected several hydrogen signals of different frequencies along a given line of observation. The data are interpreted as radiations originating in separate clouds, each traveling at a different speed.

As the resolving power of radio telescopes is increased, the distribution of neutral hydrogen gas in interstellar space can be accurately determined, thus adding to our knowledge of the structure of the universe. In contrast to visible light, the 21-cm radiation undergoes very little absorption in its passage through space, thereby making possible the exploration of more remote regions, not only in the Milky Way but also in distant galaxies which are beyond the reach of optical telescopes. With the exception of the 21-cm waves from hydrogen, no other radiations corresponding to a single frequency have been observed in the radio spectrum of outer space. Their existence, however, has been predicted and it seems highly probable that they will eventually be detected through the use of larger antennas and more sensitive receivers.

PROBLEMS

10.1. Verify the statement that there is ten million times as much "room" in the EHF spectrum as there is in the VLF band.

10.2. Assume that a station in the standard broadcast band has a vertical grounded tower of height $5\lambda/8$ and that reception by the surface wave is satisfactory at a distance of 150 miles. Find the height of the ionosphere for which the sky wave might be expected to interfere with the surface wave (see Fig. 10.4). Does this height seem to be a reasonable value?

10.3. Show that the field strength along the horizon is zero for a single vertical grounded tower one wavelength in height, as indicated in Fig. 10.5.

10.4. A station in the standard broadcast band is to be located at the center of a well populated region in the Middle West. Another station due south must be protected. The following types of antennas are proposed: (a) a single vertical mast, (b) two vertical antennas spaced a half-wave apart and fed in phase, (c) two vertical antennas spaced a quarter-wave apart with currents having a phase angle of 90°. Draw the patterns. Give reasons for the most satisfactory choice and for the rejection of the other two.

10.5. A television transmitting antenna, 528 ft high, and a receiving antenna, 52.8 ft high, are separated by a distance of 10 miles. The frequency is 70 Mc (approximately Channel 4). If the height of the receiving antenna is increased by 50 per cent, by what percentage is the resultant field strength at the receiver changed? Assume that the earth is a perfect reflector.

10.6. Solve Problem 10.5, using a frequency of 490 Mc (approximately Channel 17). Compare and discuss the results.

10.7. When a television antenna was placed at a given height, reception was acceptable. When the height was increased a short distance, reception became poor, but an additional increase in height produced better quality reception. Explain.

10.8. The transmission line of a television station is not matched to either the source or the antenna, so that both the original and the doubly reflected signals are radiated. If the line is 500 ft long and has a velocity factor of 0.93, what will be the displacement of the ghost image on a receiving screen 20 in. wide?

10.9. For the optimum performance of a conical horn, $\Delta = L' - L = 0.3\lambda$ and $\phi = 50°$ (see Fig. 10.12). For 10-cm waves find (a) the axial length L, (b) the diameter D of the aperture, in centimeters and in wavelengths.

10.10. The effective aperture area of a conical horn having optimum gain is about 50 per cent of its actual area. Considering the horn in Problem 10.9, find (a) the power gain, (b) the gain in decibels, with respect to an isotropic radiator.

10.11. Using the pulse method of radar, radio signals have been reflected from the moon. If the echo is received 2.56 sec after transmission, what is the distance between the earth and the moon?

10.12. A lightweight airborne radar has a peak power of 8 kw at 800 pulses per sec. The pulse width is 0.8 microsecond. Find: (a) the duty cycle, (b) the average power, (c) the maximum range, (d) the minimum range.

10.13. The frequency of the radiation resulting from the change in the spin of the hydrogen electron, as measured by the resonance method, is 1420.4 Mc. The first signal observed with a radio telescope had a frequency 170 kc higher. With what *velocity* was the hydrogen cloud moving with respect to the earth?

Chapter 11

WAVEGUIDES

11.1. Reasons for the Use of Waveguides. In our discussions of transmission lines and antennas we have constantly emphasized the desirability of assuming that the propagation of electromagnetic energy takes place in the space surrounding the conductors. The energy is transferred, not as the result of the motion of electrons within the wires, but as periodic disturbances in a region which has the general properties of a dielectric. In a broad sense, the energy is either *guided* or *unguided*. An open-wire transmission line or a coaxial cable, for example, guides the energy from an oscillator to an antenna, from which the radiation proceeds unguided into space.

The distinction between the two types of propagation must be somewhat arbitrary. In general, there is a guiding action when the wave is incident on a boundary between two mediums of different refractive indices. The change may be abrupt or it may take place gradually. When a radio wave is propagated by multiple-hop transmission between the earth and the ionosphere, the refractive index undergoes a sharp change at the surface of the earth, whereas the transition in the ionized layer takes place more slowly. Wave propagation in an atmospheric duct may be considered as a phenomenon resulting from changes in the refractive index of the air. While the earth and the ionosphere, and the duct, may serve to guide the waves, the radiations so directed are not ordinarily classified as guided.

Guided waves are usually specified as those which are limited in their extent by a particular experimental arrangement. In general, this consists of making use of the boundary between a conductor and an insulator or the boundary between two insulators having appreciably different refractive indices. Examples of the former have been considered in the discussions dealing with the properties of open-wire transmission lines and coaxial cables. Waves may also be guided in hollow metallic tubes, which in practice are of rectangular or circular cross section and, to a more limited extent, in dielectric rods. Tubes and rods, so used, are known as *waveguides*, in

217

the strict sense of the term, and will form the principal topic of discussion in this chapter.

Waveguides have a number of advantages when compared with other types of transmission lines. At all frequencies the heat loss in the conductors is a source of attenuation. The magnitude of the skin effect at high frequencies restricts the current effectively to a narrow layer at the surface of the conductors. As the frequency increases, this layer becomes narrower, its resistance accordingly increases, and the heat loss becomes greater. Since the resistance of the layer, for a given frequency, is inversely proportional to the radius of the conductor, the heat loss in an open-wire line exceeds that in a coaxial cable of comparable dimensions. In the latter, the greater loss takes place at the inner conductor because it has a much smaller radius than the outer metallic sheath. Other factors being equal, the hollow waveguide, having a single conductor, has a smaller heat loss than that of either an open-wire or a coaxial line.

No substance is a perfect insulator. The dielectric loss in air is negligible, but in solid insulators it may be considerable, particularly at the higher frequencies. Open-wire lines and hollow waveguides, employing air as the insulating medium, are consequently superior to cables in that they have practically no dielectric loss.

In all forms of transmission lines it is desirable to keep the radiation loss at a minimum. For this reason the coaxial cable and the waveguide have, for the most part, replaced the open-wire line. The electric and magnetic fields being confined by the outer sheath of the cable or by the walls of the guide, no radiation can pass out into space and therefore these lines are perfectly shielded.

In addition to being simpler and more rugged in construction, the hollow waveguide can transmit greater power than a coaxial cable designed to operate on the same frequency.

Analogous to the use of shorted and open stubs as reactive elements (inductances and capacitances), the principal disadvantage in a waveguide is associated with its size. Unless the frequency is very high, the dimensions of the guide must be impractically large. As will be shown later, a waveguide can transmit energy only at frequencies exceeding a certain limiting value, called the cut-off frequency, which is a function of the cross-sectional dimensions of the guide.

In Sec. 11.4 it will be shown that the wavelength in free space, corresponding to the critical frequency for a guide of rectangular cross section, operating in its dominant mode, is equal to twice the width of the pipe. Under these conditions, the use of waveguides for frequencies below 3000 Mc, or for wavelengths above 10 cm, is not generally convenient. Waveguides are like low-pass filters. Open-wire and coaxial lines, on the other hand, have no low frequency cut-off. They may even be used with direct current.

In addition to transferring energy, waveguides, like other types of transmission lines, may be used as reactances and matching devices. Shorted and open stubs have their counterparts in short sections of waveguides. Two waveguides, not of the same dimensions, have different characteristic impedances. They may be matched by connecting them to a quarter-wavelength guide, called a resonant cavity. When the sides of a waveguide are flared it becomes a horn antenna, which is essentially a device for matching the impedance of the guide with that of free space. The usefulness of these devices is, of course, confined to frequencies for which the dimensions of the guide are practicable.

11.2. A Transmission Line Analog of the Waveguide. Since a waveguide makes use of a tube with only a single conductor, the theory of its operation cannot be conveniently described in terms of voltage and current.

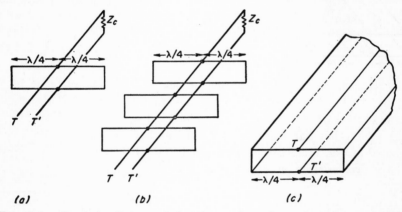

FIG. 11.1. Short-circuit transmission line analog of a rectangular waveguide.

However, certain valuable relationships between the familiar open-wire transmission line and a waveguide do exist, as may be seen from the following discussion. Let Fig. 11.1(a) represent a lossless two-wire transmission line connected to two shorted quarter-wave stubs. These stubs, as explained in Sec. 3.7, present a high impedance to the line and therefore may be regarded as insulators. As a consequence of the standing waves of voltage and current set up across the length of the stubs, they absorb no energy from the line. If the latter is terminated by its characteristic impedance, all the energy is transferred to the load.

If more stubs are connected to the line, as shown in Fig. 11.1(b), the current and voltage distributions remain unchanged. Finally, if a sufficiently large number of stubs is used, they will touch at all points forming a rectangular tube analogous to a waveguide, as illustrated in Fig. 11.1(c). The structure may be imagined as consisting of two narrow bus bars TT' and an infinite number of quarter-wave insulators.

A two-wire transmission line connected as shown in Fig. 11.1(a) and (b) would be insulated only at frequencies corresponding to those for which the stubs were a quarter-wavelength, or an odd integral multiple thereof. In contrast, a waveguide of the same dimensions will, in principle, transmit not only these particular frequencies but also all the higher frequencies. This may be seen by comparing Fig. 11.1(c) with Fig. 11.2. Keeping in mind that a waveguide may be pictured as an infinite number of quarter-wave

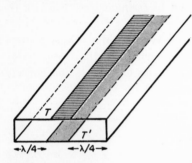

FIG. 11.2.   Rectangular waveguide operating above minimum cut-off frequency.

stubs connected to a central section of bus bars, we observe that in Fig. 11.1(c) the bus bar is very narrow, such that the length of the stubs is substantially half the width of the guide. At some higher frequency the width of the bus bar may be considered as having been increased, as illustrated in Fig. 11.2. Accordingly the length of the stubs may be assumed to have decreased in order to correspond to a quarter-wave at the new frequency.

It will be observed that this arrangement is not effective when the frequency is such that the stubs are less than a quarter-wavelength. They now present to the line a lower impedance, inductive in nature and varying with the electrical length of the stub, as described in Eq. (3.2). This inductance, in parallel with the line, short-circuits the current. Therefore, no energy is transmitted to the load.

The distribution of voltage and current in the transmission line analog of the rectangular waveguide described above is the simplest possible arrangement that satisfies the necessary conditions. For this reason it is called the dominant mode. The operation of the guide is not restricted to this mode, for, by adjusting the position of the "transmission line," infinite number of higher modes are theoretically possible. In practice, only a relatively few are useful, the dominant mode being preferred because of its low attenuation. An illustration of a higher mode is shown in Fig. 11.3.

The width of the guide is unchanged, but the transmission line is now insulated by a series of quarter-wave stubs at the left and three-quarter-wave stubs at the right, both of which present a high impedance to the line. The cut-off frequency in this instance is therefore twice that of the dominant mode.

Although it is usually desirable to operate a waveguide in a single mode, the pipe may be excited simultaneously in a series of modes, like overtones in musical instruments. While the frequencies corresponding to the various

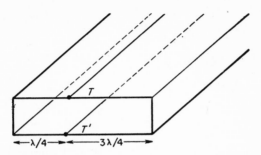

FIG. 11.3.   Illustration of rectangular waveguide operating in a higher mode.

modes in a waveguide are not necessarily integral multiples of the lowest cut-off frequency, their resultant may be considered as being equivalent to the sum of a series of harmonic components as illustrated in the case of a square wave (Sec. 1.5).

11.3. Boundary Conditions. Although certain relationships between an open-wire line and a waveguide were established in the preceding section, a more detailed analysis shows that the phenomena associated with the guide cannot be described adequately in terms of voltage and current. This statement is not intended to imply that the basic principles of energy propagation are different in the two cases. Fundamentally, the problem may always be analyzed from the point of view that the energy is transmitted through the dielectric, the conductors merely serving as guides. In view of the similarities between the physical aspects of two-wire lines and conventional circuits, particularly at the lower frequencies, it is often convenient to employ the more familiar concepts of voltage and current. The existence of only one conductor in a waveguide makes it desirable to approach the problem from a different point of view.

When we are dealing with time-varying electromagnetic fields, we must determine the distribution of these fields within a given region of space. The general procedure consists of solving the field equations and applying the boundary conditions. The solution of the equations predicts the existence within this space of an electromagnetic wave, its general characteristics being determined by the type of antenna—using the word in its most general sense—used to excite the radiation. The boundary conditions restrict the configurations of the field as a consequence of the limitations imposed by the presence of guiding surfaces. The reader is referred to Chapter 3 for examples of boundary conditions applied to the voltage and current at the termination of a transmission line.

With regard to plane electromagnetic waves in free space and those associated with open-wire and coaxial transmission lines, we recall that the directions of the electric field, the magnetic field, and the propagation of the wave are all mutually perpendicular to each other. In a waveguide it is also true that the electric and magnetic fields are perpendicular to one another, but either may have a component in the direction of wave propagation.

The assumption that the walls of a waveguide are perfect conductors requires the application of two boundary conditions. The first states that the *tangential* component of the electric field must vanish at the surface of a perfect conductor. If this were not true, the existence of a component of ε parallel to the surface would result in a flow of energy into the conductor, in accordance with Poynting's theorem. Since this energy would be equivalent to a heat loss within the metal, the definition of a perfect conductor would not be satisfied. Therefore, the electric field within the enclosure must be perpendicular to a bounding surface.

The second boundary condition states that the *normal* component of the magnetic field must vanish at the surface of a perfect conductor. Since the magnetic field is perpendicular to the electric field, which in turn is perpendicular to the conductor, the magnetic field can have no normal component at the surface and must therefore be parallel to the conductor.

In order to show that the boundary conditions stated above may also be applied to a two-conductor system, we shall first consider the propagation of a wave between two parallel conducting plates of *infinite width*. Although they do not completely enclose the field, the result obtained will enable us to interpret more clearly the propagation of a wave within a metallic enclosure. If the planes are perfectly conducting, the boundary condition that all components of the electric field tangential to the surfaces must be zero is satisfied by a field ε_y in the y-direction only (Fig. 11.4). The condition that all components of the magnetic field perpendicular to the planes must be zero is satisfied by a field $\mathcal{K}_x$ in the x-direction only. In accordance with Poynting's theorem, a plane wave, called a transverse electromagnetic (TEM) wave, is propagated in the z-direction between the plates.

If the farther end of the conductors is not terminated by an impedance matching device, standing waves are formed as on a transmission line. A slot may be cut in one of the plates and a probe inserted to measure the

wavelength, after the manner described in Sec. 3.12. Upon multiplying
this wavelength by the frequency of the radiation, the velocity of light in
the dielectric is obtained. This result is identical with the ordinary velocity
of propagation on an open-wire or coaxial transmission line.

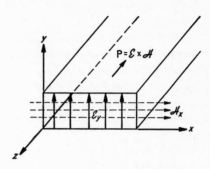

Fig. 11.4. A TEM wave is propagated
between two parallel conducting plates
of infinite width.

If, however, the wave is propagated within the enclosure of a true waveguide, the product of the wavelength, as measured with the slotted section,
and the frequency gives a result which turns out to be greater than the
velocity of light. Since it is a postulate of the theory of relativity that
energy cannot travel faster than the speed of light, it is clear that the
quantity thus calculated cannot be the velocity with which the signal is
transmitted along the waveguide.

11.4. Wave Propagation in a Rectangular Waveguide. If the parallel
plates shown in Fig. 11.4 are finite in width, being terminated by metal conductors parallel to the yz-plane, the boundary conditions cannot be satisfied
by a plane transverse wave. The tangential component of the electric field
$\mathcal{E}_y$ will vanish at the top and bottom of the guide, i.e., at the xz-planes. But
$\mathcal{E}_y$ will be parallel to the sides of the guide, the yz-planes, and thus fail to
satisfy the boundary condition there. As for the magnetic field, it will be
parallel to the top and bottom surfaces, but it will violate the boundary
condition at the sides.

However, other types of field distributions, differing from the configuration associated with a plane transverse wave, may be obtained. A
particular case is illustrated in Fig. 11.5 where, it will be noticed, the two
boundary conditions are satisfied. Since the magnetic field has components
parallel and perpendicular to the direction of wave propagation, along the
length of the guide, and only the electric field is purely transverse, this type
of wave is known as a *transverse electric* (TE) wave.

An explanation of wave propagation along the tube may be given by
making use of the principle of superposition (Sec. 5.1). It will be shown
below that two plane waves, directed *obliquely* against the sides of the guide
and thereby following a zigzag path between them, combine to produce a

resultant wave satisfying the boundary conditions and propagating energy along the enclosure with a velocity which does not conflict with the principles of relativity. In general, however, the superposition of more than two plane waves is required.

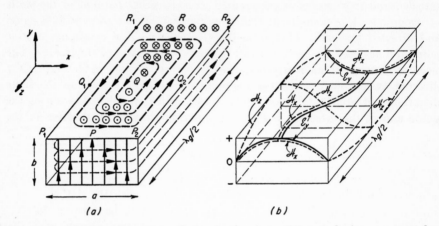

FIG. 11.5. Field configuration of the dominant or TE_{10} mode in a rectangular waveguide at a given instant of time. Cf. Fig. 11.6.

A top view of the waveguide having the field distribution of Fig. 11.5 is depicted in Fig. 11.6, with corresponding lettering for the purpose of identifying positions along the tube. *At a given time,* say $t = 0$, let the crest of the plane wavefront of the first wave A be represented by the solid line PQ_1, making an angle θ with the wall P_1R_1. The direction in which this wave is traveling is denoted by an arrow, labeled A, drawn perpendicular to the wavefront. The trough of this wave is similarly represented by the broken line Q_2R. In like manner the crest and trough of the second wave B, the front of which also subtends an angle θ with the walls of the guide, are represented by PQ_2 and Q_1R, respectively. Notice that θ may also be interpreted as the angle of incidence, i.e., the angle between the direction of the wave and the normal to the wall.

All points on a given plane wavefront are in phase. If the directions of the electric field and the energy flow are known, the direction of the magnetic field may be determined by applying Poynting's theorem (Sec. 2.5). Consider any point on the wavefront PQ_1. The direction of $\mathcal{E}_y$ is upward (toward the reader) and that of the energy flow is as indicated by the arrow A. The theorem shows that $\mathcal{3C}$ must be in the direction shown on the diagram. Since $\mathcal{3C}$ is a directed quantity, we may arbitrarily resolve it into its components, $\mathcal{3C}_z$ and $\mathcal{3C}_x$, parallel and perpendicular, respectively, to the walls of the guide. Bearing in mind that $\mathcal{E}_y$ is directed downward on the trough section of the wave, the $\mathcal{H}$-components of the other three wavefronts, PQ_2, Q_1R, and Q_2R, may be verified by an examination of the diagram.

By applying the principle of superposition to any point in the field space enclosed by the guide, it will be found that the boundary conditions are satisfied and that energy is propagated in a direction parallel to the walls of the guide. For example, at P the contribution of each wave to $\mathcal{E}_y$ is equal and directed upward. Therefore, the electric field is a maximum at this point and has no component parallel to the top or bottom of the guide. The z-components of the magnetic field, being equal in magnitude and oppositely directed, cancel each other. The x-components, however, are in the same direction and produce a resultant magnetic field parallel to the top of the guide and in the direction P_1P_2. By applying Poynting's theorem to the

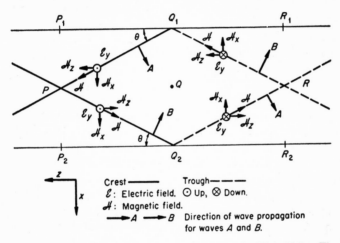

FIG. 11.6. Top view of rectangular waveguide shown in Fig. 11.5. The resultant wave is formed by the superposition of two plane waves A and B.

resultant $\mathcal{E}$ and $\mathcal{H}$ vectors at P, it will be seen that the energy flow is to the right and parallel to the z-axis.

At the point Q_1, the superposition of wavefronts PQ_1 and Q_1R shows that the electric field components parallel to the wall combine to vanish at the boundary. Likewise the x-components of the magnetic field cancel each other. The z-components, however, add to form a resultant magnetic field parallel to the boundary P_1R_1 and directed to the left. At the point Q_2, a similar line of reasoning leads to the conclusion that while both $\mathcal{E}_y$ and $\mathcal{H}_x$ vanish, as at Q_1, the resultant $\mathcal{H}_z$ is directed to the right.

As the reader may verify by considering phases intermediate between crests and troughs, wavefronts of equal positive and negative electric displacement are always superimposed at the sides of the guide. Accordingly, the resultant electric field parallel to the walls is zero. The resultant magnetic field tangential to the walls, however, is not zero, and it is oppositely directed along the opposite sides of the guide. Fig. 11.5(a) pictures the lines representing the fields as possessing characteristics ascribed to them by Faraday—the electric lines extend between the perfectly conducting walls of the guide; the magnetic lines form a series of closed loops.

It should be emphasized that the configuration described above and illustrated in Fig. 11.5(b) is a representation of the electromagnetic field at a given time, say $t = 0$. The magnitudes of the electric and magnetic components at each point vary sinusoidally with time. For example, $\mathcal{E}_y$, which is a maximum at P when $t = 0$, will be zero at this point when $t = T/4$ (Sec. 2.2).

The two plane waves, A and B, for a guide with air as the dielectric, travel back and forth between the conducting walls with a speed which is approximately equal to the velocity of light c in free space. As a result of the zigzag motion of the component waves, the energy is propagated in the direction of the axis of the guide with a velocity which is less than the speed of light, and which is designated as the *group velocity*, v_G. It is so called because it is the rate at which the group of frequencies composing a signal is propagated down the waveguide. At the walls of the guide, however, the crest of the resultant wave, for example, moves faster than the speed of light. Since this is the velocity of a surface of constant phase along the guide, it is called the wave or *phase velocity*, v_P (see Sec. 4.6 and 7.11).

The relations among these velocities may be obtained by the aid of Fig. 11.7. The wavelength associated with the component plane waves is the *perpendicular* distance between two successive crests, or other equiphase points, and is designated as λ. The component of λ, parallel to the axis of the guide, may be interpreted as the wavelength λ_z of the disturbance by which the energy is propagated. From the geometry of the figure, the relation

$$\lambda_z = \lambda \sin \theta \tag{11.1}$$

is obtained. Since the frequency of the waves is the same, their velocities are proportional to their wavelengths.

$$v_G = c \sin \theta \tag{11.2}$$

Accordingly, the group velocity can never exceed the velocity of light.

The distance between two successive equiphase points, say the crests, of the resultant wave is the wavelength λ_g of this wave. As indicated in the diagram, it may be expressed as

$$\lambda_g = \lambda/\sin \theta \tag{11.3}$$

This is the quantity which is measured by inserting a probe into a slot cut parallel to the axis of the guide.

From Eq. (11.3) the relation

$$v_P = c/\sin \theta \tag{11.4}$$

may be obtained. Although this equation indicates that the phase velocity cannot be less than the speed of light, no energy principles are violated. The phase velocity measures the speed with which a crest, if it could be observed, would travel down the guide. It is not equivalent to the rate at which energy is propagated.

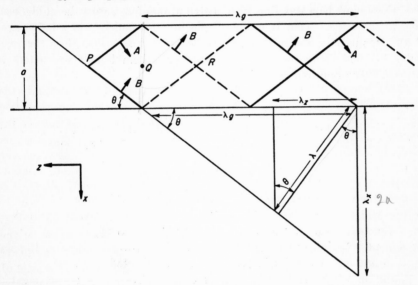

FIG. 11.7. Top view of rectangular waveguide illustrated in Figs. 11.5 and 11.6, showing the relations among λ, λ_g, λ_x, and λ_z.

The relation among the three velocities may be obtained from the product of Eq. (11.2) and (11.4)

$$v_P \cdot v_G = c^2 \tag{11.5}$$

Two special cases may be mentioned. When the wavefronts of the plane waves are perpendicular to the sides of the guide ($\theta = 90°$), the group velocity and the phase velocity are the same and are equal to c. As a consequence of the boundary condition which requires that the component of the electric field vanish at the surface of a perfect conductor, this situation may be realized only if the *sides of the guide are removed*. The component waves with their electric fields perpendicular to two parallel conducting plates are propagated as a plane wave in free space.

When the wavefronts are parallel to the sides of the guide ($\theta = 0°$), all points on a given equiphase surface reach the boundary at the same time. The phase velocity becomes infinite and the group velocity is zero. Under this condition the resultant wave merely bounces back and forth between the sides of the guide and no energy is propagated down the enclosure.

That the boundary condition requiring the resultant electric field of the elementary plane waves to vanish at the walls of the guide leads to a relation in which the angle θ depends on the wavelength of the radiation and the width a of the guide, can always be shown as follows. If $\mathcal{E}_y$ must *always* be zero at the side walls and vary sinusoidally with time at points between them, there must be a standing wave distribution of $\mathcal{E}_y$ across the guide with nodes at the walls. That is, a must be an integral multiple of a half-wavelength measured in a direction *perpendicular to the walls*. For the particular TE mode being used as an example, only a single half-wavelength is involved. The required condition is

$$a = \lambda_x/2 \qquad (11.6)$$

where λ_x is the distance between crests, measured in the x-direction, as shown in Fig. 11.7. By observing that $\cos \theta = \lambda/\lambda_x$, it may be shown that

$$\cos \theta = \lambda/2a \qquad (11.7)$$

Since the value of the cosine cannot exceed unity, this equation shows us that the width of the guide must be greater than a half-wavelength of the free-space radiation. When $a = \lambda/2$ the so-called *cut-off condition* exists. The angle θ becomes zero and, as stated above, the wave is reflected directly across the guide. The cut-off wavelength will be denoted by λ_c.

Radiation with wavelengths less than λ_c, however, may be propagated along the guide in conformity with the condition expressed by Eq. (11.7). As λ decreases, θ increases, with the result that at frequencies much higher than the cut-off value the wavefronts are almost perpendicular to the axis of the guide. Consequently the group velocity approaches the speed of light.

The assumption has been made that the walls of a waveguide are perfect conductors at which the stated boundary conditions may be applied. Since all metals have finite resistivities, this is not strictly true. The electric field does not meet the conducting surface exactly at an angle of 90°; nor is the magnetic field exactly parallel to the wall. The Poynting vector is therefore inclined slightly toward the conductor. Nearly all the energy is retained in the dielectric, but a small amount, just enough to supply the heat loss in the metal, flows into the conductor. The result may be compared to the propagation of a vertically polarized radio wave over the surface of the earth.

At the high frequencies employed in waveguides the current in the conducting walls is determined by the skin effect. Taking into account the conductivities of the metals used, the depth of penetration is found to be of the order of 10^{-4} cm. For most practical purposes the currents may be considered as existing only on the inner surfaces of the guide, i.e., the walls simulate perfect conductors. The ideal condition may be approximated in an economical manner by making the waveguide of brass and coating the inside with a thin layer of silver.

11.5. Modes in a Rectangular Waveguide. The distribution of the electric and magnetic fields in the above example of a rectangular waveguide is the dominant TE mode. It is the mode of operation having the lowest cut-off frequency for this type of guide, but it is only one of many possible configurations. For example, the standing wave distribution of the electric field across the guide may include two half-wave segments. That is, the electric field may be zero not only at the side walls but also along a plane halfway between them. The field distribution in this case is equivalent to that which would be obtained by placing two similar waveguides side by side and removing the wall between them. Other configurations may be obtained for standing wave distributions between the top and bottom of the guide in addition to those across the sides. If such distributions exist, $\mathcal{E}$ must have components in both the x- and y-directions. Provided there is no $\mathcal{E}$-component along the axis of the guide, the disturbance will have the characteristics of a TE wave. In theory the number of possible field configurations is unlimited. Practically, the operation of waveguides is confined to a few of the simpler modes.

The modes of operation in a waveguide are classified according to the field configuration. As stated previously, the guide operates in a transverse electric (TE) or a transverse magnetic (TM) mode, depending on whether the electric or magnetic lines lie in a plane perpendicular to the axis of the guide. A further description is given by affixing subscripts to the above notation: thus, TE_{mn} or TM_{mn}. For *rectangular* guides, m denotes the half-wave segments of $\mathcal{E}$ (or $\mathcal{H}$) along the larger dimension a, and n the number along the smaller dimension b. In the dominant mode described above, $\mathcal{E}$ lies entirely in the transverse plane, it has a space variation of *one* half-wavelength along a, and it shows *no* maximum or minimum along b. Accordingly the configuration is designated as a TE_{10} mode.

Since it is usually desirable that only one mode be propagated, some care must be exercised in choosing the dimensions of the guide. In all cases it is, of course, necessary that the cut-off wavelength be greater than the longest wavelength of the radiation to be transmitted. In addition, the width must not only be large enough to transmit, say the dominant mode, but it must also be small enough to exclude the higher-order modes.

If, for example, the TE_{10} mode is to be propagated, the width a must be greater than half the free-space wavelength, $\lambda/2$. But a must also be less than λ; otherwise, the TE_{20} would also be transmitted. For the TE_{10} mode, the height b may be as small as desired, provided the electric field gradient between the plates is insufficient to produce an arc-over. However, unless b is less than $\lambda/2$, a TE_{01} mode, which is like the TE_{10} mode except for its orientation within the guide, may also be present. In this case the resultant field configuration is equivalent to a TE_{11} mode (Fig. 11.8).

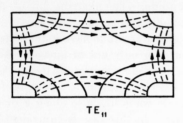 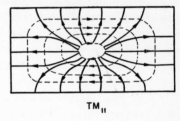

TE₁₁   TM₁₁

FIG. 11.8. Field configurations in the transverse plane for the TE_{11} and TM_{11} modes of a rectangular waveguide.

The dimensions of commercial rectangular pipes are usually such that $a/b = 2$. This is a very convenient ratio, for it provides a two-to-one frequency band over which the signals may be transmitted entirely within the dominant mode.

When the situation with respect to the fields is reversed, the magnetic field is everywhere transverse to the axis of the guide, whereas the electric field has both transverse and axial components. This type of propagation is referred to as a *transverse magnetic* (TM_{mn}) wave. The different modes are specified by the proper subscripts which are now given with reference to the magnetic field. An important difference should be noticed. As a consequence of the continuity of magnetic lines, the space variation of $\mathcal{H}$ across either dimension of the guide must be an integral number of half-wavelengths. If either m or n were zero, the entire wave would disappear. Therefore, the lowest order in which a transverse magnetic wave may be propagated is the TM_{11} mode (Fig. 11.8). Fundamentally the boundary conditions and the principles of transmission are the same for TE and TM waves. In view of this similarity in theory and the fact that relatively little practical use has been made of TM waves in *rectangular* guides, no detailed account of their characteristics will be given here.

Higher modes for either the TE or TM waves in rectangular tubes may be visualized by an extension of the method in which two similar waveguides are assumed to be placed side by side, as described earlier in this section. All the higher TE modes may be constructed from either the TE_{10}

or the TE_{11} mode by combining a group (equal to the sum of the subscripts for the former and their product for the latter) into the appropriate rectangular arrangement. Similarly all the higher TM modes may be derived from the TM_{11} pattern (see Problem 11.6).

11.6. Circular Waveguides. Electromagnetic waves may also be propagated in tubes of circular cross section. Both TE and TM waves are found to exist as in the case of rectangular guides. In applying the boundary conditions to cylindrical surfaces, it is found that the analysis can be carried out more conveniently if cylindrical coordinates are substituted for those of the ordinary or rectangular frame of reference.

In Fig. 11.9(b) a cylindrical waveguide is shown with reference to a coordinate system, r, θ, and z. The relationship of these variables to those of the cartesian system, x, y, z, may be obtained from Fig. 11.9(a). The

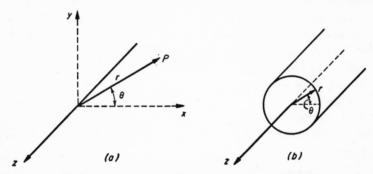

Fig. 11.9. (a) Relation between cylindrical and cartesian coordinates. (b) Cylindrical coordinates applied to a cylindrical waveguide.

z-axis is common to both systems. The displacement r is the radial distance of the point P from the z-axis. The variable θ is the angle which r or, in general, its projection on the xy-plane, makes with the positive x-axis.

The two fundamental types of waves which may exist in a circular guide are those for which either the components of $\mathcal{E}$ or the components of $\mathcal{H}$ lie wholly in planes perpendicular to the axis of the tube, which is in the z-direction. The former is designated as a TE, the latter as a TM, wave. Thus, the electric field in a TE wave may be expressed in terms of its radial and angular components, $\mathcal{E}_r$ and $\mathcal{E}_\theta$. $\mathcal{E}_z$, of course, must be zero. Similarly, for a TM wave, $\mathcal{H}_r$ and $\mathcal{H}_\theta$ may exist, but $\mathcal{H}_z$ must be zero. Reference to Fig. 11.9 shows that the notation is in conformity with the scheme used in rectangular guides.

When cylindrical coordinates are used to obtain the solution to the wave equation with the required boundary conditions, the general procedure is the same as that for the rectangular guide. In each type of guide the fields vary sinusoidally throughout with respect to time, but only along the z-axis with respect to space. The field distributions in terms of r and θ over the cross section of a circular guide are more complex, being represented graphically by what are known as Bessel functions. Although they resemble sine and cosine functions, as shown by their oscillations between positive and negative values, their amplitudes decrease, and the intervals between the points, called the roots, at which the value of a given function becomes zero are not uniformly spaced. A Bessel function may be described as roughly equivalent to a damped and slightly nonperiodic sine or cosine curve. Numerical values of Bessel functions have been tabulated and may be used in a manner similar to the familiar tables of trigonometric functions.

With regard to the integers m and n, they are also used to describe the modes of operation in a circular pipe but, as a result of the cylindrical coordinate system employed, *they do not have the same significance as in the case of a rectangular guide.* Instead, they must be interpreted in terms of the radial and angular components of the electric or magnetic field. For example, in the TE_{mn} modes the radial field $\mathcal{E}_r$, which must be perpendicular to the wall of the tube and consequently have its maximum value there, may vary cyclically between the wall and the center of the pipe. The tangential field $\mathcal{E}_\theta$, on the other hand, must vanish at the boundary. It has, therefore, been found convenient to designate m as the number of cyclic variations along the radius and n as the number around the center of a cross section of the guide.

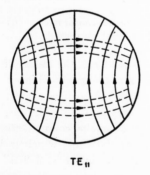 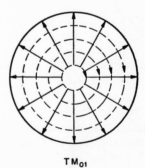

TE₁₁ TM₀₁

FIG. 11.10. Field configurations in the transverse plane for the TE_{11} and TM_{01} modes of a circular waveguide. The TE_{11} field is the dominant mode.

The field configurations of two of the lowest-order, and most often used, modes of a circular waveguide are illustrated in Fig. 11.10. The difference in the interpretation of the subscripts, with reference to the geometry of the tube, is apparent from the TM_{01} mode which cannot exist in a rectangular guide. The cut-off wavelength for a given mode varies directly with the diameter of the guide, the factor of proportionality being the root of the Bessel function for the order of the mode. It turns out that the TE_{11} mode has the lowest cut-off frequency and thus is the dominant mode in a circular guide. For this mode, $\lambda_c = 1.706d$, where d is the diameter of the tube.

Circular pipes, in comparison with rectangular guides, have several disadvantages which limit their use. Their dominant mode requires a pipe of slightly larger dimensions in order to propagate radiation of the same wavelength. The range between the dominant cut-off wavelength and that of the next higher mode is much shorter in the circular guide, thus limiting the frequency range over which signals may be transmitted in the preferred mode. In construction the allowable tolerances in dimensions are less for the circular guide. For example, a small departure from circularity produces an elliptical cross section. Radiation propagated in such an enclosure is elliptically polarized and thus has two different wavelengths in the guide.

For mechanical reasons, a circular guide must be used in an assembly where an antenna rotates with respect to a fixed rectangular guide. In this device, which is known as a rotating joint, a transition from a rectangular to a circular mode must be made.

11.7. Excitation of Waveguides. Let us consider a waveguide as a limited region of space into which energy is to be radiated. As in free

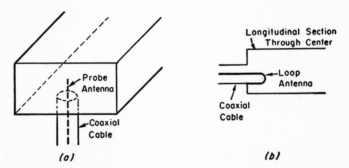

FIG. 11.11. Two methods for the excitation of a TE_{10} mode in a rectangular waveguide. (*a*) Probe at the center in the bottom of the guide is parallel to the electric field. (*b*) Plane of the loop at the end of the guide is perpendicular to the magnetic field.

space, the transference requires the aid of a coupling device, or antenna, usually in the form of a straight wire or a loop. If correctly oriented with respect to the fields of the mode to be established in the guide, either type of radiator may be used. The wire, or probe, must be in the direction of the electric field; the loop must be oriented with its plane normal to the magnetic field. The guide is ordinarily closed at one end to insure the transmission of radiation in the desired direction.

The principles may be illustrated by a description of two typical methods used to excite the TE_{10} mode in a rectangular waveguide. For convenience we shall assume that the electric field component is in the y-direction. If the inner conductor of a coaxial cable, entering the guide at the center of one of the wider surfaces, is extended across the guide, as shown in Fig. 11.11(*a*), the wire becomes an antenna which radiates an electric field parallel to the y-direction and with its maximum at the center of the guide. This field and the accompanying magnetic field, which encircles the probe, produce a configuration which satisfies the boundary conditions required for the propagation of the wave.

Fig. 11.11(*b*) indicates the manner in which a loop, formed by the inner conductor of a cable, is placed at the center of the guide where the plane of the loop is perpendicular to the direction of the magnetic field characteristic of the required mode. Accordingly, the electromagnetic field assumes the necessary configuration for the propagation of a TE_{10} wave.

The TE_{20} mode may be excited by the method shown in Fig. 11.12. The antennas in this arrangement are oppositely phased by making one cable

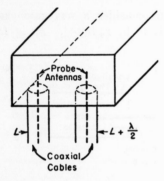

Fig. 11.12. Method for the excitation of a TE_{20} mode in a rectangular waveguide. The antennas are oppositely phased and placed at the maxima of the electric field. L indicates the length of the cable.

a half-wavelength longer than the other. Therefore the electric fields are oppositely directed in the two halves of the guide such that the larger dimension includes two segments of a standing wave pattern. The out-of-phase currents in the antennas are accompanied by magnetic fields which cancel each other along a plane parallel to the sides of the guide and midway between them.

By noting the similarity in pattern between the rectangular TE_{10} and the cylindrical TE_{11} modes, it may be seen that the latter can also be excited by a probe mounted in the cylinder after the manner shown in Fig. 11.11(*a*) for the rectangular guide. From the configuration of the cylindrical TM_{01} mode, it may also be observed that the appropriate fields may be established by inserting a probe, directed along the axis of the tube, into the end of the guide.

Sometimes it is desirable to produce the required field configuration by coupling to a primary excited guide through a hole in the wall of the tube, as in the case of the rotating joint referred to in the last section. Under these circumstances there must be a field component common to both the exciting and excited modes where the tubes are joined. Radiation may also be transferred from one guide to another of different cross section by introducing a gradual change in the dimensions of the guide. This procedure should be compared to the method of transferring energy from a waveguide into free space through a horn antenna (Sec. 10.5).

Probe and loop antennas may excite waves of different frequencies and polarizations. Because a guide acts as a high-pass filter, only those frequencies above cut-off will be transmitted. If desired, an additional separation may be effected by the insertion of a diaphragm which restricts the passage of waves to those having a wavelength shorter than the cut-off value of the opening. Unwanted polarization may be eliminated by mounting a series of parallel wires in a plane perpendicular to the axis of the guide. All components of the wave in which the electric vector is parallel to the wires are therefore reflected as explained in Sec. 6.3.

It may be observed, as a consequence of the reciprocity theorem, that a satisfactory arrangement of probes or loops for the excitation of radiation in waveguides is equally desirable for its reception.

11.8. Waveguides: Standing Waves and Characteristic Impedance. Inasmuch as the ordinary two-wire transmission line may be considered as a special form of a waveguide operating in the TEM mode, similarities in the properties or characteristics of the two devices may be expected. In particular, it has been found that the transfer of energy and the presence of standing waves in a waveguide are determined by its termination, that the concept of characteristic impedance, with appropriate modifications, is a useful property, and that elements corresponding to shorted and open stubs may be employed for the purpose of matching.

The existence of standing waves in a guide is a result of the distribution of electric and magnetic fields which are to be interpreted as the analogs of voltage and current on an open-wire transmission line. (Indeed, as indicated in earlier discussions, the phenomena associated with a transmission line may also be described in terms of its component fields.) For example, if the receiving end of a guide is terminated by a perfect conductor, the resultant electric field, in conformity with boundary conditions, is zero at the load. Additional nodes, separated by distances corresponding to half-wavelengths, are located along the guide, analogous to the distribution of voltage shown in Fig. 3.5. Also in accordance with boundary conditions, the resultant magnetic field is a maximum at the load, the standing wave pattern corresponding to the current distribution in the same figure. Here, as in all cases where the stationary wave is contained within a guide, the distance between nodes is based on the *guide wavelength* λ_g.

A waveguide, like a transmission line, is, in general, terminated by an impedance such that the incident energy is partly absorbed and partly reflected. Accordingly, the positions and relative magnitudes of maxima and minima are determined by the resistive and reactive components of the load impedance. The effect of a particular termination on the standing wave configuration of a transmission line has been described in Sec. 3.13. The results obtained there may be applied directly to the interpretation of analogous situations in a waveguide.

In transmission line theory the existence of standing waves is determined by the relation between the load impedance and the characteristic impedance of the line. The latter, substantially constant at all radio frequencies, is equal to the square root of the ratio of the inductance to the capacitance (per unit length of line). It is also calculable from the geometry of the conductors and the dielectric properties of the medium. Since the usual concept of impedance is the ratio of voltage to current, the characteristic impedance of a line matched to its load may be found conveniently by measuring the defining quantities at any point on the line.

If, however, the concept of impedance is to be associated with a waveguide, the ratio of an electric to a magnetic field must be used. As a consequence of the field components and the mode of propagation which may be selected, it is possible to define the "characteristic impedance" of a waveguide in several different ways, each of which gives a different result. The usefulness of a particular definition depends on what information regarding the properties of the guide is desired. The selection of a "best" definition is therefore a matter of convenience.

One particularly useful concept is that of the *wave impedance* Z_w which is defined as the ratio of the transverse electric to the transverse magnetic field. From this statement it may be seen that Z_w cannot be the same for TE and TM waves. It will be convenient if two expressions, one for each of these two types of waves, can be found, such that Z_w will have the same value for all modes independent of the dimensions and shape of the tube, except in the way they may affect the guide wavelength λ_g.

For any TE wave

$$Z_w = 120\pi \cdot \lambda_g/\lambda \tag{11.8}$$

For any TM wave

$$Z_w = 120\pi \cdot \lambda/\lambda_g \tag{11.9}$$

where λ is the free-space wavelength and λ_g the wavelength in the guide.

As shown in Sec. 11.4, λ_g can never be less than λ. Therefore, as the cut-off frequency is approached, $\lambda_g \to \infty$ and Z_w increases very rapidly in the case of a TE wave. On the other hand, for a TM wave, Z_w becomes smaller as the frequency nears the cut-off value. Thus, in contrast to a transmission line, the wave impedance may not be considered independent of the frequency. If a waveguide could be excited in the TEM mode, λ and λ_g would be equal, and the wave impedance would have a constant value of 120π or 377 ohms (the impedance of free space) at all frequencies.

Since rectangular guides are usually operated in the dominant TE_{10} mode, it will be of interest to obtain a useful characteristic impedance in this instance. The analysis is made on the assumption that there are no standing waves or higher modes.

Let us consider the wave impedance as the characteristic impedance of a *square area* of the wavefront in the transverse plane. This assumption is justified, as Z_w does not involve the shape and dimensions of the tube. If a square sheet of conducting material having an impedance (resistance) equal to that of a square area of the wavefront is placed perpendicular to the direction of wave propagation, no radiation will be reflected from the sheet. Accordingly, the square sheet exhibits the property of a characteristic impedance with respect to the square section of the wavefront.

Now, if a sheet of the same material and thickness, but with the cross-sectional dimensions of the guide, is placed in the transverse plane of the wave, all of the incident radiation is absorbed. Therefore, the resistance of the sheet may be interpreted as equivalent to the characteristic impedance of the guide. On the basis of the transmission line analog of a waveguide, as presented in Sec. 11.2, a current may be assumed to flow between the top and bottom of the guide through the conducting sheet. The length of the current path is b and its width is a, the letters referring to the dimensions previously assigned to the guide.

The resistance R of a uniform conducting sheet is given by

$$R = \sigma \cdot l/w \qquad (11.10)$$

where σ is the *surface resistivity*, or resistance per square, and l and w are the length and width, respectively, of the current path. (For the meaning of resistance per square, see Problem 8.4.) For a square sheet, $l = w$ and $R = \sigma$. Since Z_w is purely resistive and now refers to a square area, $Z_w = \sigma$.

Calling the resistance of the sheet having the dimensions of the guide Z_c and substituting the appropriate quantities in Eq. (11.10), we obtain

$$Z_c = Z_w \cdot b/a \qquad (11.11)$$

which may now be defined as the characteristic impedance of a rectangular guide operating in the TE_{10} mode. The equation is valid for this mode only. Although the general method may be used to obtain Z_c for other modes, considerable difficulty may be encountered because the effective length and width of the current path do not correspond to the dimensions of the guide.

As an application of this concept, standing waves may be eliminated in a waveguide by terminating it with a conducting sheet having a resistance per square equivalent to the wave impedance of the incident wave. If the tube is closed at the end, the absorbing screen is placed a quarter-wavelength ($\lambda_g/4$) from the shorted termination which, as in a transmission line, presents a high impedance to the sheet.

Another method of eliminating reflected waves at the termination of a waveguide uses a gradually tapered wedge long enough to absorb the incident radiation. These wedges are manufactured from so-called lossy substances, that is, dielectrics in which fine particles of a metal or a semiconductor are embedded.

11.9. Waveguides: Impedance Matching. Using the modified concepts of impedance discussed in the last section, ordinary transmission line theory may be applied in many cases to waveguides. One rather straightforward example is the waveguide analog of tuning stubs used to remove standing waves from an open-wire line in accordance with the principles set forth in Sec. 3.14.

These stubs are in the form of short sections of tubing, called T junctions, which are joined to the main waveguide and provided with adjustable shorting plates by means of which their reactance may be varied. The stub may be attached to the guide so that its axis is either parallel to the electric field or perpendicular to the magnetic field in the guide proper. Since the position of the stub cannot be varied along the guide conveniently, double-stub tuning is generally employed. While the operations are carried out in a manner similar to those used on a two-wire line, it should be remembered that for a rectangular guide operating in the TE_{10} mode, the characteristic impedance is that defined by Eq. (11.11) and the wavelength, as always, is λ_g.

Because T junctions may be somewhat unwieldly, an impedance matching device consisting of thin metallic plates or fins attached to a waveguide, in order to constrict its cross section as illustrated in Fig. 11.13, is often used. This arrangement is called an *iris* or a *window*. The insertion of an iris into a waveguide is equivalent to shunting a stub across a transmission line. The general procedure of matching is the same in each case. An iris (stub) is located at the correct position along the tube (line) and the separation between the edges (position of the shorting bar) is varied until the required match is obtained.

When the edges of the plates are parallel to the electric field, as shown in Fig. 11.13(a), a magnetic field, which is not propagated but receives and returns part of the energy of the wave, is set up in the immediate neighborhood of the iris. Since the energy is stored in a magnetic field, this type of

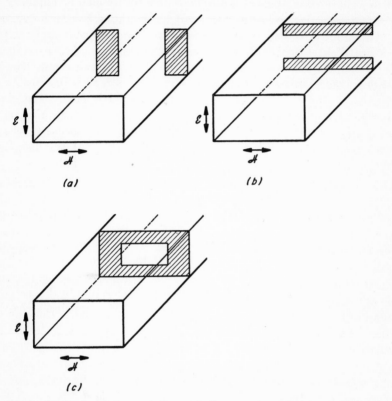

FIG. 11.13.   Irises or windows used as reactive apertures in waveguides.   (a) Inductive.   (b) Capacitive.   (c) Composite.

iris is called inductive. It is equivalent to a shorted stub, less than a quarter-wavelength, shunted across a transmission line.

When the edges of the plates are parallel to the magnetic field, as shown in Fig. 11.13(b), the electric lines extend across the edges of the aperture after the manner of a capacitor. Since the localized energy is stored in an electric field, this type of iris is called capacitive. It is equivalent to a shorted stub, between a quarter- and a half-wavelength, shunted across a transmission line.   The use of capacitive windows is limited because of the possibility of an arc-over at the high potential gradients which may exist across the edges of the aperture.

If the iris has the form shown in Fig. 11.13(c), it is either inductive or capacitive, depending on the dimensions of the opening. In the special case where the two reactances have the same value, the iris forms a *parallel* resonant circuit, which is equivalent to a shorted quarter-wave stub shunted across a transmission line. Consequently, at the resonant frequency the wave sees a high resistive impedance and passes through the window as if it were completely transparent. However, as the frequency departs from resonance, the aperture becomes increasingly opaque.

As an alternative to a T junction or an iris, a *tuning screw,* which is simply a threaded metal cylinder, like a machine screw, is inserted in the top of a rectangular waveguide, parallel to the electric field. The tuning screw is similar to a vertical antenna and its image formed by the surface of the guide. The impedance of such an antenna is capacitive when it extends less than a quarter-wavelength into the guide. If the distance is between a quarter- and a half-wavelength the impedance is inductive. Thus it is seen that the variation in the impedance of a tuning screw is analogous to that of an open stub. In practice, inductive screws are avoided because their greater length increases the danger of an arc-over. When the analog of double-stub tuning is employed, two screws are used.

In Sec. 8.8 a procedure employing the inversion property of a quarter-wave line was used to match two sections of line having different characteristic impedances. This was accomplished by inserting an intermediate quarter-wave section with a characteristic impedance equal to the geometric mean of the lines' impedances. Likewise a match can be effected between two sections of a waveguide which have different characteristic impedances.

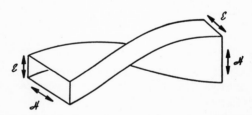

FIG. 11.14. Twist in waveguide for rotating the polarization of the wave.

In determining the dimensions of the matching element, the guide wavelength (λ_g) in the quarter-wave section must be used. Since, in a waveguide, Z_c varies with the wavelength, a match can be made only at a single frequency. This method of matching with a quarter-wave transformer is particularly useful when two guides having the same cross-sectional dimensions but containing different dielectric materials are to be connected.

When two waveguides are connected, a corner may have to be turned in order that the fields may be in the proper direction for matching. When a bend is introduced care should be taken to avoid abrupt changes which would lead to the formation of standing waves. For example, a waveguide may be bent into the arc of a circle, provided the internal dimensions are kept constant and the radius of curvature is not too small. The direction of the field may also be changed by imparting a gradual twist to the guide as shown in Fig. 11.14, where a change from vertical to horizontal polarization in the TE_{10} mode is indicated.

11.10. Dielectric Waveguides. Electromagnetic waves may also be propagated through a rod of dielectric material having a refractive index greater than that of the surrounding space. The phenomenon is similar to that observed when light passes from a medium of higher to a medium of lower refractive index (Sec. 4.6). When the angle of incidence i is less than the critical angle C, the energy is partly transmitted and partly reflected. When, however, the critical angle is exceeded, all of the energy is reflected.

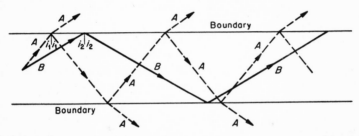

Fig. 11.15. Reflection and refraction in a dielectric waveguide. The directions of wave propagation are shown by the rays A and B. Ray A (broken line) represents a wave having a frequency below f_c. Ray B (solid line) represents a wave having a frequency above f_c.

Let us assume that uniform plane waves, traveling in the dielectric after the manner of waves in a metallic tube, as described in Sec. 11.4, are incident upon the boundary at an angle i. For a given dimension of the guide there is a minimum frequency f_c for which $i = C$. For frequencies greater than f_c, $i > C$, and all of the energy is reflected in zigzag fashion along the guide. For frequencies less than f_c, $i < C$; part of the energy is reflected within the guide and part is transmitted into the surrounding medium. (See Fig. 11.15, which may be compared advantageously with Fig. 4.19 and the accompanying description.) Thus, in general, the waves are propagated both in the dielectric and in the surrounding space.

The effectiveness of a rod as a waveguide lies in using a material with a high index of refraction and in operating at frequencies well above the cut-off value. Unlike the metallic waveguide, its dielectric counterpart has no definite cut-off frequency. A small fraction of the energy is always retained within the guide at each successive reflection however small the angle of incidence may be. The larger the diameter of the rod with respect to the wavelength, the greater is the ratio of the energy inside a dielectric waveguide to the energy outside.

The loss of radiation at the surface, however, may be turned to advantage in the dielectric rod antenna. This type of antenna is a tapered rod of some dielectric material, usually polystyrene, long enough so that most of its energy is radiated through the wall before reaching the smaller end. When the appropriate diameter of the rod is used, it turns out that much of this radiation is directed parallel to the axis of the guide. This produces a wavefront of large area. When the antenna is terminated, the equivalent of a large aperture is created which, in accordance with Huygens' principle, produces a highly directive pattern in the forward direction (Sec. 5.8). Actually the situation is similar to that which exists at the mouth of a horn. In fact, dielectric antennas may be substituted for horns, especially in arrays where the use of the latter would be inconvenient because of their size.

11.11. Slot Antennas. As stated in Sec. 11.1, the radiation in a waveguide with perfectly conducting walls is confined within the enclosure. If, however, there is a hole or slot in the wall, some of the energy will leak out into the surrounding space. When the dimension is small compared to the wavelength, the loss is unimportant. But if the slot is properly oriented with respect to the fields and is of a length equal to a half-wavelength in the guide $(\lambda_g/2)$, an appreciable amount of energy is radiated through the opening. Basically, this slot is an antenna and as such is similar to a half-wave dipole, with an important difference which will be described below.

Let us consider a perfectly conducting screen of infinite extent in which a narrow rectangular opening has been cut. The complementary screen is defined as an opaque sheet having the same dimensions as those of the aperture. Let each screen be illuminated separately by a source of electromagnetic radiation and the individual fields be investigated in the region beyond the plane of the screens. An optical law, long known as Babinet's principle, states that the sum of the two complementary fields (not the intensities) at any point is equal to the field at that point in the absence of any screen.

In Fig. 11.16(a) the vertically polarized source and the field, at the selected point P beyond the plane of the screen, are shown when no screen is present. Next, the screen containing the slot is placed in position, as illustrated in Fig. 11.16(b). The required boundary conditions at the edges of the slot are satisfied by the propagation of a vertically polarized wave on the far side of the screen. Since this field is the same as that produced without any screen, the field at P, resulting from the insertion of the complementary screen, in accordance with Babinet's principle, must be zero. If this condition is to hold, the electric field must be horizontal in order that the wave may be reflected by the conducting strip as explained in Sec. 6.3.

When Babinet's principle is applied to radio waves, it is found that the fields of the source, as well as the screens themselves, must be considered complementary. This relation is brought about by simply rotating the direction of polarization through 90°. The field obtained from the horizontally polarized source in Fig. 11.16(c) thus becomes zero at the selected point in the region beyond the plane of the screen, and Babinet's principle is satisfied.

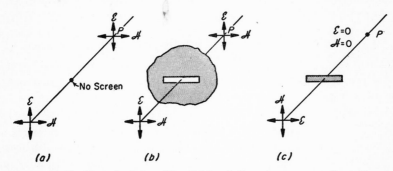

FIG. 11.16. Babinet's principle. The fields of the source, as well as the screens themselves, must be considered complementary.

As a word of caution, it should be mentioned that, for simplification, a shadow effect—in which the cross section of the beam is ideally limited to the area of the aperture—has been chosen. The reasoning may be applied to cases where diffraction is involved.

By using the extended principle a half-wave dipole may be interpreted as the complement of a slot of the same dimensions cut in an infinite plane conducting sheet. In Fig. 11.17(a) the dipole is fed by a generator placed across a very small gap at the center. Accordingly, the radiation of the dipole is horizontally polarized. On the other hand, the radiation from the complementary slot, energized by an oscillator connected across its center as shown in Fig. 11.17(b), is vertically polarized. The field pattern for each antenna therefore has the same configuration, but with this significant difference: the electric and magnetic fields are interchanged.

From this duality principle the characteristics of a slot radiator can easily be deduced from the complementary wire antenna. Since a narrow vertical slot has the same radiation pattern as that of a thin, flat, horizontal antenna of corresponding dimensions, it may be used as a radiator where horizontal polarization is required. One or more longitudinal slots in a vertical cylinder produce a circular radiation pattern in a horizontal plane. The slot radiator used in UHF television broadcasting is the complement of the stacked turnstile antenna described in Sec. 9.8. The slots, which are energized across their narrow dimension by feeders from a central coaxial

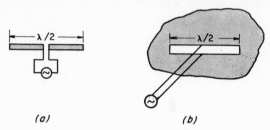

(a)   (b)

FIG. 11.17. Complementary antennas. (a) Half-wave dipole; horizontal polarization. (b) Half-wave slot in infinite sheet; vertical polarization.

cable in the vertical metal cylinder, are arranged in cross pairs and are stacked to obtain the desired vertical directivity as in the case of the turnstile antenna.

11.12. Lens Antennas. At microwave frequencies optical methods may be conveniently employed in the design of antennas. Mirrors and lenses are optical devices which readily suggest interesting possibilities. In particular, it has been shown that the parabolic reflector is especially effective in providing a highly directive field pattern. This directivity is achieved by utilizing the geometric properties of the parabola to obtain a field distribution corresponding to a plane wave across the aperture of the radiator. The same result, as will be shown below, may be obtained in the case of a lens by taking advantage of the change in phase velocity which a wave undergoes in traversing the boundary between free space and a dielectric or a waveguide.

The action of a lens depends on Snell's law (Sec. 4.6) and the equality of optical paths along all rays between two given wavefronts. The optical path is measured in terms of a wavelength which, it will be recalled, is proportional to the phase velocity of the wave in the medium. When a dielectric is used as the material of the lens, this velocity v_P is always less than the free-space velocity c. The index of refraction μ may be written

$$\mu = c/v_P = \lambda/\lambda_g \qquad (11.12)$$

where λ is the free-space wavelength and λ_g is the wavelength in the medium (cf. λ_g in a waveguide). Since, in a dielectric, μ is always greater than one,

λ_g is always less than λ. Accordingly, a given distance in the dielectric is equivalent to a greater number of wavelengths than is the same distance in space. For example, if $\mu = 1.6$ for lucite, the optical path length is 1.6 times as great as it is in air.

Fig. 11.18(a) shows a system designed to transform the spherical wavefront originating at the point P into a plane wavefront at the right-hand surface of the lens. Consider any two rays, PQR and PST, associated with

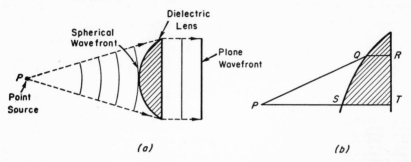

FIG. 11.18. (a) Diagram of dielectric lens. (b) Detail showing two rays associated with the wavefront.

the wavefront, as depicted in Fig. 11.18(b). Since the optical path from P to the plane wavefront must be the same for all rays,

$$PQ + \mu \cdot QR = PS + \mu \cdot ST = \text{constant} \qquad (11.13)$$

If the lens is shaped so that this condition is fulfilled, the desired plane wavefront is obtained.

Since the diameter of the lens must be large in terms of wavelengths, the weight of ordinary solid dielectrics, such as glass or polystyrene, sometimes makes them inconvenient to use. A less massive substitute is an artificial dielectric consisting of metal spheres or rods, with dimensions small compared to a wavelength, arranged in a three-dimensional array and embedded in plastic foam. Satisfactory dielectrics with a refractive index as high as 15 have been reported.

From another point of view, the dielectric lens may be likened to a device which retards the velocity of each element in the wavefront by the exact amount necessary to effect the change in its contour. The possibility of another type of lens in which the velocity of the wavefront is advanced, instead of being retarded, is suggested by the knowledge that the phase velocity in a waveguide is greater than the speed of light in a vacuum.

This type of antenna, one form of which is shown in Fig. 11.19, is called a metal-plate lens. Like the dielectric lens described above, it is designed to transform a spherical wave into a plane wave. The lens consists of conducting strips—only one is shown in the diagram—appropriately shaped and set parallel to the electric field of the source. If the plates are separated by a distance slightly greater than $\lambda/2$, .they are equivalent to a number of waveguides in parallel. As in the case of its dielectric counterpart, the focusing action of the metal-lens may be described either by the principle of the equality of optical paths or from the viewpoint of a device which *advances* the velocity of the elements in the wavefront.

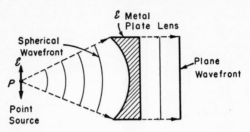

FIG. 11.19.   Diagram of $\mathcal{E}$ metal-plate lens.

In view of the points of similarity between a metal-lens and a wave-guide, the result obtained in Problem 11.7 may be used to determine the refractive index of the lens.

$$\mu = c/v_P = \sqrt{1 - (\lambda/2a)^2} \tag{11.14}$$

The index is, of course, always less than one and varies with the frequency. Consequently, the focusing is imperfect over a range of wavelengths, the effect being analogous to chromatic aberration in an optical lens.

11.13. A Radio Quarter-Wave Plate. Observations of radio waves from the sun show that they are often circularly polarized. A device, similar to a quarter-wave plate in optics (Sec. 6.4), has been developed whereby this radiation at appropriately high frequencies—say upwards of 3000 Mc—may be converted into linearly polarized waves for acceptance by a linear antenna. The arrangement consists of a series of equally spaced metal strips of which only two are shown in Fig. 11.20. The circularly polarized wave may be considered as having sinusoidal electric field components parallel and perpendicular to the planes of the strips, each component traveling with a different phase velocity in the intervening spaces.

In the case of the perpendicular component, assuming the plates to be perfect conductors, the electric field is everywhere normal to the surface of the metal strips and the magnetic field is parallel to their larger dimension. This wave component is a TEM wave and will therefore travel with a downward velocity which is substantially the same as that in free space. In the case of the parallel component, the electric vector is parallel to the planes of the strips, although it must vanish at their surfaces. The magnetic vector, however, has a component not only across the space separating the plates, but also in the direction of wave propagation. This field configuration represents a TE wave traveling with a phase velocity which depends on the separation of the plates and which is always greater than the free-space velocity, as in a waveguide.

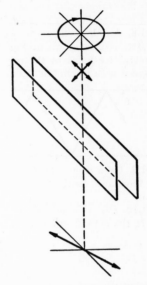

FIG. 11.20. Principle of the radio quarter-wave plate. Arrows show direction of electric field.

The difference in phase between the two components of the circularly polarized wave is either 90° or 270°. The width of the strips may be chosen such that the phase difference between the emergent components is 180° or 0°. The circularly polarized wave is therefore resolved into a linearly polarized wave. When used with a parabolic reflector, the quarter-wave plate is placed in front of the linear element, the strips being set at an angle of 45° with the antenna.

PROBLEMS

11.1. Assume that Fig. 11.5(a) represents the field configuration of the TE_{10} mode in a rectangular guide when $t = 0$. Sketch the field configurations when $t = T/4$ and $t = T/2$.

11.2. Determine the critical frequency for the dominant mode of a rectangular waveguide with air as a dielectric and having the dimensions $a = 5$ cm and $b = 2.5$ cm.

11.3. In Problem 11.2, find the guide wavelength, the phase velocity, and the group velocity at a wavelength of 4 cm in air for the dominant mode.

11.4. Using 4 cm waves in air, find the wave impedance and the characteristic impedance of the TE_{10} mode for the waveguide in Problem 11.2.

11.5. Find the angle θ that the component plane waves of the TE_{10} mode of Problem 11.3 make with the axis of the guide.

11.6. Using the appropriate TE_{10}, TE_{11}, or TM_{11} field configuration in a rectangular waveguide, construct a transverse section of the (a) TE_{30}, (b) TE_{22}, (c) TM_{22} modes.

11.7. Show that in a rectangular waveguide operating in the TE_{10} mode the guide wavelength is given by

$$\lambda_g = \lambda / \sqrt{1 - (\lambda/2a)^2}$$

11.8. An electromagnetic wave may be propagated over a zigzag path within a dielectric rod as shown in Fig. 11.21. What is the largest possible angle for θ if the refractive index of the rod is 2 and the surrounding medium is air? What is the speed with which the signal travels *along the rod* for this angle?

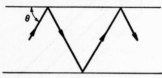

FIG. 11.21. Dielectric rod for Problem 11.8.

11.9. On a single sheet of graph paper plot v_P/c and v_G/c against λ for values of λ from zero to the cut-off wavelength. Discuss the physical significance of the curves.

11.10. On a single sheet of graph paper plot μ against λ for values of λ from zero to the cut-off wavelength. Discuss the physical significance of the curve.

REFERENCES

References for additional reading are given in the list below. Prepared in conformity with the author's express purpose of writing a book primarily for readers with a background of elementary physics and mathematics through analytic geometry, these references are designed to provide such readers not only with further details but also with the increased understanding that comes from other points of view.

ALBERT, ARTHUR L., *Electrical Communication*, 3d Edition, John Wiley & Sons, Inc., New York, 1950. Carefully selected topics embracing the entire field of electrical communication are covered with a limited use of mathematics. Many standard definitions of electrical terms are included.

A.R.R.L. Antenna Book, 8th Edition, American Radio Relay League, West Hartford, Conn., 1956. Eminently readable and most economical in price, the text has been thoroughly worked over in its successive editions as a result of contributions from the practical experiences of amateurs. Since the book is designed for operators of widely varying backgrounds, the presentation must of necessity be essentially physical rather than mathematical in character.

BROWN, THOMAS B., *Foundations of Modern Physics*, 2d Edition, John Wiley & Sons, Inc., New York, 1949. Written with the idea of presenting modern physics in both an exact and an elementary manner, this volume includes interesting and important material on the wave characteristics of light, electromagnetic waves, and the photoelectric effect. Experiment is emphasized as a basis for the theory.

HAUSMANN, ERICH AND SLACK, EDGAR P., *Physics*, 4th Edition, D. Van Nostrand Co., Inc., Princeton, N. J., 1957. For the reader who wishes to review the necessary principles of elementary physics this widely used text will be particularly clear and helpful. The topics are presented in conventional sequence with special emphasis on the fundamentals of the science.

KIVER, MILTON S., *UHF Radio Simplified*, D. Van Nostrand Co., Inc., Princeton, N. J., 1945. Although the book of this title is out of print, it is generally available in libraries. The chapters on transmission lines, waveguides, antennas, and wave propagation are written in simple nonmathematical language. By comparing lower-frequency phenomena the author emphasizes the essential unity of all radio. An expanded and revised edition, *Introduction to UHF Circuits*, was published in 1955.

LITTLE, NOEL C., *Physics*, D. C. Heath & Co., Boston, 1953. One of the few introductory texts which does not follow the traditional approach to the study of physics, this book provides the reader with a fresh appreciation of the topics he wishes to review. For example, all wave phenomena are considered as a unified subject. An informal style, the author talking directly to his reader, is combined with a careful presentation of fundamental principles.

NATIONAL BUREAU OF STANDARDS, Ionospheric Radio Propagation, *Circular 462*, U. S. Government Printing Office, Washington, 1948. This publication contains the best summary of ionospheric phenomena. Included are charts and nomograms for calculating maximum usable frequencies from the monthly bulletins issued by the Bureau of Standards, *Basic Radio Propagation Predictions Three Months in Advance,* CRPL-D.

Radar Electronic Fundamentals, TM 11-466 or Navships 900,016, U. S. Government Printing Office, Washington, 1943. The Army and Navy versions are essentially the same. These manuals contain practically nothing on radar systems as such. The chapters on the physical properties of transmission lines, waveguides, and antennas are clearly written.

ROBERTSON, JOHN K., *Introduction to Optics,* 4th Edition, D. Van Nostrand Co., Inc., Princeton, N. J., 1954. The theoretical aspects of wave optics are analyzed without the use of the calculus. Chapter 6, in which much use has been made of graphical methods, is strongly recommended for a study of wave motion.

SOUTHWORTH, GEORGE C., *Principles and Applications of Waveguide Transmission,* D. Van Nostrand Co., Inc., Princeton, N. J., 1950. Written by a pioneering researcher in the development of waveguides, much of the text assumes an appreciable mathematical background on the part of the reader. Two selections, however, may be read with profit. Chapter 1 contains valuable material of an introductory and historical nature. Chapter 6 provides an excellent descriptive account of the transmission of electromagnetic energy, using the familiar concepts of electric and magnetic fields.

TERMAN, FREDERICK E., *Electronic and Radio Engineering,* 4th Edition, McGraw-Hill Book Co., New York, 1955. This book gives a thorough coverage of the principles of radio engineering. The topics are arranged for easy reference and the reasoning is carried out in terms of physical rather than mathematical concepts. An important feature is the large number of problems and exercises. Directions for using the Smith chart are given in Chapter 4.

TERMAN, F. E. AND PETTIT, J. M., *Electronic Measurements,* McGraw-Hill Book Co., New York, 1952. Experimental procedures for measuring the various properties of transmission lines, antennas, and waveguides are given in detail.

ANSWERS TO PROBLEMS

CHAPTER 1

1. 1.32 microseconds.   2. 7.07×10^{-2} cm; 4.44×10^5 cm/sec, upward; $- 2.79 \times 10^{12}$ cm/sec^2; 9.95×10^3 mi/hr; 2.85×10^9 g.   3. 1.27 per sec.   4. 795 kc. 5. 5.00 cm.   6. 6.7×10^{-3} sec.   7. Derivation.   8. Graphs.   9. Derivation. 10. Proof.   11. 500 cycles/sec; 15.9 volts.   12. 50. $\pm$ 0.25 cycles/sec.   13. 5.60 volts.   14. Graph.

CHAPTER 2

1. (a) 7.35 ft; (b) 2.40 ft.   2. 1700 kc; no.   3. 3.48 in.; 1.50 ft.   4. 7.98 cm; $- 9.06$ cm; 1.22 cm.   5. $\lambda/12$; 18λ.   6. Proof.   7. Proof.   8. 5.3×10^{-9} watt/meter^2; 377 ohms.   9. Derivation.   10. 6.67×10^{-14} joule.

CHAPTER 3

1. 4 ft; 245 Mc; 1, 3, 5 ft.   2. 4 ft; 245 Mc; 0, 2, 4, 6 ft.   3. 60 cm; 500 Mc. 4. 39.6 cm; 500 Mc.   5. 200 volts; 100 volts.   6. (a) 45.0 ohms; 44.4 ohms; (b) 44.7 ohms.   7. 0.0333 amp; 0.00358 amp.   8. (a) 9.45 cm; (b) 46.1 cm.   9. (a) 46.8 cm; (b) 28.9 cm.   10. (a) 900 ohms; (b) 100 ohms; (c) 386 ohms. 11. V_{min} and I_{max} at the load; 500 volts and 5.0 amp; 1000 volts and 2.5 amp. 12. (a) 0.231 microhenry; (b) 2.57 micro-microfarads.   13. (a) 150 ohms; (b1) 1.82 amp; 546 volts; (b2) 1.82 amp; 546 volts; (b3) 3.65 amp; 274 volts.

CHAPTER 4

1. 3.10×10^8 Mc.   2. 46.5 mi.   3. Derivation.   4. Construction.   5. Construction.   6. Construction.   7. Construction.   8. 5.25 mi; 1.56 mi; 0.61 x^2 $+ 6.86$ $y^2 = 4.18$.   9. 63°.   10. Construction; 27.0, 24.5, 22.5, 21.0°.   11. 28.3 mi.   12. (a) 1060 ft; (b) 90 ft.   13. 15%.

CHAPTER 5

1. Amplitude: 1.73 that of components; frequency: same.   2. Construction. 3. 8°.   4. Proof.   5. Construction.   6. Construction.   7. Construction.   8. Construction.   9. Construction.   10. Construction.   11. Construction.   12. Proof.   13. 2.93 mi.   14. Construction.   15. Proof.

CHAPTER 6

1. 1/4.   2. Proof.   3. 57.2°.   4. 8.82×10^{-5} cm.

CHAPTER 7

1. 2.22×10^{15} per sec; 1.47×10^{-18} joule.   2. 1.80×10^6 meters/sec.   3. 1.06×10^6 meters/sec.   4. 300 km; 186 mi.   5. 1 inch; 15 km.   6. (a) 400 waves; (b) 9900 microseconds; (c) 10 watts.   7. 364 km; 7100 microseconds.   8. 605 mi. 9. 3.53 cm.   10. 18.1 cm.   11. 54.3 cycles/sec.   12. Diagram.

CHAPTER 8

1. 84.4 microhenrys.   2. Proof.   3. 39.8 mv.   4. Proof.   5. Construction. 6. Construction.   7. Construction.   8. Graph.   9. $r_L \rightarrow \infty$.   10. Phase difference of 180°.   11. 146 ohms; phase shift of 180°.   12. 1.20×10^{-5} cm.   13. 78.2°.   14. Proof.   15. (a) 3.98 meters; (b) 0.   16. 1.54 meters; 0.77 meter; 105 ohms.

CHAPTER 9

1. Construction.   2. Construction.   3. Construction.   4. Construction.   5. Construction.   6. Construction.   7. Construction.   8. Construction.   9. Construction.   10. (a) 1.1 microwatts/meter^2; (b) 60.4 db.   11. (a) 0; (b) 2.2 db. 12. 8 λ^2; 8 meters^2.   13. Proof.   14. (a) 1.52 microwatts; (b) 1.52×10^{-4} microwatt.   15. $L/\sqrt{\pi}$.   16. (a) 1 mv; (b) 10^{-9} watt; (c) 80 db.   17. $\lambda/2 = 2.62$ ft.

CHAPTER 10

1. Proof.   2. 130 mi.   3. Proof.   4. Cardioid.   5. Increased 48.5%.   6. Decreased 40%.   7. Explanation.   8. 0.42 in.   9. (a) 29 cm; 2.9 λ; (b) 27 cm; 2.7 λ.   10. (a) 36; (b) 15.6 db.   11. 235,000 mi.   12. (a) 6.4×10^{-4}; (b) 5 watts; (c) 116 mi; (d) 392 ft.   13. 2.2 mi/sec toward the earth.

CHAPTER 11

1. Diagrams.   2. 3000 Mc.   3. 4.36 cm; 3.28×10^{10} cm/sec; 2.75×10^{10} cm/sec.   4. 412 ohms; 206 ohms.   5. 66.4°.   6. Construction.   7. Proof.   8. 60°; 7.5×10^7 meters/sec.   9. Graph.   10. Graph.

INDEX

Ion, 106
Ionization, 105
Ionosphere, chemical composition, 109, 115
  critical frequency, 112
  fading, 118–120
  group velocity, 123
  layers, 108, 109, 115
  magnetic field, 110, 125–127
  maximum usable frequency, 112
  modus operandi, 122–127
  multiple-hop transmission, 114, 118
  optimum traffic frequency, 113
  optimum working frequency, 113
  phase velocity, 123
  reflection, 110, 114
  refraction, 110, 116
  skip distance, 113
  skip zone, 113
  Snell's law applied to, 124
  solar effects, 110
  transmission line analog, 125
  variations, 109, 115
  virtual height, 111
Isotropic radiator, 164

Jansky, 212
Jim Creek Valley, 180

Kennelly-Heaviside layer, 108
Kirchhoff's law, 22

L antenna, 182
Lecher wire system, 34
Lens antenna, dielectric, 244
  metal-plate, 245
Line-of-sight, 67
Lissajous figures, 11, 15
Longitudinal wave, 19, 21
Loop, 28
Loop antenna, 171–174, 233
Loran, 79
Lossy substances, 238

Magnetic dipole, 173
Magnetic field, 2
Marconi, 203
Maximum power transfer, 146
Maxwell's laws, 23

Mean free path, 107
Menzel, 110
Mirage, 66
Model measurements, 153
Modes in waveguides, 229, 232
Momentum, 18
Multiplication of patterns, 159–163
Mutual impedance, 168

Near zone, 132
Newton's laws of motion, 3, 7, 18, 121
Nichols and Tear, 54
Night error, 173
Node, 28
Noise, 137, 156, 180
Nulls, 83

Open-circuited line, 33
  input impedance, 39
Optical path, 244
Optimum height, 185
Optimum pattern, 162
Ordinary ray, 99, 127

Parabolic cylinder, 57
Paraboloid, 56
Parameters, lumped, 40–42
  uniformly distributed, 42–44
Parasitic arrays, 167–171
Peak-to-peak, 14
Period, 4
Periodic function, 5
Phase velocity, 62, 123, 226
Phasor, 5, 82
Photoelectric effect, 106
Photon, 106
Pi (π) section, 43
Planck's constant, 106
Polarization, circular, 103
  elliptical, 102
  light waves, 97
  linear, 98
  radio antennas, 102, 184, 195
  radio waves, 97, 100
  waveguides, 241
Polaroid, 98
Power density, 149
Poynting vector, 24, 151, 228
Protection, 155